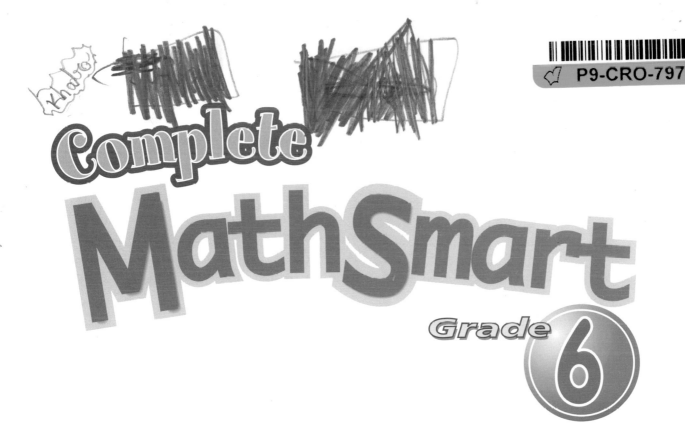

Complete MathSmart

Grade 6

 Contents

Section 1

Overview

In this section, Grade 6 students sharpen their fraction and decimal skills previously developed in Grade 5.

They learn to relate fractions to decimals, percents, rates and ratios, and to estimate answers involving decimals. New fraction skills include adding and subtracting fractions with unlike denominators as well as dividing whole numbers by fractions and dividing fractions by fractions.

Decimal operations include using brackets as well as applying the correct order of operations in evaluating mathematical expressions.

Introducing Percent

1. Write thirty-seven percent in 2 different ways.

   a.   37 %   b. $\dfrac{37}{100}$

2. Write the percent that represents the shaded parts.

   $\dfrac{75}{100} = 75\%$

3. Colour 50% of the square.

HINTS:

- Percent (%) means a part of 100 or out of 100.

  e.g.   Kate got 92 out of 100 on her test, which means she got 92% .

- Percent can be expressed in different ways.

  e.g.   ninety-two percent or 92% or $\dfrac{92}{100}$

Write the percent that represents the shaded part of each 100-square grid.

①   63%

② 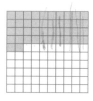   42%

③   18%

④   _____

⑤   _____

⑥   _____

Estimate what percent of each shape is shaded.

⑦   _____

⑧   _____

⑨   _____

⑩   _____

⑪    _____

⑫   _____

⑬   _____

⑭   _____

Colour each 100-square grid according to the given percents.

⑮

27 %

⑯

76 %

⑰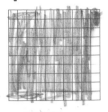

92 %

⑱

48 %

Colour the given percent of each shape.

⑲

20 %

⑳

50 %

㉑

10 %

㉒

50%

On each line segment, mark and label the percents.

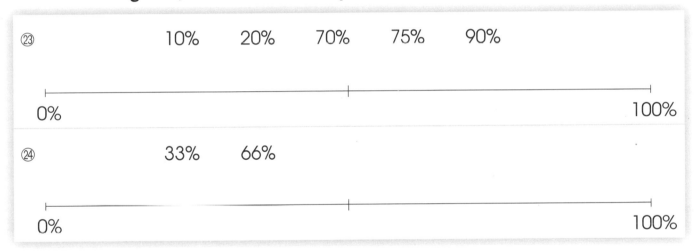

㉓   10%   20%   70%   75%   90%

0%   100%

㉔   33%   66%

0%   100%

Estimate the percent of each line segment marked by each letter.

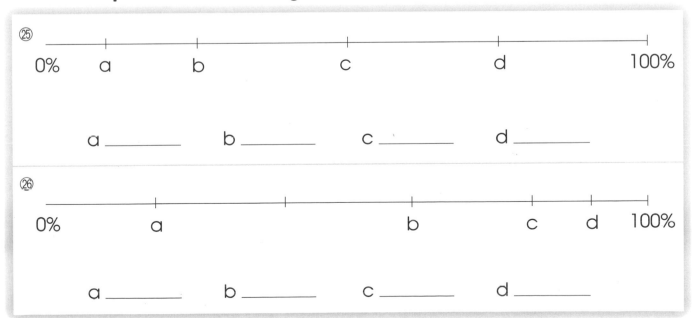

㉕

0%   a   b   c   d   100%

a _____   b _____   c _____   d _____

㉖

0%   a   b   c   d   100%

a _____   b _____   c _____   d _____

Label the 100% mark on each line segment.

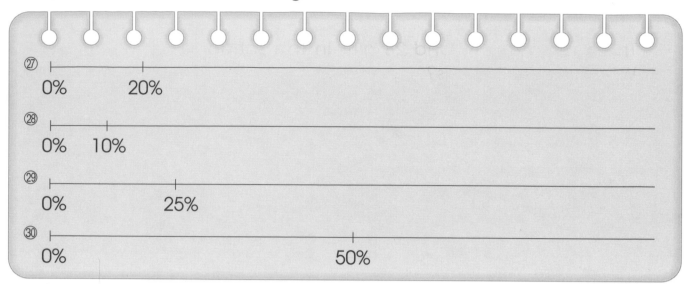

㉗ 0% 20%

㉘ 0% 10%

㉙ 0% 25%

㉚ 0% 50%

Rewrite the following percents using % .

③① 7 out of 100 = _____

③② sixty-five percent = _____

③③ 99 out of 100 = _____

③④ one hundred percent = _____

③⑤ $\frac{36}{100}$ = _____

③⑥ $\frac{20}{100}$ = _____

③⑦ $\frac{200}{100}$ = _____

③⑧ $\frac{8}{100}$ = _____

③⑨ $\frac{72}{100}$ = _____

④⓪ $\frac{45}{100}$ = _____

Rewrite the following percents as fractions with 100 as the denominator.

④① 9% = _____

④② 16% = _____

④③ 20% = _____

④④ 108% = _____

④⑤ 300% = _____

④⑥ 62% = _____

④⑦ 82% = _____

④⑧ 33% = _____

④⑨ 51% = _____

Look at the floor plan and complete the table.

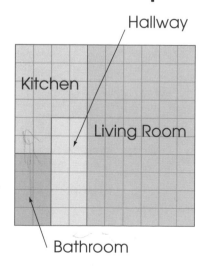

Hallway

Kitchen

Living Room

Bathroom

Room	Number of squares	Percent of the total floor area
㊿ Living Room		
㈤① Kitchen		
㈤② Hallway		
㈤③ Bathroom		

Answer the questions.

54. There are 72 boys and 28 girls in the school yard. What percent are girls? _____

55. 60 out of 100 Canadians are female. What percent is this? _____

56. 47 out of 100 students are girls.
    a. What percent of the students are girls? _____
    b. What percent of the students are boys? _____

57. 38 students have a computer at home and 62 do not have a computer.
    a. What percent of the students have a computer? _____
    b. What percent of the students do not have a computer? _____

58. All the clothes sold in a shop are at 40% discount. What percent of the original price do you pay? _____

59. A bicycle is sold at 55% of the original price. What is the discount in percent? _____

60. 10 out of 50 apples in the basket are red. What percent of the apples are red? _____

61. Dave gets 90% on a test. What does this mean?

_____

Just for Fun

Find the rule.

Write a rule that relates the first 2 columns to the 3rd column. Then follow the rule to write another set of numbers in the 4th row.

Rule : _____

5	8	14
9	6	16
8	12	21

Rate and Unit Price

Which is the better buy? 3 kg of cat food for
$3.78 or 5 kg for $5.95?

3 kg for $3.78 :

3.78 ÷ 3 = 1.26
The unit price is $1.26 per kg.

5 kg for $5.95 :

5.95 ÷ 5 = 1.19
The unit price is $1.19 per kg.

So 5 kg for $5.95 is the better buy.

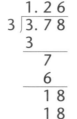

HINTS:

- Rate is a comparison between quantities of different units.

   e.g. $0.65 per box; 0.5 L per person;
        0.05 mm/sheet; $1.69/kg

- To calculate the unit price, divide the total cost by the amount. Then round the answer to the nearest cent if necessary.

- Remember to put the decimal point in the correct place in the product or quotient when doing multiplication or division with decimal numbers.

- To round a number, the digit immediately after the digit to be retained must be considered.

Find the unit price for each item mentally.

 ①

$ _____ / bag

②

$ _____ / box

 ③ $ 4.20

$ _____ / bottle

④

$ _____ / can

⑤ $ 10.00

$ _____ / packet

 ⑥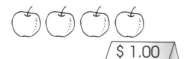

$ _____ / apple

⑦ $ 0.99

$ _____ / bottle

⑧

$ _____ / bag

Calculate the unit price for each item. Round to the nearest cent if necessary.

Unit Price

⑨   2 kg of cereal for $5.20 $ _____

⑩   5 bars of chocolate for $4.50 $ _____

⑪   3 notebooks for $1.75 $ _____

⑫   2 CDs for $24.80 $ _____

⑬   2 pizzas for $12.40 $ _____

⑭   6 spicy chicken wings for $4.99 $ _____

Calculate the total cost for each purchase.

Total Cost

⑮   3 bottles of orange juice at $0.79 each $ _____

⑯   5 ten-pack pencils at $0.87 each $ _____

⑰   4 T-shirts at $4.99 each $ _____

⑱   6 hamburgers at $2.60 each $ _____

⑲   2 boxes of laundry detergent at $7.96 each $ _____

⑳   8 correction pens at $3.75 each $ _____

Find the unit price for each quantity. Round to the nearest cent if necessary. Put a ✓ in the box for the better buy.

Item	Total Cost	Unit Price	Better Buy
㉑ Orange juice	3 cans for $1.95		
	4 cans for $2.65		
㉒ Pansy	2 pots for $4.25		
	3 pots for $6.35		

Solve the problems. Show your work. Round your answers to the nearest hundredth if necessary.

㉓ Susanne's hair grows 0.83 cm per month. How long does it grow in 6 months?

It grows _____ cm in 6 months.

㉔ Peggy saves $12.50 per week. How much can she save in 5 weeks?

㉕ Gas sells at $0.75 per litre. How much do 4 litres cost?

㉖ Brenda buys 2 litres of spring water for $1.42. What is the price per litre?

㉗ Mark builds a 24.4-m long fence using 9 posts. How far apart are two adjacent posts?

㉘ Bill buys 2 pairs of shoes at $39.95 per pair. How much does he pay?

㉙ 6 friends go to Canada's Wonderland. They spend $87.00 altogether. How much does each spend if each spends an equal amount?

㉚ 2.5 litres of pop is divided equally among 8 friends. How much does each drink?

㉛ Kate drinks 2 glasses of milk daily. Each glass contains 0.3 L of milk. How much milk does she drink per week?

㉜ Susan earns $22.50 for 5 hours of babysitting. Bob earns $12.75 for 3 hours. Who is better paid?

㉝ 3 T-shirts are sold for $14.70.

    a. What is the price for each T-shirt?

    b. How much do 5 T-shirts cost?

㉞ Baby Sue weighed 3.2 kg at birth. She gains 150 g per week. How many kg does she weigh at 6 weeks?

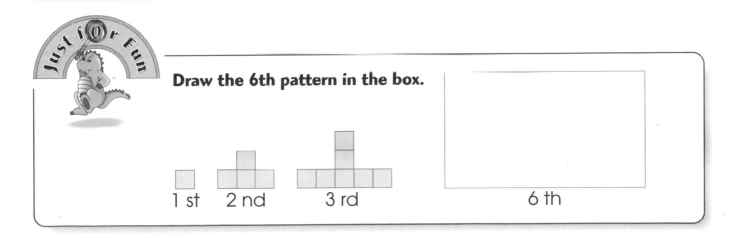

Draw the 6th pattern in the box.

1 st   2 nd   3 rd   6 th

③ Ratio and Rate

During an 8-week period, Ruth reads 10 books and David reads 14 books.

1. How many books does David read per week?

   Books David reads per week = David's reading rate $= \dfrac{14}{8} = 1.75$ books/week

2. What is the ratio of the number of books read by Ruth to the number of books read by David?

   The ratio is 10 : 14 or 5 : 7.

3. What fraction of the total does Ruth read?

   Total number of books read by Ruth and David = 10 + 14 = 24

   Fraction of the total Ruth reads :

   $\dfrac{10}{24} = \dfrac{5}{12}$ ⟵ reduce to lowest terms

HINTS:

- Ratio is a comparison of two quantities.

  e.g. There are 3 boys and 4 girls.

  The ratio of boys to girls is 3 to 4.

- A ratio can be expressed in different ways.

  e.g. 3 to 4,   3 : 4, $\dfrac{3}{4}$

- To find equivalent ratios, multiply or divide each term by the same number other than 0.

  e.g. $\dfrac{10}{14} = \dfrac{10 \div 2}{14 \div 2} = \dfrac{5}{7} = \dfrac{5 \times 3}{7 \times 3} = \dfrac{15}{21}$

- A ratio is usually written in lowest terms or simplest form.

  e.g. $\dfrac{5}{7}$ is in simplest form because the only common factor of the terms is 1.

Look at the pictures. Write each ratio.

① Boys to girls : _____3 : 4_____

② Girls to boys : _____

③ Boys to children : _____

④ Girls to children : _____

⑤ Dogs to cats : _____

⑥ Cats to dogs : _____

⑦ Cats to animals : _____

⑧ Dogs to animals : _____

⑨ Apples to oranges : _____

⑩ Oranges to apples : _____

⑪ Apples to fruits : _____

⑫ Oranges to fruits : _____

Write each ratio in two other ways.

⑬ 2 : 3   _____   _____   ⑭ 5 to 9   _____   _____

⑮ 15 to 4   _____   _____   ⑯ 7 : 11   _____   _____

⑰ 6 to 13   _____   _____   ⑱ 7 : 12   _____   _____

⑲ $\dfrac{3}{8}$ _____   _____   ⑳ $\dfrac{6}{17}$ _____   _____

Write 2 equivalent ratios for each ratio.

㉑ 3 : 1   _____   _____   ㉒ 4 : 2   _____   _____

㉓ 2 : 6   _____   _____   ㉔ 8 : 10   _____   _____

㉕ 6 : 9   _____   _____   ㉖ 7 : 4   _____   _____

㉗ 2 : 1   _____   _____   ㉘ 6 : 15   _____   _____

Write each ratio in simplest form.

㉙ 10 : 15   _____   ㉚ 22 : 25   _____

㉛ 12 : 16   _____   ㉜ 36 : 45   _____

㉝ 14 : 35   _____   ㉞ 98 : 4   _____

㉟ 95 : 10   _____   ㊱ 91 : 63   _____

㊲ 120 : 1000   _____   ㊳ 30 : 45   _____

㊴ 75 : 25   _____   ㊵ 6 : 72   _____

Look at the flowers. Write the items that each ratio compares.

㊶ 4 : 2   Rose : Tulip

㊷ 3 : 4   _____ : _____

㊸ 3 : 9   _____ : _____

㊹ 2 : 3   _____ : _____

㊺ 4 : 9   _____ : _____

㊻ 9 : 2   _____ : _____

Rose   Tulip   Daisy

Complete the following table to show how much water is needed to cook the various amounts of rice. Answer the questions.

㊼

Rice (cup)	1	2	3	4	5	6	7	8
Water (cup)	2	4						

㊽ What is the ratio of water to rice in lowest terms? _____

㊾ How many cups of water are needed to cook 12 cups of rice? _____ cups

㊿ How many cups of rice can be cooked with 20 cups of water? _____ cups

51 What is the ratio of rice to the mixture of water and rice? _____

Calculate each rate.

52 Walking 50 km in 5 hours

Rate: _____

53 Reading 20 books in 4 weeks

Rate: _____

54 Writing 200 words in 10 minutes

Rate: _____

55 Turning 14 pages in 7 minutes

Rate: _____

Solve the problems. Show your work.

56 Sheila reads 9 books in 12 days and Karen reads 5 books in 8 days. Who reads faster?

Sheila's reading rate : _____

Karen's reading rate : _____

_____ reads faster.

57 Debbie reads 150 words in 12 minutes.

a. What is her reading rate?

b. How many words will she read in 20 minutes?

58. Mr Wong drives 90 km in 2 hours and Mrs Ling drives 126 km in 3 hours. Who drives faster?

59. Special offer: "Buy 4 pairs of socks for $7.50 and get 1 pair free." What is the cost per pair?

60. David eats 6 slices of pizza and Dan eats 4 slices.

    a. What is the ratio of the number of slices Dan eats to the number of slices David eats?

    b. What is the ratio of the number of slices eaten by David to the total number of slices eaten by both?

61. Fred drives 96 km in 2 hours and Ivan drives 120 km in 3 hours. Calculate:

    a. Fred's speed.

    b. Ivan's speed.

    c. the ratio of Fred's speed to Ivan's speed.

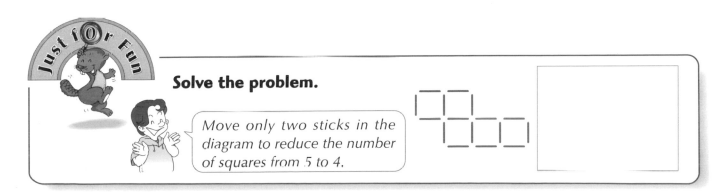

Solve the problem.

Move only two sticks in the diagram to reduce the number of squares from 5 to 4.

Relating Fractions to Decimals, Percents, Rates and Ratios

1. Convert $\frac{5}{7}$ to a decimal correct to the nearest hundredth.

$$= 0.71$$

⟵ round the quotient to hundredths place

$$\begin{array}{r} 0.7\,1\,4 \\ 7\overline{\smash{)}5.0} \\ 4\,9 \\ \hline 1\,0 \\ 7 \\ \hline 3\,0 \\ 2\,8 \\ \hline 2 \end{array}$$

2. Convert 0.15 to a fraction.

$$0.15 = \frac{15}{100} = \frac{15 \div 5}{100 \div 5} = \frac{3}{20}$$

⟵ 0.15 has 2 decimal places, so put 2 zeros in the denominator; then reduce the fraction to simplest form

3. Convert $\frac{11}{25}$ to a percent.

$$\frac{11}{25} = \frac{11 \times 4}{25 \times 4} = \frac{44}{100} = 44\%$$

⟵ change the denominator to 100 by multiplying each term by 4

4. Billy has completed 6 out of 8 pages of his homework.

a. What fraction of the homework has he completed?

$$\frac{6}{8} = \frac{6 \div 2}{8 \div 2} = \frac{3}{4}$$ He has completed $\frac{3}{4}$ of his homework.

b. What is the ratio of the completed homework to the incomplete homework?

$$6 : 2 = 3 : 1$$ The ratio is 3 : 1.

c. What percent of the homework has he done?

$$\frac{6}{8} = \frac{3}{4} = \frac{3 \times 25}{4 \times 25} = \frac{75}{100} = 75\%$$

He has done 75% of his homework.

Convert each fraction to a percent.

① $\dfrac{7}{10} = \dfrac{70}{100} = \underline{70}$ %

② $\dfrac{2}{5} = \dfrac{}{} = \underline{}$ %

③ $\dfrac{3}{4} = \dfrac{}{} = \underline{}$ %

④ $\dfrac{1}{2} = \dfrac{}{} = \underline{}$ %

⑤ $\dfrac{1}{20} = \dfrac{}{} = \underline{}$ %

⑥ $\dfrac{4}{5} = \dfrac{}{} = \underline{}$ %

⑦ $\dfrac{19}{25} = \dfrac{}{} = \underline{}$ %

⑧ $\dfrac{19}{200} = \dfrac{}{} = \underline{}$ %

HINTS:

- Convert fractions to decimals :

  Divide the numerator by the denominator. Continue dividing until the remainder is zero or there are enough decimal places.

  e.g. $\frac{2}{3} = 0.67$ ⟵ round to the nearest hundredth

- Convert fractions to percents :

  Multiply or divide each term by the same number to change the denominator to 100.

- Convert decimals to fractions :

  Write the decimal part as numerator with a denominator of 10, 100, 1000, etc.

  e.g. $0.07 = \frac{7}{100}$ ⟵ number of zeros in the denominator equals the number of decimal places

- Remember to reduce the fraction to simplest form.

Convert each percent to a fraction in simplest form.

⑨   50% = $\dfrac{50}{100}$ = _____   ⑩   35% = —— = _____

⑪   8% = —— = _____   ⑫   18% = —— = _____

⑬   15% = —— = _____   ⑭   60% = —— = _____

Write each fraction as a decimal.

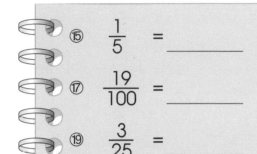

⑮ $\dfrac{1}{5}$ = _____   ⑯ $\dfrac{1}{4}$ = _____

⑰ $\dfrac{19}{100}$ = _____   ⑱ $\dfrac{7}{10}$ = _____

⑲ $\dfrac{3}{25}$ = _____   ⑳ $\dfrac{27}{200}$ = _____

Write each decimal as a fraction in simplest form.

㉑   0.65 = —— = _____   ㉒   0.22 = —— = _____

㉓   0.25 = —— = _____   ㉔   0.9 = —— = _____

㉕   0.15 = —— = _____   ㉖   0.84 = —— = _____

Complete the table.

	Ratio	Fraction	Decimal	Percent
㉗	2 : 5	$\dfrac{2}{5}$		
㉘			0.35	
㉙				27 %
㉚		$\dfrac{3}{4}$		

Choose and write the decimal that comes between each pair of numbers.

0.96   0.55   0.86   0.25   0.8   0.08

㉛ $\frac{1}{2}$ ______ 70%

㉜ 90% ______ $\frac{4}{5}$

㉝ 85% ______ $\frac{3}{4}$

㉞ $\frac{1}{10}$ ______ 30%

㉟ $\frac{5}{100}$ ______ 10%

㊱ 99% ______ $\frac{9}{10}$

Choose and write the fraction that comes after each pair of numbers.

$\frac{9}{10}$ $\frac{19}{20}$ $\frac{8}{10}$ $\frac{1}{10}$ $\frac{1}{5}$ $\frac{17}{25}$

㊲ 40% 0.25 ______

㊳ 0.8 92% ______

㊴ 0.7 72% ______

㊵ 0.1 15% ______

㊶ 75% 0.7 ______

㊷ 75% 0.8 ______

Write >, < or = in each box.

㊸ 0.25 ☐ 60%

㊹ 0.24 ☐ $\frac{6}{25}$

㊺ 30% ☐ $\frac{1}{2}$

㊻ $\frac{3}{4}$ ☐ 70%

㊼ $\frac{4}{5}$ ☐ 75%

㊽ $\frac{3}{20}$ ☐ 0.16

Write each group of numbers in order from least to greatest.

㊾ 0.1 $\frac{1}{4}$ 20% ______________________

㊿ 70% $\frac{3}{4}$ 0.73 ______________________

(51) $\frac{3}{25}$ 10% 0.15 ______________________

Solve the problems. Show your work.

52. Look at the word FRIEND. Round your answers in b. and c. to the nearest percent.

    a. What fraction of the letters in the word FRIEND are vowels?

    b. What percent of the letters are vowels?

    c. What percent are consonants?

53. Annie collects $24 and Betty collects $12 for a local charity.

    a. What is the ratio of the amount Annie collects to the amount Betty collects?

    b. What fraction of the total amount is collected by Annie?

54. In a Grade 6 class, 18 of the 30 students have brown eyes.

    a. What fraction of the students have brown eyes?

    b. What percent have brown eyes?

    c. What is the ratio of the students having brown eyes to those who do not have brown eyes?

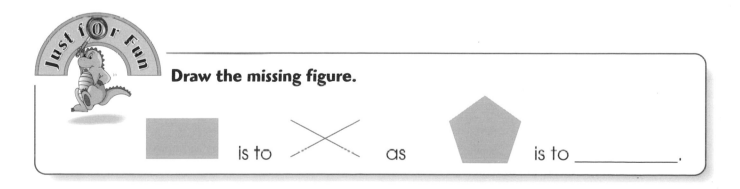

Draw the missing figure.

is to _____ as _____ is to _____.

Adding and Subtracting Decimals

1. $93.749 - 53.818 + 29.271$
    $= 39.931 + 29.271$
    $= 69.202$

2. $59 - 3.2 + 9.784$
    $= 55.8 + 9.784$
    $= 65.584$

$$
\begin{array}{r}
\overset{8\ 12\ 17}{9\cancel{3}.\cancel{7}49} \\
-\ 53.818 \\
\hline
39.931
\end{array}
\qquad
\begin{array}{r}
\overset{1\ 1\ \ 1}{39.931} \\
+\ 29.271 \\
\hline
69.202
\end{array}
\qquad
\begin{array}{r}
\overset{8\ 10}{59.\cancel{0}} \\
-\ 3.2 \\
\hline
55.8
\end{array}
\qquad
\begin{array}{r}
\overset{1\ 1}{55.800} \\
+\ 9.784 \\
\hline
65.584
\end{array}
$$

← write zeros to fill the empty decimal places

└ align the decimal ┘ points

Find the sums or differences mentally.

① $2.912 + 3$ = _____

② $5.784 + 6$ = _____

③ $9.854 - 2$ = _____

④ $12.469 - 3.4$ = _____

⑤ $7.2 + 9.1$ = _____

⑥ $9.81 - 1.51$ = _____

⑦ $2.981 - 1.4$ = _____

⑧ $5.829 - 1.829$ = _____

⑨ $6.975 - 3.675$ = _____

⑩ $15.862 - 5.862$ = _____

⑪ $10.948 + 25$ = _____

⑫ $211.984 - 1.984$ = _____

⑬ $8 + 2.195 - 0.195$ = _____

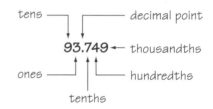

HINTS:

*   tens — decimal point
    93.749 ← thousandths
    ones — hundredths
    tenths

*   1 tenth = 10 hundredths
    1 tenth = 100 thousandths
    1 hundredth = 10 thousandths

*   Align the decimal points when doing vertical addition or subtraction. Write zeros to fill the empty decimal places.

*   Don't forget to put the decimal point in the correct place in the answer.

*   To change the order of operations in multi-step operations, move the number together with the sign immediately in front of it.

*   You can get the same answer by changing the order of operations.

    e.g. $93.749 - 53.818 + 29.271$
    $= 39.931 + 29.271$
    $= 69.202$

    or $93.749 - 53.818 + 29.271$
    $= 93.749 + 29.271 - 53.818$
    $= 123.020 - 53.818$
    $= 69.202$

Do the calculation.

⑭
```
    6.070
+   3.039
```

⑮
```
    7.453
+   8.498
```

⑯
```
   59.307
+  28.838
```

⑰
```
    2.981
-   1.790
```

⑱
```
    7.920
-   1.875
```

⑲
```
    8.000
-   3.998
```

⑳
```
    8.280
+   2.839
```

㉑
```
    0.799
+   0.958
```

㉒
```
    9.999
+   5.084
```

㉓
```
    9.000
-   5.231
```

㉔
```
   12.250
-   3.987
```

㉕
```
   15.200
+   9.297
```

㉖
```
    3.298
+   2.762
```

㉗
```
   10.092
+   5.979
```

㉘
```
    3.412
+   2.598
```

㉙
```
   10.582
-   9.289
```

㉚
```
   26.529
-  11.478
```

㉛
```
   16.793
-   8.654
```

㉜
```
  300.000
- 194.509
```

㉝
```
  106.423
+ 218.659
```

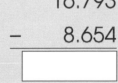

Write the following numbers.

㉞ Three thousand two hundred ninety-seven and thirty-two hundredths _____

㉟ One hundred ten and ninety-seven thousandths _____

㊱ The sum of three hundredths and twenty-six thousandths _____

㊲ The difference between seven tenths and two hundredths _____

Write the correct numbers.

㊳ 9 tenths = _____ hundredths

㊴ 7 hundredths = _____ thousandths

㊵ 40 thousandths = _____ hundredths

㊶ 80 hundredths = _____ tenths

Find the answers. Show your work.

㊷ $9 - 3.294 + 1.429$

㊸ $17.219 + 209.91 - 63.258$

㊹ $12 - 1.9 - 0.874$

㊺ $5.239 + 7.298 - 8.799$

㊻ $100 - 9.29 - 0.984$

㊼ $15.9 + 8.92 - 7.345$

Find the answers only if they are between 10 and 20.

⑱
$$
\begin{array}{r}
8.294 \\
+ \quad 3.846 \\
\hline
\end{array}
$$

㊾
$$
\begin{array}{r}
37.981 \\
- \quad 18.249 \\
\hline
\end{array}
$$

㊿
$$
\begin{array}{r}
7.248 \\
+ \quad 2.619 \\
\hline
\end{array}
$$

51
$$
\begin{array}{r}
17.843 \\
+ \quad 12.981 \\
\hline
\end{array}
$$

52
$$
\begin{array}{r}
48.123 \\
- \quad 29.843 \\
\hline
\end{array}
$$

53
$$
\begin{array}{r}
9.999 \\
+ \quad 10.098 \\
\hline
\end{array}
$$

54
$$
\begin{array}{r}
35.555 \\
- \quad 10.999 \\
\hline
\end{array}
$$

55
$$
\begin{array}{r}
29.849 \\
- \quad 19.298 \\
\hline
\end{array}
$$

56
$$
\begin{array}{r}
12.598 \\
+ \quad 7.981 \\
\hline
\end{array}
$$

Solve the problems. Show your work.

57 If A = 5.984 + 2.198 and B = 9.104 + 7.293, find:
   a. A.   b. B.

   c.   the sum of A and B.   d.   the difference between A and B.

Insert + or – to make each number sentence true.

① Insert only three + or – signs: 1   2   3   4   5   6   7   =   55

② Insert only four + or – signs: 1   2   3   4   5   6   7   =   55

6 Multiplying and Dividing Decimals

1. 9.321 x 5
    = 46.605

$$
\begin{array}{r}
9.321 \\
\times \quad 5 \\
\hline
46.605
\end{array}
$$

⎫ 3 decimal places in the factors

← 3 decimal places in the product
← align all numbers on the right-hand side

2. 1523 × 0.01 = 15.23
   ↑   ↑
   2 decimal places   2 decimal places
   in the factor   in the product

place a decimal point in the quotient above the one in the dividend

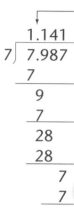

$$
\begin{array}{r}
1.141 \\
7\overline{)7.987} \\
7 \\
\hline
9 \\
7 \\
\hline
28 \\
28 \\
\hline
7 \\
7 \\
\end{array}
$$

3.   7.987 ÷ 7
     = 1.141

4. 2.394 × 100 = 239.4
   ↑
   2 zeros   move the decimal
                point 2 places right

5. 723.1 ÷ 10 = 72.31
   ↑
   1 zero   move the decimal
               point 1 place left

HINTS:

- When multiplying a decimal by a whole number, the number of decimal places in the product is the same as that in the question.

- When dividing a decimal by a whole number, put the decimal point in the quotient directly above the dividend.

- When multiplying a decimal by 10 or 100, move the decimal point 1 place or 2 places right. The number of places moved equals the number of zeros.

- When dividing a decimal by 10, 100, etc., move the decimal point 1 place, 2 places, etc. left. The number of places moved equals the number of zeros.

Find the answers mentally.

① 3.241 × 2 = _____

② 3.984 ÷ 100 = _____

③ 0.523 ÷ 10 = _____

④ 12 × 0.01 = _____

⑤ 125 × 0.1 = _____

⑥ 8.4 ÷ 7 = _____

⑦ 1.2 × 5 = _____

⑧ 75.937 × 100 = _____

⑨ 529.1 ÷ 100 = _____

⑩ 39.8 ÷ 10 = _____

⑪ 3.693 ÷ 3 = _____

⑫ 6.824 ÷ 2 = _____

Find the answers.

⑬ 2.931×5	⑭ 3.924×7
⑮ 1.487×4	⑯ 4.878×6
⑰ 3.099×8	⑱ 3.763×3
⑲ $7.917 \div 3$	⑳ $8.472 \div 6$
㉑ $14.835 \div 5$	㉒ $16.568 \div 8$
㉓ $49.83 \div 2$	㉔ $13.31 \div 2$
㉕ 2.569×9	㉖ $57.617 \div 7$

Fill in the blanks.

㉗ _____ × 100 = 52.8

㉘ _____ × 2 = 5.8

㉙ _____ × 3 = 7.2

㉚ _____ ÷ 2 = 5.1

㉛ _____ ÷ 5 = 1.2

㉜ 12.93 ÷ _____ = 1.293

㉝ 5.8 ÷ _____ = 2.9

㉞ 7.3 × _____ = 73

Put the decimal point in the right place and add the correct number of zeros, if necessary, to make each number sentence true.

㉟ 3 2 × 1 0 = 3.2

㊱ 3 5 × 8 = 0.2 8

㊲ 1.4 5 × 7 = 1 0 1 5

㊳ 2 1 2 × 5 = 1.0 6

㊴ 5 ÷ 6 = 8 3 3

㊵ 5.1 ÷ 4 = 1 2 7 5

㊶ 9 1 3 ÷ 4 = 2.2 8 2 5

㊷ 1 3 6 ÷ 8 = 0.0 1 7

Complete only those questions with a product between 5 and 10. Then list the answers in order from least to greatest in ㊿.

㊸ 1.981 × 3	㊹ 2.191 × 5	㊺ 0.897 × 6
㊻ 3.998 × 4	㊼ 0.723 × 8	㊽ 0.701 × 9
㊾ 3) 1 9.8 2 4	㊿ 5) 2 3.4 5 5	51 8) 0.1 3 6

52 _____

Solve the problems. Show your work.

㊾ Joe is building 6 shelves. Each shelf is 0.825 m long. What length of plywood must he buy?

He must buy _____ m of plywood.

㊿ 8 identical books take up 33.68 cm on a bookshelf. How thick is each book?

㊻ The price of a share in ABC Corporation is $2.937. How much do 7 shares cost? Round your answer to the nearest cent.

㊼ There are about 3.283 feet in 1 metre. How many feet are there in 5 metres?

㊽ If A = 5.923 × 2, B = 33.981 ÷ 3 and C = 6.094 × 3, calculate:
a. A, B, C   b. A + B − C   c. A − B + C

Look for the pattern.

Find the sum of the first 6 terms in this pattern.
2.4 + 1.2 + 0.6 + ...

Sum of the first 6 terms = _____

Estimating Answers to Operations with Decimals

7

1. $9.83 + 7.19 \approx 17$
    estimate $10 + 7 = 17$

2. $98.78 \div 4.82 \approx 20$
    estimate $100 \div 5 = 20$

3. $29.235 - 17.592 \approx 11$
    estimate $29 - 18 = 11$

4. $93.48 \times 0.95 \approx 93$
    estimate $93 \times 1 = 93$

HINTS:

- When rounding a number, consider the digit immediately after the digit to be retained. Round up if the digit is 5 or more; otherwise, round down.

- Estimate an answer by rounding each decimal to the nearest whole number. Then do the operations.

Estimate the answer to each problem to the nearest whole number.

① $59.823 - 17.197$

estimate _____ − _____ = _____

② $73.243 + 89.981$

estimate _____ + _____ = _____

③ 3.923×1.894

estimate _____ × _____ = _____

④ $3.923 \div 1.894$

estimate _____ ÷ _____ = _____

⑤ $15.8 \div 3.9$

estimate _____ ÷ _____ = _____

⑥ $36.25 \div 5.83$

estimate _____ ÷ _____ = _____

⑦ $12.14 \div 4.98$

estimate _____ ÷ _____ = _____

⑧ $100.48 \div 25.01$

estimate _____ ÷ _____ = _____

⑨ $143.72 \div 11.98$

estimate _____ ÷ _____ = _____

⑩ $200.2 - 78.9$

estimate _____ − _____ = _____

⑪ $5.98 + 9.90$

estimate _____ + _____ = _____

⑫ 19.65×2.73

estimate _____ × _____ = _____

Estimate first. Then find the sums and differences.

⑬ 19.98 − 9.87 = _____

estimate _____

⑭ 100.63 − 79.34 = _____

estimate _____

⑮ 29.72 − 18.98 = _____

estimate _____

⑯ 212.49 − 183.91 = _____

estimate _____

⑰ 200.61 − 198.98 = _____

estimate _____

⑱ 200.61 + 198.98 = _____

estimate _____

⑲ 5.92 + 2.78 + 12.10 = _____

estimate _____

⑳ 10.12 + 8.92 − 7.85 = _____

estimate _____

Estimate the unit prices and put a ✓ in the circle beside the better buy in each purchase. Check your answers using a calculator.

㉑ | CAT FOOD |

    10 kg for $13.45   ◯

    4 kg for $5.95   ◯

㉒ | CRAYONS |

    12 crayons for $0.99   ◯

    72 crayons for $7.25   ◯

㉓ | SPRING WATER |

    1.25 L for $0.69   ◯

    2 L for $0.99   ◯

㉔ | TIN FOIL |

    15 m for $2.15   ◯

    100 m for $9.95   ◯

㉕ | APPLES |

    3 kg for $3.89   ◯

    5 kg for $5.29   ◯

㉖ | WRITING PAPER |

    10 packs for $7.90   ◯

    15 packs for $12.90   ◯

Estimate each total cost to the nearest dollar. Check your answers using a calculator.

Estimated Total Cost

㉗   12 cans of soup at $0.59 each   _____

㉘   6 pairs of socks at $4.49 each   _____

㉙   8 bottles of coke at $1.19 each   _____

㉚   9 bottles of detergent at $2.23 each   _____

Estimate the price of each item. Then estimate the total cost of each sales receipt to the nearest dollar.

㉛

EASY GROCERY

BANANAS	$1.49
HAM	$3.29
CHEESE	$5.25
MILK	$1.99
APPLES	$3.49
YOGURT	$2.99

Estimated total [   ]

㉜

CHEAPER SUPERMARKET

3 @ $1.45
LETTUCE   _____

2 @ $6.75
PIZZA   _____

2 DOZENS @ $1.79
EGGS   _____

2 LOAVES @ $1.84
BREAD   _____

5 @ $0.99
TURKEY PIE   _____

Estimated total [   ]

㉝

ABC GROCERY

2 bags @ $3.99
ORANGES   _____

3 bags @ $3.29
COOKIES   _____

2 @ $0.79
AVOCADOS   _____

Estimated total [   ]

Solve the problems. Show your work.

㉞ Joe earns $6.75 per hour in a job after school. Estimate his monthly earnings to the nearest dollar if he works 50 hours per month.

He earns about _____ monthly.

㉟ Mr Johnson goes to the hardware store. He buys 6 batteries at $2.25 for 2 and 12 light bulbs at $2.49 for 3. About how much change will he get from a $20 bill?

He gets about _____ change.

㊱ Betty buys some clothes in a "10% off" sale. Estimate how much money she saves to the nearest dollar.

Item	Original Price
Dress	$69.95
Sweater	$49.65
Pants	$109.50
Shorts	$19.70

She saves about _____ .

Just for Fun

Find Big Bob's height.

Little Lennie and Big Bob are out for an evening walk. Little Lennie is 1.2 m tall and casts a 2-m shadow on the road. How tall is Big Bob if he casts a 3-m shadow?

Big Bob is _____ m tall.

Calculating Percents

1. What is 25% of 200?

    × 2

    $$\frac{25}{100} = \frac{50}{200}$$ ←— 200 is the total

    × 2

    25% of 200 is 50.

2. What is 16% of 25?

    ÷ 4

    $$\frac{16}{100} = \frac{4}{25}$$ ←— 25 is the total

    ÷ 4

    16% of 25 is 4.

3. What percent is 17 out of 20?

    × 5

    $$\frac{17}{20} = \frac{85}{100}$$ ←— change denominator to 100

    × 5

    17 out of 20 is 85%.

HINTS:

- To calculate the percent of a whole :

  Set up a proportion. Multiply or divide the numerator and denominator by the same number to change the denominator to 100.

- To calculate a certain percent of a whole :

  Write the percent as a fraction. Multiply or divide the numerator and denominator by the same number to make the denominator equal to the total amount. The numerator is the amount of that percent.

Find the missing numbers mentally.

① $\frac{15}{20} = \frac{\square}{100}$

② $\frac{12}{25} = \frac{\square}{100}$

③ $\frac{12}{50} = \frac{\square}{100}$

④ $\frac{240}{300} = \frac{\square}{100}$

⑤ $\frac{30}{100} = \frac{\square}{50}$

⑥ $\frac{17}{100} = \frac{\square}{200}$

⑦ $\frac{25}{\square} = \frac{50}{100}$

⑧ $\frac{30}{\square} = \frac{15}{100}$

⑨ $\frac{72}{100} = \frac{\square}{25}$

⑩ $\frac{90}{100} = \frac{\square}{20}$

⑪ $\frac{45}{300} = \frac{\square}{100}$

⑫ $\frac{1}{5} = \frac{\square}{100}$

⑬ $\frac{3}{4} = \frac{\square}{100}$

⑭ $\frac{\square}{100} = \frac{11}{20}$

⑮ $\frac{60}{100} = \frac{15}{\square}$

⑯ $\frac{3}{\square} = \frac{75}{100}$

Find the amounts. Show your calculation.

		Calculation	Amount
⑰	10% of $50		
⑱	25% of $300		
⑲	75% of $400		
⑳	24% of $25		

Find the percents. Show your calculation.

		Calculation	Percent
㉑	4 out of 50		
㉒	9 out of 20		
㉓	7 out of 25		
㉔	29 out of 50		

Answer the questions. Show your work.

㉕ Billy gets 19 out of 25 on a test. What is his test percentage?

㉖ Margie gets 80% on an essay. What is her mark out of 20?

㉗ Andy gets 18 out of 25 on a test and May gets 16 out of 20 on another test. Who has the better grade?

Solve the problems. Show your work.

㉘ 6 out of 25 students in a Grade 6 class are girls. What percent of the class are girls?

_____ % of the class are girls.

㉙ Tim has done 60% of 5 pages of his homework. How many pages has he completed?

㉚ 4 out of 5 people in Britain are English. What percent of the people in Britain are English?

㉛ 9 out of 20 people surveyed floss their teeth. What percent of the people use floss?

㉜ 65% of the voters in Canada voted in an election. If there are 10 million eligible voters, how many people voted?

㉝ There are 140 students in the school orchestra. 77 of them are girls.

    a. What fraction of the students are girls?

    b. What percent of the students are girls?

    c. What percent of the students are boys?

Answer the following questions.

㉞ There are 28 girls and 22 boys swimming in a pool.

    a.   What percent of the swimmers are boys?

    b.   What percent of the swimmers are girls?

㉟ Tom bought a $10 T-shirt in a sale for $7.

    a.   What was the amount reduced?

    b.   What percent of the original price did Tom pay?

    c.   What was the percent off the original price?

㊱ Sally bought a bicycle for 40% off.

    a.   What percent of the original price did Sally pay?

    b.   What fraction of the original price did Sally pay?

    c.   If the regular price was $200, how much did Sally pay?

Help Sally solve the problem.

$$\triangle + \triangle + \blacksquare = \blacksquare + \blacksquare$$

Find 2 different possible pairs of values for $\triangle$ and $\blacksquare$.

① $\triangle$ = _____ $\blacksquare$ = _____

② $\triangle$ = _____ $\blacksquare$ = _____

Midway Review

Circle the letter which represents the correct answer to each problem.

① 2 litres of dishwasher liquid cost $6.49. What is the cost per litre?

A. $3.24   B. $3.25   C. $12.98   D. $4.49

② Gas costs $0.74 per litre. What is the cost of 10 litres of gas?

A. $10.74   B. $7.40   C. $74.00   D. $8.00

③ What is the price of 9 potatoes if 6 potatoes cost $1.49?

A. $2.24   B. $2.98   C. $2.49   D. $3.49

④ A cyclist cycles 34 km in 2 hours. How far will she cycle in 5 hours at the same speed?

A. 170 km   B. 68 km   C. 85 km   D. 44 km

⑤ Dave and Dan share a 12-slice pizza in the ratio 2 : 1. How many slices does Dan get?

A. 6 slices   B. 8 slices   C. 9 slices   D. 4 slices

⑥ 45% written as a fraction in lowest terms is

A. $\dfrac{9}{20}$ B. 0.45   C. $\dfrac{45}{100}$ D. $\dfrac{11}{20}$

⑦ 8 out of 25 people surveyed drink tea. What percent of those surveyed drink tea?

A. 8%   B. 40%   C. 32%   D. 35%

⑧ There are 14 million workers in Canada. About 1.4 million are unemployed. What percent of workers are unemployed?

A. 14%   B. 1%   C. 10%   D. 1.4%

⑨ A basket contains 150 apples. 30% of the apples are red. How many apples are not red?

   A. 105   B. 45   C. 120   D. 50

⑩ If $\dfrac{24}{100} = \dfrac{?}{300}$, then ? is

   A. 8   B. 72   C. 27   D. 80

⑪ What is 80% of $120?

   A. $76   B. $106   C. $86   D. $96

⑫ Barry gets 70% on a test. If the test is out of 25, what is the mark Barry gets?

   A. 17   B. 18   C. 17.5   D. 20

⑬ In a class,18 students have brown eyes and 9 students have blue eyes. What is the ratio of blue-eyed students to brown-eyed students?

   A. 2 : 1   B. 1 : 2   C. 2 : 3   D. 3 : 2

Write each group of numbers in order from least to greatest.

⑭ $\dfrac{2}{5}$ $\dfrac{3}{25}$ 35%   0.15   _____

⑮ 82% $\dfrac{17}{20}$ $\dfrac{3}{4}$ 0.73   _____

⑯ $\dfrac{12}{25}$ 0.55 $\dfrac{27}{50}$ 51%   _____

Estimate each answer to the nearest whole number.

⑰ $7.98 + 9.04 - 6.92 - 1.91$ ≈ _____

⑱ $13.75 - 6.17 + 1.82 - 4.62$ ≈ _____

⑲ 9.83×1.49 ≈ _____   ⑳ $53.9 \div 5.78$ ≈ _____

㉑ $63.45 \div 6.87$ ≈ _____   ㉒ 12.24×9.71 ≈ _____

Find the answers. Show your work for ㉓ - ㉜.

㉓ 2.984 + 3.487	㉔ 3.487 − 2.984
㉕ 5.91 + 9.79 − 3.48	㉖ 15.249 − 8.62 + 5.174
㉗ 9.836 × 9	㉘ 26.964 ÷ 7
㉙ 0.242 × 6	㉚ 3.795 ÷ 3
㉛ 14.865 ÷ 5	㉜ 2.945 × 7

㉝ 149.2 ÷ 100 = _____   ㉞ 47 × 0.01 = _____

㉟ 2.593 × 100 = _____   ㊱ 18.9 ÷ 100 = _____

㊲ 12.785 × 10 = _____   ㊳ 8.942 ÷ 10 = _____

Fill in the boxes.

㊴ ☐ × 4 = 9.6   ㊵ ☐ ÷ 6 = 4.5   ㊶ 3.9 × ☐ = 39

㊷ ☐ ÷ 100 = 3.2   ㊸ ☐ × 10 = 83   ㊹ 6.53 × ☐ = 13.06

㊺ 96.45 ÷ ☐ = 9.645   ㊻ 0.43 × ☐ = 43   ㊼ ☐ ÷ 4 = 0.175

Write True (T) or False (F) for each statement.

48 $12 - 1.9 > 9.2 + 1.4$ (   )   49 $3 \times 12.4 = 12.4 \times 3$ (   )

50 $100 - 3.1 = 3.1 - 100$ (   )   51 $12.00 = 12$ (   )

52 $100 + 3.1 = 3.1 + 100$ (   )   53 $16.494 \div 2 < 2.749 \times 3$ (   )

Solve the problems. Show your work.

54 Tim has read 75% of his book. He has read 300 pages. How many pages are there in his book?

There are _____ pages in his book.

55 There are 19 girls and 6 boys in a class. What percent of the class are boys?

56 There are 50 candies in a bag. 20 of them are red. What is the ratio of red candies to those of other colours?

57 Carol gets $\frac{27}{50}$ and Dave gets $\frac{11}{20}$ on two different tests. Who gets the lower grade?

58 Mary types 200 words in 10 minutes and Mike types 450 words in 25 minutes. Who types faster?

59 Bill and Bob start running from the same place. Bill runs at 8 km/h and Bob runs at 10 km/h. How far apart are they after $\frac{1}{2}$ hour?

More Operations with Decimals

1. $1.7 + 3.7 \times 5 = 1.7 + 18.5 = 20.2$ ⟵ do the multiplication first

2. $10.2 \div 2 \times 3 = 5.1 \times 3 = 15.3$ ⟵ do the multiplication and division in order from left to right

3. $(1.2 + 2.3) \div 5 = 3.5 \div 5 = 0.7$ ⟵ do the operations in the brackets first

4. Mrs Kerr buys 10 cans of juice at 0.79 each. She pays with a $10 bill. How much change does she get?

   $10.00 - 10 \times 0.79 = 10.00 - 7.90 = 2.10$

   She gets $2.10 change.

Find the answers using the correct order of operations. Show all steps.

HINTS:

- For mixed operations, do × and ÷ first, and then do + and −.

- For × and ÷, calculate in order from left to right.

- For number sentences with brackets, do all the operations in the brackets first.

① $0.3 + 2 \times 1.2$	
② $9.5 - 3 \times 1.1$	
③ $0.4 + 10.2 \div 2$	④ $12.4 - 10 \times 0.2$
⑤ $50 \times 0.1 \div 2.5$	⑥ $10.2 \div 2 + 7.1$
⑦ $9.3 \div 3 \times 2$	⑧ $13.5 \times 2 \div 3$
⑨ $2.1 \times 3 + 5.2 \times 2$	⑩ $4 \times 2.1 - 3 \times 1.1$

⑪ $12.5 \div 5 - 3.2 \div 2$

⑫ $5 \times 1.2 + 18.9 \div 9$

⑬ $3 \times 3.24 - 1.23$

⑭ $5.78 - 1.23 \times 4$

⑮ $5.91 \times 2 \div 3$

⑯ $12.4 \div 4 - 1.9$

⑰ $12 - 5.91 \times 2$

⑱ $0.93 + 1.98 \div 3$

⑲ $1.12 + 36.39 \div 3$

⑳ $10.55 \div 5 - 3.33 \div 3$

㉑ $(1.2 + 9.8) \times 0.2$

㉒ $(2.9 + 1.1) \div 2$

㉓ $(9.8 - 3.5) \div (8.1 - 5.1)$

㉔ $2.1 \times 9 \div 3 \times 2$

㉕ $5.92 - 2.87 + 1.23 \times 2$

㉖ $1.7 \times 3 - 2.1 \div 7$

㉗ $10 - 1.982 + 3.054$

㉘ $12.9 \div 3 \times 10 \times 0.1$

㉙ $2.4 \times 2 \times 5 \times 10$

㉚ $100.2 \div 2 - 5.4 \times 2$

Solve the problems. Show your work.

③ Jane buys 5 chocolate bars at $1.25 each. She pays with a $10 bill. How much change does she get?

She gets _____ change.

③ Brenda buys 2 pairs of jeans. She pays $100 and gets $9.70 change. How much does each pair cost?

③ Look at Mrs Smith's shopping list: (Note: lb represents pound)

5 lbs of bananas at $0.39/lb

3 lbs of apples at $0.69/lb

10 lbs of potatoes at $0.29/lb

How much does she pay in all?

③ Mr Brown buys 3 magazines at $2.25 each and 2 books at $5.99 each. How much change does he get from $20?

③ Write a shopping problem which has the following solution.

$$10.00 - 5 \times 1.19$$
$$= 10.00 - 5.95$$
$$= 4.05$$

The answer is $4.05.

Use the following exchange rates to solve the problems. Show your work.

$$C\$1 = US\$0.664 = £0.449 = HK\$5.173$$

㊱ Gary is on a "Round the World" trip. His first stop is London, England, where he exchanges C$100 into £. He buys a sweater for £25. How much in £ has he left?

He has £ _____ left.

㊲ His next stop is Hong Kong. He exchanges C$100 into HK$ and then buys a shirt for HK$200.

   a.   How much in HK$ has he left?

   b.   What is the approximate value of the amount left in C$?

㊳ In New York, Gary exchanges C$100 into US$. He buys a theatre ticket for US$50 and a souvenir for US$9.80.

   a.   How much in US$ has he left?

   b.   What is the approximate value of the amount left in C$?

Help Sally complete the number sentences.

Write + , – , x or ÷ in the ◯ . Add brackets if necessary.

① 4◯4◯4◯4 = 3   ② 4◯4◯4◯4 = 6

③ 4◯4◯4◯4 = 7   ④ 4◯4◯4◯4 = 9

Equivalent Fractions, Simplifying and Comparing Fractions

EXAMPLES

1. Write 3 fractions which are equivalent to $\frac{2}{3}$.

$$\frac{2}{3} = \frac{4}{6} = \frac{6}{9} = \frac{8}{12}$$

$$\uparrow \qquad \uparrow \qquad \uparrow$$
$$\frac{2 \times 2}{3 \times 2} \quad \frac{2 \times 3}{3 \times 3} \quad \frac{2 \times 4}{3 \times 4}$$

2. Order the following fractions from least to greatest using < .

$$\frac{9}{8} , \frac{9}{12} , \frac{7}{8} , \frac{1}{4} , \frac{5}{8} , \frac{6}{16} , \frac{5}{4}$$

$$\frac{9}{12} = \frac{9 \div 3}{12 \div 3} = \frac{3}{4} = \frac{3 \times 2}{4 \times 2} = \frac{6}{8} \qquad\qquad \frac{1}{4} = \frac{1 \times 2}{4 \times 2} = \frac{2}{8}$$

$$\frac{6}{16} = \frac{6 \div 2}{16 \div 2} = \frac{3}{8} \qquad\qquad\qquad\qquad \frac{5}{4} = \frac{5 \times 2}{4 \times 2} = \frac{10}{8}$$

write the equivalent fractions with 8 as the denominator

compare the numerators

$$\therefore \quad \frac{2}{8} < \frac{3}{8} < \frac{5}{8} < \frac{6}{8} < \frac{7}{8} < \frac{9}{8} < \frac{10}{8}$$

$$\therefore \quad \frac{1}{4} < \frac{6}{16} < \frac{5}{8} < \frac{9}{12} < \frac{7}{8} < \frac{9}{8} < \frac{5}{4}$$

HINTS:

- To find an equivalent fraction, multiply or divide the numerator and denominator by the same number.

- To compare fractions, find their equivalent fractions with the same denominator and then compare the numerators. Remember that the final answers must be written in terms of the original fractions.

- To simplify a fraction is to reduce the fraction to lowest terms or simplest form.

Simplify the following fractions.

① $\frac{90}{100}$ = _____   ② $\frac{15}{33}$ = _____

③ $\frac{49}{56}$ = _____   ④ $\frac{38}{40}$ = _____

⑤ $\frac{990}{1000}$ = _____   ⑥ $\frac{77}{121}$ = _____

⑦ $\frac{56}{72}$ = _____   ⑧ $\frac{45}{54}$ = _____   ⑨ $\frac{55}{70}$ = _____   ⑩ $\frac{48}{80}$ = _____

⑪ $\frac{42}{77}$ = _____   ⑫ $\frac{16}{48}$ = _____   ⑬ $\frac{3}{45}$ = _____   ⑭ $\frac{44}{120}$ = _____

Write 3 equivalent fractions for each of the following fractions.

⑮　$\dfrac{5}{9}$ _____　_____　_____

⑯　$\dfrac{7}{8}$ _____　_____　_____

⑰　$\dfrac{9}{10}$ _____　_____　_____

⑱　$\dfrac{15}{100}$ _____　_____　_____

Write each group of fractions from least to greatest using < . Show your work.

⑲　$\dfrac{5}{9}$, $\dfrac{2}{3}$, $\dfrac{17}{18}$, $\dfrac{7}{9}$

⑳　$\dfrac{4}{5}$, $\dfrac{9}{10}$, $\dfrac{14}{20}$, $\dfrac{3}{4}$

㉑　$\dfrac{3}{4}$, $\dfrac{4}{3}$, $\dfrac{5}{3}$, $\dfrac{5}{6}$, $\dfrac{3}{2}$

㉒　$\dfrac{16}{15}$, $\dfrac{8}{5}$, $\dfrac{4}{3}$, $\dfrac{9}{10}$, $\dfrac{10}{15}$

Place each of the following numbers on the number line below.

㉓　$1\dfrac{1}{4}$, $1\dfrac{1}{2}$, $\dfrac{3}{4}$, $1\dfrac{3}{4}$, $1\dfrac{2}{3}$, $\dfrac{2}{3}$, $\dfrac{7}{8}$

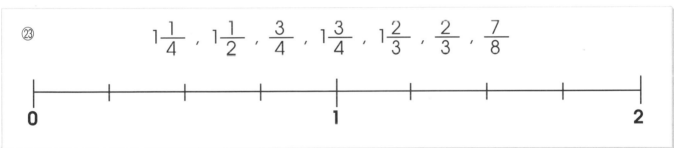

Write each group of the mixed numbers from greatest to least using > .

㉔　$2\dfrac{3}{4}$, $2\dfrac{7}{8}$, $1\dfrac{7}{8}$, $1\dfrac{3}{4}$, $2\dfrac{1}{2}$, $2\dfrac{5}{8}$

_____

㉕　$3\dfrac{4}{5}$, $3\dfrac{9}{10}$, $3\dfrac{1}{2}$, 3 , $3\dfrac{1}{8}$, $3\dfrac{1}{4}$

_____

Write the following improper fractions as mixed numbers in lowest terms.

㉖ $\dfrac{10}{6} = $ _____ ㉗ $\dfrac{20}{16} = $ _____ ㉘ $\dfrac{38}{36} = $ _____

㉙ $\dfrac{22}{7} = $ _____ ㉚ $\dfrac{18}{10} = $ _____ ㉛ $\dfrac{28}{21} = $ _____

㉜ $\dfrac{37}{12} = $ _____ ㉝ $\dfrac{95}{9} = $ _____ ㉞ $\dfrac{60}{14} = $ _____

Match each of the letters A → H on the number line with the following fractions.

㉟

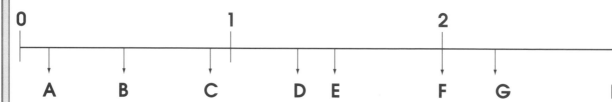

$$\dfrac{17}{6} \ , \ \dfrac{9}{4} \ , \ \dfrac{8}{4} \ , \ \dfrac{3}{2} \ , \ \dfrac{4}{3} \ , \ \dfrac{1}{8} \ , \ \dfrac{9}{10} \ , \ \dfrac{1}{2}$$

A = _____ B = _____ C = _____ D = _____

E = _____ F = _____ G = _____ H = _____

Complete each of the following statements using > , < or = .

㊱ $\dfrac{1}{3}$ ☐ $\dfrac{1}{4}$ ㊲ $1\dfrac{1}{2}$ ☐ $\dfrac{30}{20}$ ㊳ $1\dfrac{1}{8}$ ☐ $1\dfrac{1}{12}$

㊴ $\dfrac{40}{15}$ ☐ $2\dfrac{2}{3}$ ㊵ $\dfrac{15}{20}$ ☐ $\dfrac{4}{3}$ ㊶ $\dfrac{16}{10}$ ☐ $\dfrac{3}{2}$

㊷ $\dfrac{7}{12}$ ☐ $\dfrac{7}{15}$ ㊸ $\dfrac{11}{14}$ ☐ $\dfrac{33}{42}$ ㊹ $\dfrac{5}{16}$ ☐ $\dfrac{1}{4}$

Shade the diagrams to illustrate that $1\dfrac{1}{2} > 1\dfrac{1}{3} > 1\dfrac{1}{4}$.

㊺

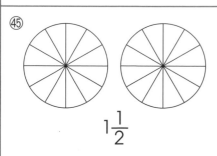

$1\dfrac{1}{2}$

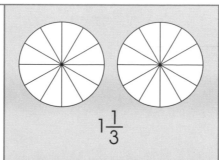

$1\dfrac{1}{3}$

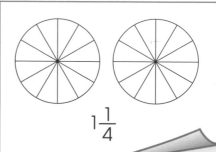

$1\dfrac{1}{4}$

48   COMPLETE MATHSMART (GRADE 6)

Find 6 different pairs of equivalent fractions from the list below.

$$\frac{30}{36}, \frac{28}{32}, \frac{21}{24}, \frac{15}{18}, \frac{5}{10}, \frac{10}{9}, \frac{1}{2}, \frac{2}{3}, \frac{9}{10}, \frac{14}{21}, \frac{30}{27}, \frac{27}{30}$$

㊻ ______ = ______   ㊼ ______ = ______   ㊽ ______ = ______

㊾ ______ = ______   ㊿ ______ = ______   (51) ______ = ______

Solve the problems. Show your work.

(52) Jack can buy a $\frac{1}{4}$ lb hamburger for \$1.00 or a $\frac{1}{3}$ lb hamburger for \$1.30. Which is the better buy? Explain.

(53) Pat has finished 9 out of 10 pages of his homework and Paul has finished 7 out of 8 pages of his homework. Who has completed the larger part of his homework?

(54) Bill states that $\frac{5}{4} < \frac{7}{6} < \frac{9}{8} < \frac{17}{16}$ because $5 < 7 < 9 < 17$. Explain what is wrong with his reasoning.

Look for the pattern and find the rule.

Write the rule that connects the first 2 columns to the 3rd column. Then write another set of numbers that fits the pattern.

18	3	7
24	6	5
30	3	11

Rule: ______________________________

Adding and Subtracting Fractions with Like Denominators

1. $\frac{3}{4} + \frac{5}{4} = \frac{3+5}{4} = \frac{8}{4} = 2$

2. $\frac{13}{18} - \frac{5}{18} = \frac{13-5}{18} = \frac{8}{18} = \frac{4}{9}$

3. $3\frac{1}{4} - 2\frac{3}{4} = \frac{13}{4} - \frac{11}{4} = \frac{13-11}{4} = \frac{2}{4} = \frac{1}{2}$

Find the answers mentally.

① $\frac{5}{7} - \frac{3}{7}$ = _____

② $\frac{5}{7} + \frac{1}{7}$ = _____

③ $\frac{12}{13} - \frac{5}{13}$ = _____

④ $\frac{3}{9} + \frac{5}{9}$ = _____

HINTS:

• To add or subtract fractions with like denominators, add or subtract the numerators and leave the denominator the same.

• To add or subtract mixed numbers, either change the mixed numbers to improper fractions before adding or subtracting or add/subtract the whole numbers and fractions separately.

• Remember to simplify the final answer.

⑤ $\frac{5}{6} - \frac{5}{6}$ = _____

⑥ $\frac{15}{18} + \frac{2}{18}$ = _____

⑦ $\frac{18}{10} - \frac{9}{10}$ = _____

⑧ $\frac{25}{27} - \frac{2}{27}$ = _____

⑨ $\frac{13}{11} - \frac{12}{11}$ = _____

⑩ $\frac{27}{45} + \frac{11}{45}$ = _____

⑪ $\frac{8}{11} + \frac{2}{11}$ = _____

⑫ $\frac{11}{35} + \frac{13}{35}$ = _____

⑬ $\frac{19}{28} + \frac{8}{28}$ = _____

⑭ $\frac{132}{144} + \frac{11}{144}$ = _____

⑮ $\frac{92}{100} - \frac{89}{100}$ = _____

⑯ $\frac{8}{9} - \frac{2}{9} - \frac{1}{9}$ = _____

⑰ $\frac{11}{15} + \frac{1}{15} + \frac{2}{15}$ = _____

⑱ $\frac{3}{8} + \frac{1}{8} + \frac{3}{8}$ = _____

⑲ $\frac{7}{12} + \frac{1}{12} - \frac{3}{12}$ = _____

Find the sums and differences. Reduce the answers to lowest terms.

20. $\dfrac{19}{20} - \dfrac{9}{20}$ = _____ = _____

21. $\dfrac{15}{16} + \dfrac{1}{16}$ = _____ = _____

22. $\dfrac{29}{30} - \dfrac{9}{30}$ = _____ = _____

23. $\dfrac{13}{5} + \dfrac{7}{5}$ = _____ = _____

24. $\dfrac{26}{11} - \dfrac{4}{11}$ = _____ = _____

25. $\dfrac{15}{18} - \dfrac{5}{18}$ = _____ = _____

26. $\dfrac{15}{14} - \dfrac{8}{14}$ = _____ = _____

27. $\dfrac{13}{21} + \dfrac{1}{21}$ = _____ = _____

28. $\dfrac{21}{28} + \dfrac{3}{28}$ = _____ = _____

29. $\dfrac{17}{100} + \dfrac{23}{100}$ = _____ = _____

30. $\dfrac{11}{54} - \dfrac{2}{54}$ = _____ = _____

31. $\dfrac{8}{56} - \dfrac{1}{56}$ = _____ = _____

32. $\dfrac{7}{56} + \dfrac{9}{56}$ = _____ = _____

33. $\dfrac{41}{40} - \dfrac{21}{40}$ = _____ = _____

34. $\dfrac{77}{50} - \dfrac{2}{50}$ = _____ = _____

35. $\dfrac{17}{25} + \dfrac{3}{25}$ = _____ = _____

36. $\dfrac{29}{74} + \dfrac{17}{74}$ = _____ = _____

37. $\dfrac{13}{80} + \dfrac{27}{80}$ = _____ = _____

38. $\dfrac{19}{35} + \dfrac{11}{35}$ – _____ = _____

39. $\dfrac{27}{42} - \dfrac{13}{42}$ – _____ = _____

Do only those questions that have an answer between 1 and 2. Then list the answers from least to greatest in ㊾ using < .

40. $\dfrac{3}{8} + \dfrac{4}{8}$ = _____

41. $\dfrac{9}{8} - \dfrac{3}{8}$ = _____

42. $\dfrac{11}{16} + \dfrac{7}{16}$ = _____

43. $\dfrac{15}{6} - \dfrac{11}{6}$ = _____

44. $\dfrac{15}{2} - \dfrac{9}{2}$ = _____

45. $\dfrac{9}{10} + \dfrac{8}{10}$ = _____

46. $\dfrac{27}{32} + \dfrac{19}{32}$ = _____

47. $\dfrac{25}{12} - \dfrac{5}{12}$ = _____

48. $\dfrac{1}{9} + \dfrac{7}{9}$ = _____

49. _____

Write the answers as whole numbers or mixed numbers in lowest terms.

50. $1\frac{1}{4} + \frac{1}{4} =$ _____

51. $2\frac{3}{8} - \frac{1}{8} =$ _____

52. $\frac{7}{9} + 2\frac{2}{9} =$ _____

53. $4\frac{1}{5} + \frac{4}{5} =$ _____

54. $\frac{5}{7} + 3\frac{2}{7} =$ _____

55. $2\frac{5}{16} - 1\frac{1}{16} =$ _____

56. $1\frac{3}{4} + 1\frac{1}{4} =$ _____

57. $3\frac{5}{6} - 2\frac{1}{6} =$ _____

58. $3\frac{1}{5} - 1\frac{3}{5} =$ _____

59. $3\frac{1}{4} - 1\frac{3}{4} =$ _____

60. $1\frac{2}{3} + 3\frac{1}{3} =$ _____

61. $6\frac{7}{9} - 5\frac{1}{9} =$ _____

Write the missing fractions.

62. $\frac{2}{3} +$ ☐ $= 1$

63. $\frac{5}{8} +$ ☐ $= 1$

64. $\frac{7}{9} -$ ☐ $= 0$

65. $\frac{3}{4} -$ ☐ $= \frac{1}{2}$

66. $1\frac{1}{2} +$ ☐ $= 2$

67. $\frac{1}{4} +$ ☐ $= \frac{1}{2}$

68. $\frac{1}{3} -$ ☐ $= \frac{1}{6}$

69. $\frac{1}{6} +$ ☐ $= \frac{1}{3}$

70. $1\frac{3}{8} -$ ☐ $= \frac{3}{4}$

71. ☐ $+ \frac{5}{10} = \frac{4}{5}$

72. ☐ $- \frac{2}{5} = \frac{3}{5}$

73. ☐ $+ 1\frac{5}{7} = 3$

Complete the following statements using > , < or =.

74. $\frac{5}{8} - \frac{1}{8}$ ◯ $\frac{1}{16} + \frac{1}{16}$

75. $1\frac{3}{4} - 1\frac{1}{4}$ ◯ $\frac{1}{4} + \frac{1}{4}$

76. $\frac{3}{5} + \frac{1}{5}$ ◯ $\frac{2}{3} + \frac{1}{3}$

77. $1\frac{5}{6} - \frac{1}{6}$ ◯ $2\frac{11}{12} - 1\frac{7}{12}$

78. $\frac{9}{10} + \frac{3}{10}$ ◯ $2\frac{3}{5} - 1\frac{2}{5}$

79. $1\frac{13}{14} + \frac{9}{14}$ ◯ $1\frac{3}{7} + 1\frac{3}{7}$

Answer the questions.

⑧⓪   Brian and Brenda are digging a large hole to plant a tree. Brian digs $\frac{3}{4}$ of the hole.

     a. What fraction of the hole must Brenda dig?   _____

     b. What is the difference between the amount of work done by Brian and Brenda?   _____

⑧①   Gord, Graham, Gary and Gerald buy 3 pizzas. Greedy Gord eats 1 pizza. The remaining pizzas are divided evenly among the other three boys.

     a. How much pizza does each of the other three boys get?   _____

     b. If each pizza is cut into 6 slices, how many slices does Gerald get?   _____

⑧②   A bag of marbles contains 5 red, 8 green, 12 white and 5 black marbles.

     a. What fraction of the marbles are either white or black?   _____

     b. What fraction of the marbles are green?   _____

     c. What fraction of the marbles are not green?   _____

     d. What is the sum of your answers to a. and b.?   _____

     e. What fraction of the marbles are neither white nor black? _____

     f. What is the sum of your answers to a. and e.?   _____

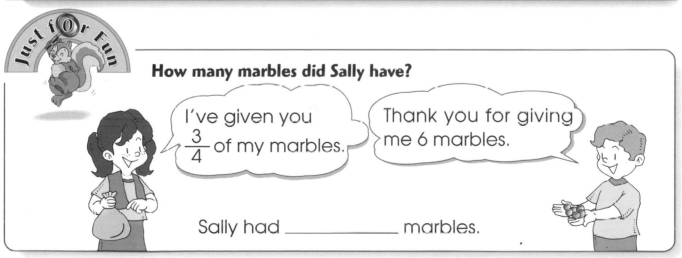

Just for Fun

How many marbles did Sally have?

I've given you $\frac{3}{4}$ of my marbles.

Thank you for giving me 6 marbles.

Sally had _____ marbles.

Adding Fractions with Unlike Denominators

1. Find the least common multiple of 4 and 6.
   The first six multiples of 4 : 4 , 8 , 12 , 16 , 20 , 24
   The first six multiples of 6 : 6 , 12 , 18 , 24 , 30 , 36
   The first two common multiples of 4 and 6 : 12 , 24
   The least common multiple (L.C.M.) of 4 and 6 : 12

2. $1\frac{1}{2} + \frac{1}{4}$
   $= 1\frac{2}{4} + \frac{1}{4}$ ← equivalent fractions with a common denominator 4
   $= 1\frac{3}{4}$

3. $\frac{1}{4} + \frac{1}{6}$
   $= \frac{3}{12} + \frac{2}{12}$ ← the common denominator is the least common multiple of 4 and 6
   $= \frac{5}{12}$

HINTS:

- The least common multiple (L.C.M.) is the smallest number that is a multiple of the given numbers.

- Adding 2 fractions with unlike denominators: Write equivalent fractions with a common denominator first. Then add the numerators of the equivalent fractions.

- Adding 2 mixed numbers:
  Add the whole numbers and fractions separately or change the mixed numbers to improper fractions before adding.

- Remember to reduce the sum to lowest terms. If the sum is an improper fraction, change it to a mixed number.

Write the least common multiple (L.C.M.) of each set of numbers.

① 4 , 2 _____

② 3 , 6 _____   ③ 2 , 6 _____   ④ 5 , 10 _____

⑤ 5 , 15 _____   ⑥ 7 , 14 _____   ⑦ 7 , 21 _____

⑧ 8 , 4 _____   ⑨ 8 , 16 _____   ⑩ 12 , 24 _____

⑪ 3 , 9 _____   ⑫ 9 , 18 _____   ⑬ 10 , 30 _____

⑭ 20 , 40 _____   ⑮ 30 , 5 _____   ⑯ 17 , 51 _____

⑰ 13 , 39 _____   ⑱ 3 , 6 , 9 _____   ⑲ 4 , 6 , 8 _____

Add the fractions. Simplify your answers.

20 $\dfrac{1}{3} + \dfrac{1}{6}$

21 $\dfrac{1}{2} + \dfrac{1}{6}$

22 $\dfrac{7}{10} + \dfrac{1}{5}$

23 $\dfrac{4}{15} + \dfrac{1}{5}$

24 $\dfrac{1}{12} + \dfrac{1}{24}$

25 $\dfrac{9}{10} + \dfrac{1}{30}$

26 $\dfrac{11}{21} + \dfrac{1}{7}$

27 $\dfrac{3}{8} + \dfrac{1}{4}$

28 $\dfrac{6}{7} + \dfrac{1}{14}$

29 $\dfrac{4}{17} + \dfrac{1}{51}$

30 $\dfrac{1}{3} + \dfrac{2}{9}$

31 $\dfrac{4}{39} + \dfrac{2}{13}$

32 $\dfrac{1}{9} + \dfrac{5}{18}$

33 $\dfrac{3}{40} + \dfrac{7}{20}$

34 $\dfrac{5}{12} + \dfrac{7}{24}$

35 $\dfrac{3}{8} + \dfrac{9}{16}$

First determine the **L.C.M.** for the denominators in each question. Then add the fractions.
Show all your work.

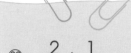

36 $\dfrac{2}{5} + \dfrac{1}{6}$ = _____

    = _____

37 $\dfrac{1}{2} + \dfrac{1}{5}$ = _____

    = _____

38 $\dfrac{1}{7} + \dfrac{2}{9}$ = _____

    = _____

39 $\dfrac{3}{8} + \dfrac{2}{11}$ = _____

    = _____

40 $\dfrac{4}{9} + \dfrac{1}{5}$ = _____

    = _____

41 $\dfrac{2}{3} + \dfrac{1}{4}$ = _____

    = _____

42 $\dfrac{1}{6} + \dfrac{4}{9}$ = _____

    = _____

43 $\dfrac{1}{15} + \dfrac{3}{20}$ = _____

    = _____

44 $\dfrac{1}{4} + \dfrac{1}{3} + \dfrac{1}{5}$ = _____

    = _____

45 $\dfrac{1}{3} + \dfrac{1}{6} + \dfrac{2}{9}$ = _____

    = _____

Add the fractions. Give the answers as mixed numbers.

46 $1\dfrac{4}{5} + \dfrac{5}{6}$ = _____

    = _____

47 $2\dfrac{7}{9} + \dfrac{8}{12}$ = _____

    = _____

48 $\dfrac{5}{6} + 1\dfrac{5}{18}$ = _____

    = _____

49 $4\dfrac{1}{6} + 1\dfrac{7}{8}$ = _____

    = _____

50 $1\dfrac{7}{8} + 2\dfrac{1}{4}$ = _____

    = _____

51 $2\dfrac{3}{5} + 3\dfrac{2}{3}$ = _____

    = _____

Write the addition sentences for the following diagrams.

52  _____

53  _____

Complete the diagrams to illustrate the following addition sentences.

54	$\dfrac{1}{3} + \dfrac{1}{6} = \dfrac{1}{2}$	+
55	$\dfrac{1}{2} + \dfrac{2}{3} = 1\dfrac{1}{6}$	+

Solve the problems. Show your work.

56 Anna read a book with 120 pages. She read 30 pages on the first day and 10 pages on the second day. What fraction of the book did she read

  a. on the first day? _____

  b. on the second day? _____

  c. by the end of the second day?

_____ = _____

57 Gerry chopped a tree into 50 logs. He gave 15 logs to his friends and kept the rest.

  a. What fraction of the total did he give away? _____

  b. What fraction of the total did he keep for himself? _____

  c. What is the sum of your answers to a. and b.?

_____ = _____

Look for the pattern.
Write the next term.
$\dfrac{1}{8}$ $\dfrac{1}{4}$ $\dfrac{3}{8}$ $\dfrac{5}{8}$ _____

13 Subtracting Fractions with Unlike Denominators

1. $\dfrac{1}{2} - \dfrac{1}{3}$

   $= \dfrac{3}{6} - \dfrac{2}{6}$ ← equivalent fractions with common denominator 6

   $= \dfrac{1}{6}$

2. $3\dfrac{5}{6} - 1\dfrac{3}{8}$

   $= 3\dfrac{20}{24} - 1\dfrac{9}{24}$ ← L.C.M. of 6 and 8 is 24

   $= 2\dfrac{11}{24}$ ← subtract the whole numbers and fractions separately

HINTS:

- To subtract 2 fractions with unlike denominators:

  Write equivalent fractions with a common denominator first. Then subtract the numerators of the equivalent fractions.

- The common denominator of a group of fractons is the least common multiple (L.C.M.) of the denominators.

3. $1\dfrac{1}{16} - \dfrac{1}{12}$

   $= \dfrac{17}{16} - \dfrac{1}{12}$ ← change the mixed number to an improper fraction

   $= \dfrac{51}{48} - \dfrac{4}{48}$ ← write equivalent fractions with common denominator 48

   $= \dfrac{47}{48}$

- To subtract 2 mixed numbers:

  Subtract the whole numbers and fractions separately or change the mixed numbers to improper fractions before subtracting.

- Reduce the difference to lowest terms.

- If the difference is an improper fraction, change it to a mixed number.

Subtract the fractions. Show your work.

① $\dfrac{1}{6} - \dfrac{1}{12}$ = _____

     = _____

② $\dfrac{7}{20} - \dfrac{1}{40}$ = _____

     = _____

③ $\dfrac{9}{10} - \dfrac{11}{30}$ = _____

     = _____

④ $\dfrac{3}{8} - \dfrac{1}{16}$ = _____

     = _____

⑤ $\dfrac{1}{2} - \dfrac{11}{30}$ = _____

     = _____

⑥ $\dfrac{3}{7} - \dfrac{5}{14}$ = _____

     = _____

Subtract the fractions. Give your answers in lowest terms. Show your work.

⑦ $\dfrac{2}{3} - \dfrac{1}{8}$

⑧ $\dfrac{3}{5} - \dfrac{2}{7}$

⑨ $\dfrac{3}{4} - \dfrac{1}{5}$

⑩ $\dfrac{1}{2} - \dfrac{2}{9}$

⑪ $1\dfrac{3}{4} - \dfrac{1}{6}$

⑫ $2\dfrac{5}{8} - 1\dfrac{1}{10}$

⑬ $\dfrac{5}{6} - \dfrac{3}{10}$

⑭ $2\dfrac{5}{6} - \dfrac{3}{8}$

⑮ $4\dfrac{1}{10} - 2\dfrac{2}{25}$

⑯ $3\dfrac{7}{12} - 3\dfrac{1}{18}$

⑰ $1\dfrac{1}{2} - 1\dfrac{1}{3}$

⑱ $2\dfrac{1}{3} - 1\dfrac{1}{2}$

⑲ $2\dfrac{5}{6} - 1\dfrac{1}{2}$

⑳ $2\dfrac{1}{6} - 1\dfrac{1}{3}$

㉑ $2\dfrac{1}{4} - 1\dfrac{1}{28}$

㉒ $1\dfrac{1}{12} - \dfrac{3}{4}$

Subtract the smaller fraction from the larger one for each pair of fractions. Show your work.

㉓ $\dfrac{1}{2}$, $\dfrac{2}{3}$ _____ = _____

㉔ $\dfrac{1}{4}$, $\dfrac{1}{3}$ _____ = _____

㉕ $\dfrac{1}{5}$, $\dfrac{3}{7}$ _____ = _____

㉖ $\dfrac{3}{4}$, $\dfrac{7}{8}$ _____ = _____

Fill in the boxes.

㉗ $\dfrac{5}{9} - \dfrac{\square}{9} = \dfrac{1}{9}$

㉘ $\dfrac{1}{4} - \dfrac{1}{6} = \dfrac{1}{\square}$

㉙ $\dfrac{1}{2} - \dfrac{1}{\square} = \dfrac{1}{6}$

㉚ $\dfrac{\square}{5} - \dfrac{1}{10} = \dfrac{1}{2}$

㉛ $\dfrac{\square}{3} + \dfrac{2}{9} = \dfrac{8}{9}$

㉜ $\dfrac{1}{\square} + \dfrac{1}{3} = \dfrac{7}{12}$

Find the differences. Change the whole numbers to improper fractions before subtracting. Show your work.

㉝ $3 - 1\dfrac{5}{6} - \dfrac{1}{3} =$ _____

$=$ _____

㉞ $5 - 3\dfrac{3}{14} - 1\dfrac{4}{7} =$ _____

$=$ _____

㉟ $4 - \dfrac{2}{5} - 1\dfrac{3}{10} =$ _____

$=$ _____

㊱ $3 - \dfrac{3}{4} - 1\dfrac{3}{8} =$ _____

$=$ _____

Write the subtraction sentences illustrated by the following diagrams and shade the last diagram to match each answer.

㊲

_____

㊳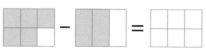

_____

Solve the problems. Show your work.

㊴ Jim wants to paint $\frac{3}{4}$ of his living room on Saturday. He has already painted $\frac{2}{3}$ of the room. What fraction of the room remains to be painted to meet his target?

_____ of the room remains to be painted.

㊵ Sandy has to wait $\frac{2}{3}$ hour for a train. What fraction of an hour does she still have to wait after $\frac{1}{2}$ hour?

㊶ Bob spent $2\frac{1}{12}$ hours to do his homework on Monday and $1\frac{1}{3}$ hours on Tuesday. How much longer did he spend on Monday than Tuesday?

㊷ Sally read $\frac{1}{12}$ of a story book on Saturday and $\frac{1}{3}$ on Sunday.

a. By what fraction of the whole book did she read on Saturday less than that on Sunday?

b. What fraction of the book has not been read by Sally?

㊸ Tom bought an apple pie. Bob ate $\frac{1}{4}$ of it and Sally ate $\frac{1}{6}$. What fraction of the pie was left for Tom?

Look for the pattern. Write the next 3 terms.

20   18   2   16   14   2   _____   _____   _____

Multiplying Fractions by Whole Numbers

EXAMPLES

1. Calculate the product of 6 and $\frac{2}{3}$.

   $6 \times \frac{2}{3} = \frac{12}{3} = 4$ ⟵ multiply the numerator or $6 \times \frac{2}{3} = \frac{6}{1}^{2} \times \frac{2}{3}_{1} = 4$ ⟵ simplify before
   by the whole number   multiplying

   $6 \times \frac{2}{3} = \frac{2}{3} + \frac{2}{3} + \frac{2}{3} + \frac{2}{3} + \frac{2}{3} + \frac{2}{3} = 4$

2. What is $\frac{5}{8}$ of 4?

   $\frac{5}{8} \times 4 = \frac{20}{8} = \frac{5}{2} = 2\frac{1}{2}$ ⟵ convert the improper fraction to a mixed number

   ⌐ multiply the whole number by the numerator

3. $3\frac{1}{3} \times 6 = \frac{10}{3} \times 6$ ⟵ convert the mixed number   or $\frac{10}{3}_{1} \times \frac{6}{1}^{2} = 20$
                                   to an improper fraction

   $= \frac{60}{3}$ ⟵ multiply the whole number
              by the numerator

   $= 20$ ⟵ reduce to lowest terms

HINTS:

- Multiplying a fraction by a whole number is the repeated addition of a fraction.

  e.g. $3 \times \frac{1}{3} = \frac{1}{3} + \frac{1}{3} + \frac{1}{3} = 1$

- To multiply a fraction by a whole number, multiply the numerator by the whole number and reduce the product to lowest terms.

- To multiply a mixed number, change it to an improper fraction first.

- If the product is an improper fraction, change it to a mixed number.

- A shortcut : divide the whole number and the denominator by their common factor before multiplying.

Find the products.

① $\frac{1}{2} \times 2 =$ _____

② $\frac{1}{3} \times 3 =$ _____

③ $\frac{3}{2} \times 2 =$ _____

④ $\frac{5}{7} \times 7 =$ _____

⑤ $\frac{1}{4} \times 4 =$ _____

⑥ $\frac{3}{5} \times 5 =$ _____

⑦ $\frac{1}{5} \times 10 =$ _____   ⑧ $\frac{1}{7} \times 21 =$ _____   ⑨ $\frac{7}{10} \times 10 =$ _____

Find the products either by simplifying or multiplying the whole numbers by the numerators.

⑩ $\frac{3}{8} \times 2$ = _____

⑪ $\frac{1}{14} \times 7$ = _____

⑫ $\frac{1}{3} \times 2$ = _____

⑬ $\frac{1}{4} \times 2$ = _____

⑭ $\frac{1}{5} \times 4$ = _____

⑮ $\frac{1}{8} \times 2$ = _____

⑯ $\frac{1}{12} \times 9$ = _____

⑰ $\frac{1}{16} \times 4$ = _____

⑱ $\frac{1}{6} \times 3$ = _____

⑲ $\frac{1}{9} \times 6$ = _____

⑳ $\frac{1}{24} \times 8$ = _____

㉑ $\frac{1}{54} \times 9$ = _____

㉒ $\frac{1}{7} \times 5$ = _____

㉓ $\frac{2}{15} \times 5$ = _____

㉔ $\frac{1}{16} \times 12$ = _____

㉕ $\frac{5}{6} \times 18$ = _____

㉖ $16 \times \frac{7}{8}$ = _____

㉗ $14 \times \frac{5}{7}$ = _____

㉘ $10 \times \frac{3}{5}$ = _____

㉙ $15 \times \frac{2}{3}$ = _____

㉚ $39 \times \frac{7}{13}$ = _____

㉛ $\frac{7}{10} \times 100$ = _____

㉜ $\frac{8}{25} \times 100$ = _____

㉝ $\frac{3}{20} \times 40$ = _____

㉞ $\frac{5}{9} \times 63$ = _____

㉟ $\frac{7}{8} \times 56$ = _____

㊱ $\frac{7}{2} \times 8$ = _____

㊲ $144 \times \frac{7}{12}$ = _____

㊳ $\frac{3}{56} \times 7$ = _____

㊴ $80 \times \frac{5}{20}$ = _____

Find the products. Convert the mixed numbers to improper fractions before multiplying.

㊵ $2\frac{1}{2} \times 2$ = _____

= _____

㊶ $3\frac{1}{3} \times 3$ = _____

= _____

㊷ $1\frac{3}{8} \times 8$ = _____

= _____

㊸ $2\frac{2}{5} \times 5$ = _____

= _____

㊹ $10\frac{1}{2} \times 2$ = _____

= _____

㊺ $5\frac{2}{3} \times 3$ = _____

= _____

Find the products. Then list them from smallest to largest in (55).

(46) $\frac{4}{15} \times 20 =$ ______	(47) $\frac{5}{15} \times 10 =$ ______	(48) $\frac{7}{8} \times 12 =$ ______
(49) $\frac{2}{25} \times 30 =$ ______	(50) $\frac{1}{10} \times 25 =$ ______	(51) $\frac{1}{14} \times 49 =$ ______
(52) $\frac{1}{22} \times 121 =$ ______	(53) $\frac{5}{6} \times 10 =$ ______	(54) $2\frac{3}{16} \times 2 =$ ______
(55) ______		

Fill in the boxes.

(56) $\frac{1}{12} \times \square = \frac{5}{12}$

(57) $\frac{3}{\square} \times 5 = \frac{15}{17}$

(58) $\frac{\square}{18} \times 12 = \frac{2}{3}$

(59) $\frac{5}{\square} \times 2 = 5$

(60) $1\frac{1}{3} \times \square = 4$

(61) $\frac{5}{\square} \times 4 = 10$

(62) $\frac{3}{4} \times \square = 15$

(63) $21 \times \frac{4}{\square} = 12$

(64) $8 \times \frac{\square}{16} = \frac{3}{2}$

Calculate only those questions with a product between 1 and 2.

(65) $\frac{3}{2} \times 3 =$ ______	(66) $\frac{1}{2} \times 3 =$ ______	(67) $\frac{3}{7} \times 3 =$ ______
(68) $\frac{3}{25} \times 10 =$ ______	(69) $\frac{2}{77} \times 49 =$ ______	(70) $\frac{2}{3} \times 4 =$ ______
(71) $6 \times \frac{5}{9} =$ ______	(72) $\frac{4}{5} \times 7 =$ ______	(73) $10 \times \frac{11}{12} =$ ______

Find the quantities.

(74) $\frac{3}{4}$ of a year ______ months

(75) $\frac{1}{3}$ of a 24-box package of orange juice ______ boxes

(76) $\frac{1}{6}$ of a day ______ hours

(77) $\frac{2}{5}$ of September ______ days

(78) $\frac{1}{4}$ of a 12-can package of pop ______ cans

Solve the problems. Show your work.

⑦⑨ A cake recipe calls for $\frac{2}{3}$ cup of sugar. Judy wants to make double the recipe. How much sugar does she need?

She needs _____ cups of sugar.

⑧⓪ Bob buys 3 bags of flour. Each bag contains $1\frac{1}{2}$ lbs of flour. How much flour does he buy?

⑧① A juice glass holds $\frac{1}{3}$ litre. How much juice is needed to fill 12 glasses?

⑧② Michelle, Mike and Mandy each watch TV for $1\frac{3}{4}$ hours on Monday. How much TV do they watch among them?

⑧③ Mrs Jones serves chicken soup for dinner. Mr and Mrs Jones and 4 older children have $\frac{1}{2}$ litre each, and the 3 smaller children have $\frac{1}{3}$ litre each. How much soup is consumed?

Find the number.

I'm a whole number. One-eighth of me is $1\frac{7}{8}$. What number am I?

The number is _____.

Dividing Whole Numbers by Fractions

1. What is the reciprocal of $\frac{3}{4}$?

   Reciprocal of $\frac{3}{4}$ is $\frac{4}{3}$ ⟵ switch the numerator and denominator

2. How many quarters are there in 2?

   $2 \div \frac{1}{4}$

   $= 2 \times \frac{4}{1}$ ⟵ multiply by the reciprocal of the divisor

   $= 8$

   There are eight quarters in 2.

3. How many $\frac{2}{3}$ pizzas are there in 4 pizzas?

   $4 \div \frac{2}{3}$ or $4 \div \frac{2}{3}$

   $= 4 \times \frac{3}{2}$ $= \overset{2}{4} \times \frac{3}{2_1}$ ⟵ simplify before multiplying

   $= \frac{12}{2}$ $= 2 \times 3$

   $= 6$ ⟵ reduce the answer to lowest terms $= 6$

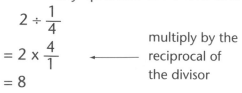

Write the reciprocal of each fraction.

① $\frac{7}{6}$ _____

② $\frac{4}{5}$ _____

③ $\frac{9}{10}$ _____

④ $\frac{7}{8}$ _____

⑤ $\frac{5}{7}$ _____

⑥ $\frac{4}{11}$ _____

⑦ $\frac{2}{4}$ _____

⑧ $\frac{5}{6}$ _____

⑨ $\frac{1}{4}$ _____

⑩ $\frac{1}{8}$ _____

⑪ $\frac{6}{13}$ _____

⑫ $\frac{8}{12}$ _____

⑬ $\frac{2}{9}$ _____

⑭ $\frac{1}{15}$ _____

HINTS:

- The reciprocal of a fraction is the fraction with the numerator and denominator switched.

  e.g. the reciprocal of $\frac{2}{3}$ is $\frac{3}{2}$

- To divide a whole number by a fraction, multiply the whole number by the reciprocal of the fraction.

- If the divisor is a mixed number, change it to an improper fraction before multiplying.

- Remember to reduce the answer to lowest terms.

- A shortcut : divide the whole number and the denominator of the reciprocal by their common factor before multiplying.

Do the division mentally.

⑮ $3 \div \dfrac{1}{2}$ = _____ ⑯ $4 \div \dfrac{1}{3}$ = _____ ⑰ $2 \div \dfrac{1}{3}$ = _____

⑱ $5 \div \dfrac{1}{2}$ = _____ ⑲ $10 \div \dfrac{1}{3}$ = _____ ⑳ $2 \div \dfrac{1}{5}$ = _____

㉑ $1 \div \dfrac{1}{6}$ = _____ ㉒ $15 \div \dfrac{1}{2}$ = _____ ㉓ $7 \div \dfrac{1}{5}$ = _____

㉔ $1 \div \dfrac{1}{14}$ = _____ ㉕ $2 \div \dfrac{1}{10}$ = _____ ㉖ $9 \div \dfrac{1}{12}$ = _____

㉗ $100 \div \dfrac{1}{2}$ = _____ ㉘ $25 \div \dfrac{1}{3}$ = _____ ㉙ $32 \div \dfrac{1}{2}$ = _____

Calculate.

㉚ $6 \div \dfrac{2}{3}$ = _____ ㉛ $12 \div \dfrac{2}{7}$ = _____ ㉜ $5 \div \dfrac{5}{9}$ = _____

㉝ $15 \div \dfrac{5}{6}$ = _____ ㉞ $12 \div \dfrac{4}{5}$ = _____ ㉟ $10 \div \dfrac{10}{13}$ = _____

㊱ $20 \div \dfrac{10}{17}$ = _____ ㊲ $100 \div \dfrac{50}{51}$ = _____ ㊳ $4 \div \dfrac{4}{7}$ = _____

㊴ $14 \div \dfrac{7}{8}$ = _____ ㊵ $18 \div \dfrac{9}{11}$ = _____ ㊶ $30 \div \dfrac{6}{7}$ = _____

Change the mixed numbers to improper fractions, and then calculate.

㊷ $6 \div 1\dfrac{1}{2}$

= _____

= _____

㊸ $10 \div 1\dfrac{1}{4}$

= _____

= _____

㊹ $5 \div 1\dfrac{2}{3}$

= _____

= _____

Write the quotients as mixed numbers.

㊺ $3 \div \dfrac{2}{3}$ = _____ ㊻ $7 \div \dfrac{2}{5}$ = _____ ㊼ $6 \div \dfrac{4}{5}$ =

Complete the chart below following the given example.

Diagram	Division Sentence
Example 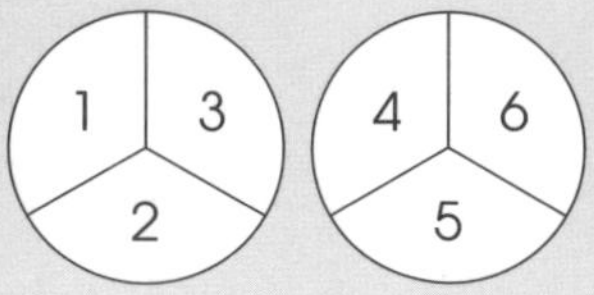 (two circles divided in thirds: circle 1 contains 1, 2, 3; circle 2 contains 4, 5, 6)	$2 \div \dfrac{1}{3} = 6$
48 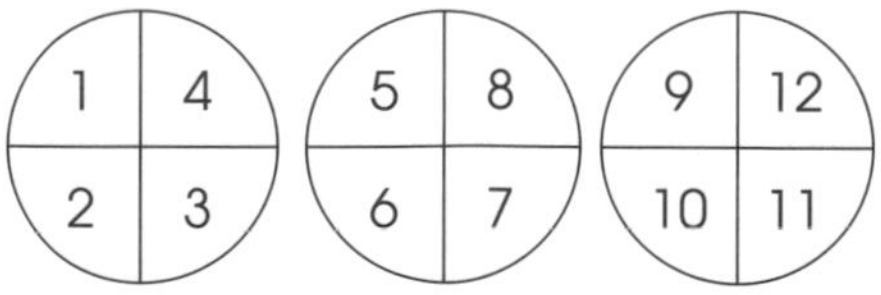 (three circles divided in quarters: 1, 2, 3, 4; 5, 6, 7, 8; 9, 10, 11, 12)	
49	$2 \div \dfrac{1}{4} =$
50 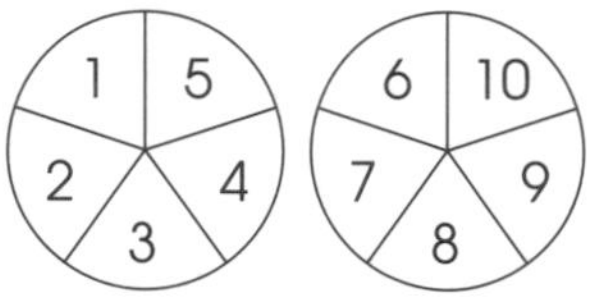 (two circles divided in fifths: 1, 2, 3, 4, 5; 6, 7, 8, 9, 10)	
51	$3 \div \dfrac{1}{2} =$
52 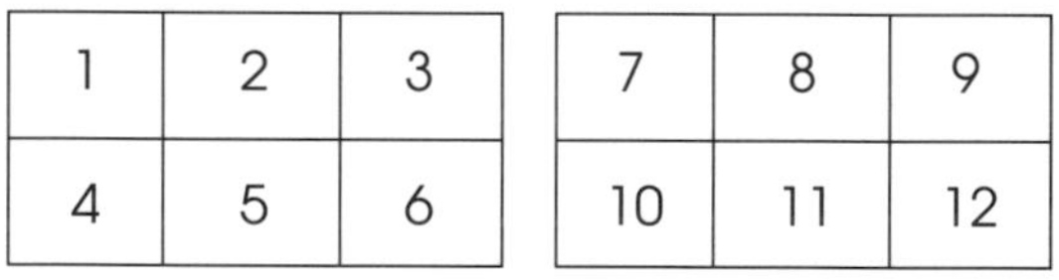 (two rectangles divided into six boxes: 1, 2, 3, 4, 5, 6; 7, 8, 9, 10, 11, 12)	
53	$1 \div \dfrac{1}{8} =$
54 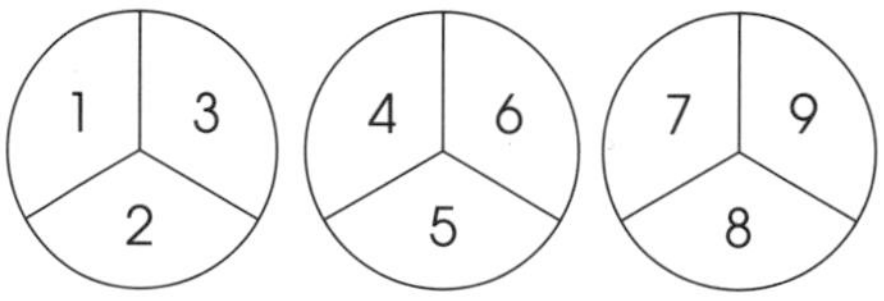 (three circles divided in thirds: 1, 2, 3; 4, 5, 6; 7, 8, 9)	
55	$1 \div \dfrac{1}{4} =$
56	$3 \div \dfrac{1}{5} =$

Fill in the boxes.

57) $12 \div \boxed{} = 24$

58) $\boxed{} \div \dfrac{1}{3} = 12$

59) $2 \div \boxed{} = 8$

60) $\boxed{} \div \dfrac{2}{3} = 3$

61) $3 \div \boxed{} = 2$

62) $\boxed{} \div 2\dfrac{1}{2} = 4$

Solve the problems. Show your work.

63) 6 pizzas are ordered for a class party. If each student eats $\dfrac{3}{8}$ of a pizza, how many students can have pizza?

_____ students can have pizza.

64) Bob has $3 in his pocket and all the coins are quarters. How many coins does Bob have?

65) Carol buys 3 cakes for her birthday party. If each guest can have $\dfrac{1}{8}$ of a cake, how many guests are there at Carol's party?

66) Barbara has 6 metres of fabric to make mini skirts. Each skirt needs $1\dfrac{1}{2}$ metres of fabric. How many skirts can Barbara make?

Just for Fun

What is the number?

Bob and Sally are facing each other. Bob writes a four-digit number between 1500 and 2000 on a transparency. Sally reads the same number on the opposite side without inverting or flipping the transparency. The four-digit number is _____.

 **More Operations with Fractions**

1. $\dfrac{3}{5} \times 4\dfrac{1}{6}$ or $\dfrac{3}{5} \times 4\dfrac{1}{6}$

$= \dfrac{3}{5} \times \dfrac{25}{6}$ ⟵ convert the mixed number to an improper fraction

$= \dfrac{75}{30}$ ⟵ multiply the numerators and multiply the denominators

$= \dfrac{5}{2}$ ⟵ reduce to lowest terms

$= 2\dfrac{1}{2}$ ⟵ change back to a mixed number

$= \dfrac{3}{\underset{1}{5}} \times \dfrac{\overset{5}{25}}{\underset{2}{6}}$ ⟵ simplify by dividing the numerators and denominators by their common factors

$= \dfrac{5}{2}$

$= 2\dfrac{1}{2}$

2. $\dfrac{4}{5} \div \dfrac{2}{5}$ — invert the fraction immediately after ÷ sign and change ÷ to x

$= \dfrac{4}{\underset{1}{5}} \times \dfrac{\overset{1}{5}}{2}$ ⟵ simplify by dividing the numerator and denominator by their common factor 5

$= \dfrac{\overset{2}{4}}{1} \times \dfrac{1}{\underset{1}{2}}$ ⟵ simplify by dividing the numerator and denominator by their common factor 2

$= 2$

HINTS:

- To multiply two fractions, multiply their numerators and denominators respectively.

- A shortcut : simplify the fractions by dividing the numerators and denominators by their common factors.

- Change mixed numbers to improper fractions before multiplying.

- Remember to reduce the answer to lowest terms.

Find the answers mentally. All the answers are whole numbers.

① $\dfrac{2}{3} \times \dfrac{3}{2}$ = _____

② $\dfrac{9}{8} \times \dfrac{8}{3}$ = _____

③ $\dfrac{5}{7} \times \dfrac{14}{5}$ = _____   ④ $\dfrac{2}{3} \div \dfrac{1}{3}$ = _____   ⑤ $\dfrac{6}{11} \div \dfrac{2}{11}$ = _____

⑥ $\dfrac{4}{9} \times \dfrac{9}{2}$ = _____   ⑦ $\dfrac{5}{1} \times \dfrac{12}{5}$ = _____   ⑧ $\dfrac{15}{2} \times \dfrac{8}{3}$ = _____

⑨ $\dfrac{4}{7} \div \dfrac{2}{7}$ = _____   ⑩ $\dfrac{2}{3} \div \dfrac{1}{3}$ = _____   ⑪ $\dfrac{7}{5} \div \dfrac{7}{20}$ = _____

⑫ $\dfrac{16}{5} \div \dfrac{4}{5}$ = _____   ⑬ $\dfrac{3}{7} \div \dfrac{1}{7}$ = _____   ⑭ $\dfrac{7}{12} \div \dfrac{1}{12}$ = _____

Calculate. Show your work.

(15) $\dfrac{5}{9} \times \dfrac{18}{25}$

(16) $\dfrac{7}{8} \times \dfrac{4}{21}$

(17) $\dfrac{2}{3} \times \dfrac{12}{5}$

(18) $\dfrac{9}{4} \times \dfrac{8}{3}$

(19) $\dfrac{3}{2} \times \dfrac{2}{3}$

(20) $\dfrac{7}{12} \times \dfrac{2}{21}$

Calculate. Show your work.

(21) $\dfrac{3}{7} \div \dfrac{1}{2}$

(22) $\dfrac{4}{9} \div \dfrac{2}{3}$

(23) $\dfrac{1}{6} \div \dfrac{7}{12}$

(24) $\dfrac{5}{8} \div \dfrac{11}{12}$

(25) $\dfrac{7}{6} \div \dfrac{5}{6}$

(26) $\dfrac{3}{2} \div \dfrac{3}{4}$

Find the answers. Show your work.

(27) $1\dfrac{2}{3} \div \dfrac{1}{3}$

(28) $2\dfrac{1}{2} \div \dfrac{1}{4}$

(29) $2\dfrac{1}{2} \div 1\dfrac{1}{4}$

(30) $\dfrac{1}{2} \div 1\dfrac{1}{2}$

(31) $1\dfrac{1}{2} \times 1\dfrac{1}{3}$

(32) $\dfrac{2}{3} \times 1\dfrac{1}{2}$

(33) $\dfrac{3}{7} \times 2\dfrac{1}{3}$

(34) $\dfrac{1}{5} \times 2\dfrac{1}{2}$

(35) $3\dfrac{1}{8} \times 1\dfrac{1}{5}$

(36) $6\dfrac{2}{3} \times 2\dfrac{1}{4}$

(37) $3\dfrac{2}{5} \div 1\dfrac{2}{3}$

(38) $7\dfrac{1}{2} \div \dfrac{5}{6}$

Find the answers to the following multi-step questions. Show the steps. Remember to multiply or divide before adding or subtracting.

㉟ $3 - \dfrac{1}{2} \times 5$	㊵ $\dfrac{2}{3} + \dfrac{1}{3} \times 5$
㊶ $\dfrac{1}{2} \times \dfrac{2}{3} + \dfrac{1}{3} \times 2$	㊷ $\dfrac{1}{2} - \dfrac{1}{2} \div 2$
㊸ $\dfrac{1}{6} \times \dfrac{2}{3} \div \dfrac{1}{2}$	㊹ $2\dfrac{2}{5} \times \dfrac{7}{12} \div 7$
㊺ $\dfrac{6}{7} + 5\dfrac{5}{7} \times \dfrac{5}{8}$	㊻ $2\dfrac{7}{8} - 4\dfrac{1}{2} \div 2\dfrac{2}{5}$

Do the following questions using division and illustrate your answers with diagrams.

Example   How many quarters are there in $1\dfrac{1}{4}$?
$$1\dfrac{1}{4} \div \dfrac{1}{4} = \dfrac{5}{4} \times \dfrac{4}{1} = 5$$

㊼ How many thirds are there in $1\dfrac{2}{3}$?

㊽ How many halves are there in $1\dfrac{1}{2}$?

㊾ How many sixths are there in $1\dfrac{5}{6}$?

Solve the problems. Show your work.

㊿ Brian works for $1\frac{1}{4}$ hours on his Math homework. Barry only works half as long. How long does Barry spend on his Math homework?

Barry spends _____ hour on his Math homework.

51 An oak tree is $9\frac{1}{2}$ m tall. A willow tree is half as tall as the oak tree. How tall is the willow tree?

52 Sue's garden is a rectangle which measures $2\frac{1}{2}$ metres by $1\frac{1}{2}$ metres. Calculate:

a. the perimeter of the garden.

b. the area of the garden.

53 A pizza parlour makes 7 pizzas. 12 people buy $\frac{1}{8}$ of a pizza each and 5 people buy $\frac{1}{2}$ a pizza each. How much pizza is left?

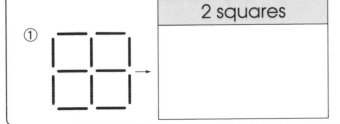 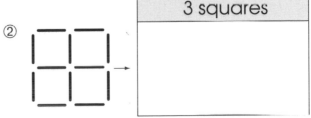

Draw the new pattern in each box.
Remove 2 sticks in each case to form the required pattern.

Circle the letter which represents the correct answer in each problem.

① 1.2 + 3.4 x 2 equals

    A. 9.2   B. 4.6   C. 8.0   D. 6.8

② 12.2 ÷ 2 − 1 equals

    A. 12.2   B. 6.0   C. 1.22   D. 5.1

③ $\frac{144}{160}$ reduced to lowest terms is

    A. $\frac{7}{8}$ B. $\frac{9}{10}$ C. $\frac{72}{80}$ D. $\frac{12}{40}$

④ Which statement is correct?

    A. $\frac{3}{2} < \frac{3}{4}$ B. $\frac{2}{3} > \frac{3}{4}$ C. $\frac{3}{4} > \frac{2}{3}$ D. $\frac{3}{4} = \frac{2}{3}$

⑤ $\frac{5}{12} - \frac{1}{12}$ in lowest terms is

    A. $\frac{4}{12}$ B. $\frac{6}{12}$ C. $\frac{1}{2}$ D. $\frac{1}{3}$

⑥ The sum of $\frac{1}{2} + \frac{2}{3}$ is

    A. $\frac{7}{6}$ B. $\frac{3}{5}$ C. $\frac{3}{6}$ D. $\frac{2}{6}$

⑦ The number of quarters in $2\frac{3}{4}$ is

    A. 5   B. 11   C. 12   D. 16

⑧ $3 ÷ \frac{1}{2}$ equals

    A. $\frac{3}{2}$ B. 2   C. 6   D. $4\frac{1}{2}$

⑨ $\frac{2}{3} × 1\frac{1}{2}$ equals

    A. 1   B. $1\frac{1}{3}$ C. $\frac{1}{3}$ D. $1\frac{1}{21}$

⑩ $\frac{3}{4} - \frac{1}{3}$ equals

A. 2   B. $\frac{1}{6}$ C. $\frac{5}{12}$ D. $\frac{1}{2}$

⑪ Half of $3\frac{1}{4}$ is

A. $1\frac{1}{8}$ B. $6\frac{1}{2}$ C. $1\frac{1}{2}$ D. $1\frac{5}{8}$

⑫ The sum of 2 fractions is $\frac{1}{2}$. One of the fractions is $\frac{1}{8}$. The other fraction is

A. $\frac{3}{8}$ B. $\frac{5}{8}$ C. $\frac{1}{4}$ D. $\frac{1}{6}$

⑬ $1 \div \frac{3}{4}$ equals

A. $\frac{3}{4}$ B. $1\frac{1}{3}$ C. $1\frac{1}{4}$ D. $1\frac{3}{4}$

⑭ The sum of $\frac{1}{4} + \frac{1}{6}$ in lowest terms is

A. $\frac{1}{10}$ B. $\frac{1}{5}$ C. $\frac{5}{12}$ D. $\frac{10}{24}$

⑮ The least common multiple of 12 and 18 is

A. 36   B. 72   C. 216   D. 9

⑯ Which of the following fractions is the smallest?

A. $\frac{5}{6}$ B. $\frac{2}{3}$ C. $\frac{3}{4}$ D. $\frac{7}{12}$

⑰ $\frac{132}{144}$ in lowest terms is

A. $\frac{13}{14}$ B. $\frac{11}{12}$ C. $\frac{66}{72}$ D. $\frac{44}{48}$

⑱ The answer to $\frac{1}{2} + \frac{1}{2} \times \frac{1}{2}$ is

A. $\frac{1}{2}$ B. $\frac{3}{2}$ C. $\frac{1}{4}$ D. $\frac{3}{4}$

19. What is $\frac{8}{25}$ of 100?

    A. 32   B. $100\frac{8}{25}$ C. $\frac{108}{25}$ D. $99\frac{17}{25}$

20. A jug is used to fill 6 glasses of juice. If the jug holds 2 litres, how much juice is in each glass?

    A. $\frac{1}{6}$ litre   B. $\frac{1}{3}$ litre   C. 6 litres   D. 12 litres

21. Paul works for $1\frac{3}{4}$ hours. He is paid $6 per hour. How much does he earn?

    A. $7.75   B. $7.50   C. $10.50   D. $12.00

22. A box of paper weighs $\frac{1}{2}$ kg. How many boxes of paper weigh $4\frac{1}{2}$ kg?

    A. 9   B. 4   C. $2\frac{5}{6}$ D. 5

23. The area of a square with length $\frac{3}{4}$ m is

    A. $\frac{6}{8}$ m^2 B. 3 m^2 C. $\frac{6}{4}$ m^2 D. $\frac{9}{16}$ m^2

24. The perimeter of the square in 23 is

    A. $\frac{6}{8}$ m   B. 3 m   C. $\frac{6}{4}$ m   D. $\frac{9}{16}$ m

Write the answers in simplest form.

25. $\frac{3}{4} + \frac{1}{5} = $ _____

26. $2\frac{3}{7} + 1\frac{5}{14} = $ _____

27. $1\frac{1}{4} + \frac{5}{8} = $ _____

28. $8 - 2\frac{7}{10} = $ _____

29. $\frac{1}{3} - \frac{1}{4} = $ _____

30. $2\frac{1}{5} - 1\frac{13}{20} = $ _____

31. $20 \times \frac{5}{12} = $ _____

32. $9\frac{3}{5} \times 2 = $ _____

33. $6\frac{2}{3} \times 2\frac{1}{4} = $ _____

34. $\frac{21}{23} \div 7 = $ _____

35. $\frac{5}{9} \div \frac{1}{3} = $ _____

36. $\frac{11}{14} \div \frac{22}{35} = $ _____

③⑦ $1\frac{5}{6} - \frac{3}{4} = $ _____

③⑧ $\frac{8}{15} \times \frac{5}{24} = $ _____

③⑨ $3 \div \frac{2}{7} = $ _____

④⓪ $8 \times \frac{3}{16} = $ _____

④① $\frac{5}{6} \div 15 = $ _____

④② $4\frac{2}{5} + 3\frac{7}{10} = $ _____

④③ $2\frac{1}{2} + \frac{1}{4} + \frac{1}{8} = $ _____

④④ $6 - 2\frac{1}{2} - 1\frac{5}{6} = $ _____

④⑤ $5\frac{5}{6} - \frac{1}{2} + \frac{1}{3} = $ _____

④⑥ $3\frac{1}{2} + 1\frac{5}{6} - \frac{3}{4} = $ _____

④⑦ $1\frac{7}{18} + \frac{1}{6} - \frac{2}{3} = $ _____

④⑧ $5 - 2\frac{2}{5} + \frac{3}{10} = $ _____

Fill in the boxes.

④⑨ $2 \div \boxed{} = 6$

⑤⓪ $\boxed{} \times \frac{2}{3} = 1\frac{1}{3}$

⑤① $\frac{1}{2} + \boxed{} = \frac{5}{6}$

⑤② $\frac{5}{8} - \boxed{} = \frac{1}{2}$

⑤③ $\frac{16}{3} \div \boxed{} = 1$

⑤④ $\frac{16}{3} \times \boxed{} = 1$

⑤⑤ $2\frac{1}{2} + \boxed{} = 4$

⑤⑥ $7\frac{1}{4} - \boxed{} = 6\frac{1}{2}$

⑤⑦ $3\frac{1}{4} \times \frac{4}{5} = \boxed{}$

State True (T) or False (F) for each statement.

⑤⑧ $\frac{3}{4} > \frac{5}{7}$ ⬭

⑤⑨ $2\frac{1}{2} = \frac{10}{4}$ ⬭

⑥⓪ $\frac{3}{4} + \frac{3}{5} = \frac{6}{9}$ ⬭

⑥① $\frac{1}{2} + \frac{2}{3} < 1$ ⬭

⑥② $\frac{121}{77} = \frac{22}{14}$ ⬭

⑥③ $100 \div \frac{1}{4} = 25$ ⬭

⑥④ $100 \times \frac{1}{4} = 25$ ⬭

⑥⑤ $\frac{100}{25} = \frac{1}{4}$ ⬭

⑥⑥ $\frac{25}{125} = \frac{2}{10}$ ⬭

⑥⑦ $2\frac{1}{3} < \frac{7}{3}$ ⬭

Solve the problems. Show your work.

68   Ben is reading a book with 320 pages. He read $\frac{3}{16}$ of the book on the first day and $\frac{1}{8}$ on the second day.

     a.   What fraction of the book did he read over the two days?

     b.   What fraction of the book remains to be read?

     c.   How many pages of the book remains to be read?

69   Bob has a bag of 100 marbles. $\frac{1}{4}$ of the marbles are either white or red. $\frac{1}{2}$ of the marbles are blue. 15 marbles are red.

     a.   How many marbles are either white or red?

     b.   How many marbles are white?

     c.   How many marbles are blue?

     d.   What fraction of the marbles are neither white, red nor blue?

70   John buys 5 loaves of bread at $1.79 each. He pays with a $10 bill. How much change does he get?

Section II

Overview

In Section I, fraction and decimal skills were emphasized. In this section, they are built upon and used in money and other applications.

Other topics included in this section are percent, ratio and rate applications. Students also learn the concepts of integers and number theory and the relationship between time, distance and speed.

Geometry units cover areas, perimeters, angles, symmetry, 2-D and 3-D figures, as well as mass and volume.

Data Management topics include bar and circle graphs. Probability applications include constructing tree diagrams.

Algebra is introduced in the context of evaluating algebraic expressions and solving simple equations. Transformation, coordinates and patterning are also included in this section.

Calculate. Do not use a calculator.

①
```
    4.03
-   2.98
```

②
```
    1806
    3904
+   4090
```

③
```
    5.43
x      6
```

④
```
      59
x     27
```

⑤
```
9 ) 7380
```

⑥
```
5 ) 32.4
```

Find the answers mentally.

⑦ 30 900 ÷ 300 = _____

⑧ 50 x 59 x 2 = _____

⑨ 4 x 12 x 25 = _____

⑩ 61.2 ÷ 6 = _____

⑪ 0.01 x 100 = _____

⑫ 801 ÷ 100 = _____

Use multiplication and addition to check each of the following answers. Put a check mark ✔ in the circle if the answer is correct.

⑬ 2955 ÷ 5 = 591   ◯ Check _____

⑭ 3939 ÷ 7 = 564   ◯ Check _____

⑮ 2390 ÷ 6 = 398...2   ◯ Check _____

Estimate each answer by rounding the number to the nearest ten or thousand. Put a check mark ✔ in the circle if the answer is reasonable.

⑯ 49 x 79 = 4081   ◯ Estimate _____

⑰ 3576 ÷ 8 = 447   ◯ Estimate _____

⑱ 52 x 41 = 213   ◯ Estimate _____

Complete the charts below.

⑲

Decimal	0.7	a.	b.	0.5	0.08	1.13
Fraction with 10 or 100 as denominator	$\frac{7}{10}$	$\frac{29}{100}$	$1\frac{35}{100}$	c.	d.	e.

⑳

Mixed number	$1\frac{1}{2}$	a.	b.	$1\frac{1}{4}$	$4\frac{2}{5}$	$3\frac{7}{8}$
Improper fraction	$\frac{3}{2}$	$\frac{7}{3}$	$\frac{31}{7}$	c.	d.	e.

Fill in the next 3 terms for each of the following patterns.

㉑ 1, 2, 4, 7, 11, _____ , _____ , _____

㉒ 2, 4, 8, 16, 32, _____ , _____ , _____

㉓ 3, 4, 6, 7, 9, _____ , _____ , _____

㉔ 100, 95, 85, 80, 70, _____ , _____ , _____

Calculate the area (A) and perimeter (P) of each of the following shapes.

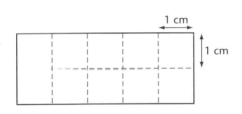
1 cm / 1 cm

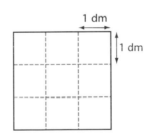
1 dm / 1 dm

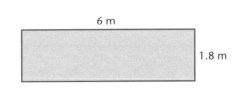
6 m / 1.8 m

㉕ A = _____ cm²

P = _____ cm

㉖ A = _____ dm²

P = _____ dm

㉗ A = _____ m²

P = _____ m

If Box A is 400 g, determine the mass of the other boxes and answer the question.

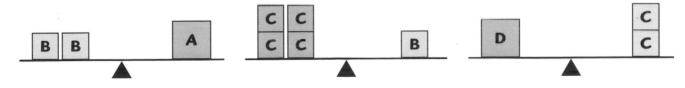

㉘ B = _____ g

㉙ C = _____ g

㉚ D = _____ g

㉛ How many D boxes would make up a mass of 1 kg ? _____

Answer the questions.

㉜ On Sports Day, 300 cans of coke were bought at $0.35 each. How much did they cost in all? $ _____

㉝ 20 boxes of biscuits were purchased at $2.75 per box. How much did they cost in all? $ _____

㉞ 15 boxes of biscuits purchased were eaten. What fraction of the biscuits purchased were left over?   _____

㉟ The students were divided into 36 equal teams of 9. How many students were there in all?   _____ students

㊱ Give 4 other possible ways to divide all the students into equal groups. Use a calculator if necessary.

_____ groups of _____ students; _____ groups of _____ students;

_____ groups of _____ students; _____ groups of _____ students

㊲ A jug holds 1.5 L of water. The water is poured equally into 10 glasses. How much water is in each glass?   _____ mL

Which of these nets would form a prism or a pyramid? Put a check mark ✔ in the circle for the net that could form a prism or a pyramid.

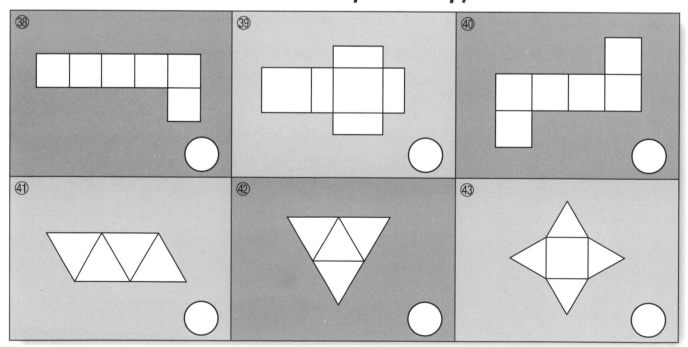

Write the coordinates of the points on the grid and complete the sentence.

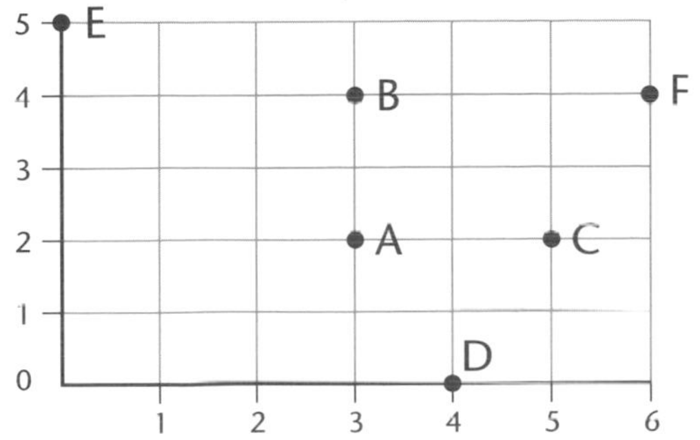

(44) A (____ , ____)　　B (____ , ____)

C (____ , ____)　　D (____ , ____)

E (____ , ____)　　F (____ , ____)

(45) The shape formed by joining A , B and C with straight lines is a ____________ .

Put a check mark ✔ in the circle if the shape can form a tiling pattern.

(46)

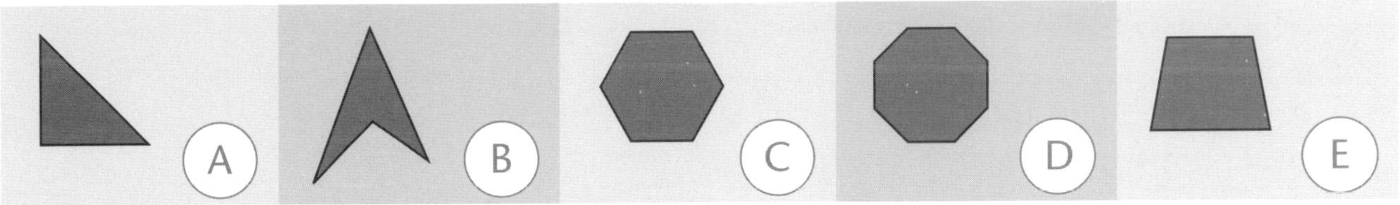

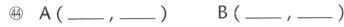

Draw the transformed images.

(47) Rotate the triangle $\frac{1}{2}$ turn.

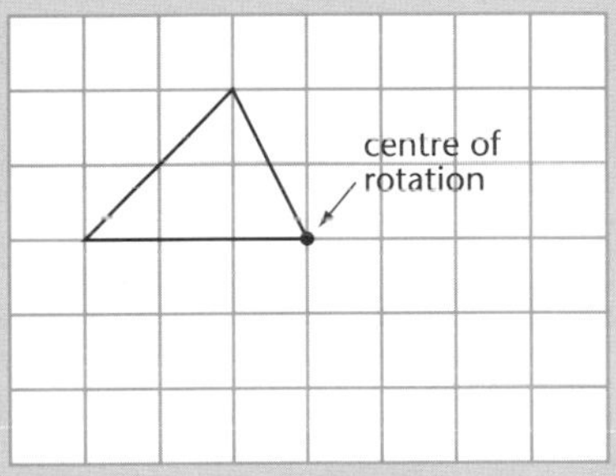

(48) Translate the triangle 4 units right and 1 unit down.

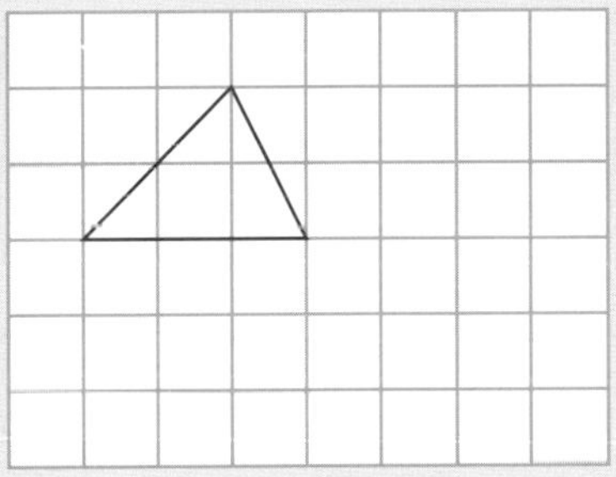

(49) Reflect the triangle in the line given.

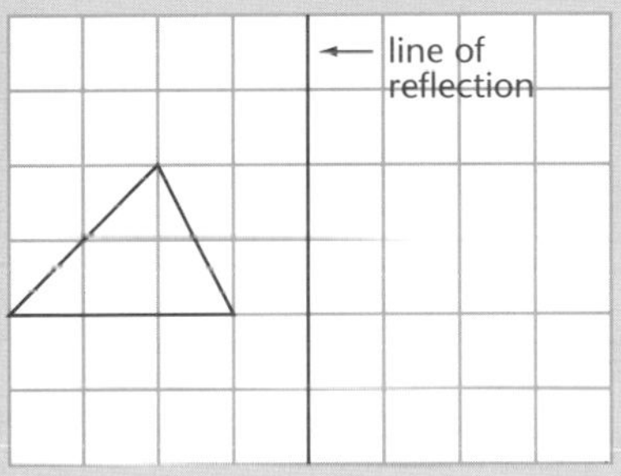

Look at the tiling pattern. Describe each of the following transformations. Write reflection, rotation or translation.

(50) B → C ____________

(51) A → D ____________

(52) C → F ____________

(53) A → E ____________

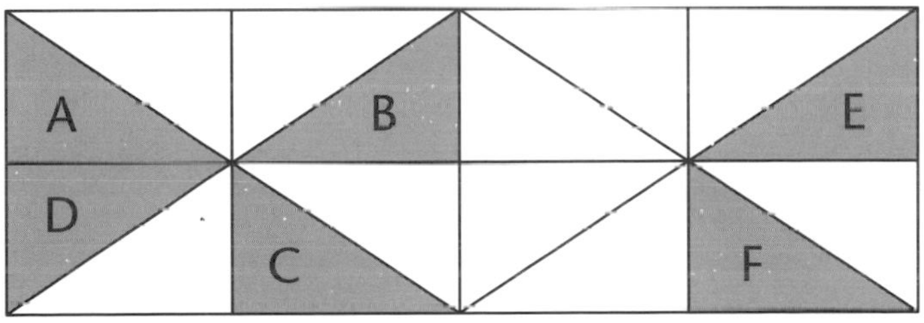

Find the volume of the stone and the apple.

(54) Volume of the stone = ________ cm^3

(55) Volume of the apple = ________ cm^3

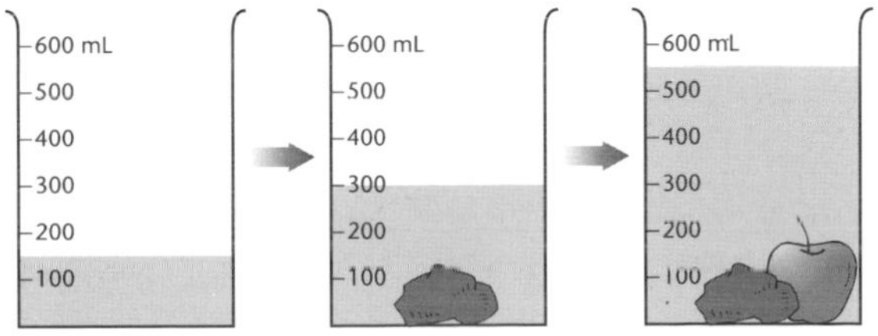

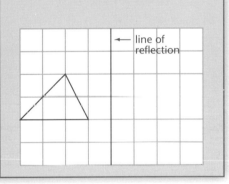

1 Operations with Whole Numbers

Find the sums or differences.

①
```
  1234
  3456
  5678
+  789
_____
```

②
```
  3926
  1503
  2198
+  492
_____
```

③
```
  8006
   123
   899
+    7
_____
```

**Quick Tip**

When doing addition, remember to add the correct digit carried over from the column to the right. It may be greater than 1 for addition with more than 2 addends.

④ 58 239 – 2120 = _____

⑤ 50 000 – 6348 = _____

Examples

① a 3-digit number x a 2-digit number

```
   239
x   28
_____
  1912
  4780
_____
  6692
```

Steps:
• Multiply the ones.
• Multiply the tens.
• Add the products.

② a 4-digit number ÷ a 2-digit number

```
       104 R6
    _____
25 ) 2 606
     2 5
    _____
      106
      100
    _____
        6
```

Steps:
• Divide the hundreds.
• Bring down the tens. Divide the tens.
• Bring down the ones. Divide the ones.
• Write the remainder.

Find the products.

⑥
```
   523
x   14
_____
```

⑦
```
   278
x   36
_____
```

⑧
```
   901
x   49
_____
```

⑨
```
   645
x   28
_____
```

Find the quotients.

⑩ 13) 598

⑪ 27) 4914

⑫ 36) 1408

⑬ 13) 5908

Estimate the answers by rounding each number to the nearest thousand. Then find the exact answers.

		Estimate	Answer
⑭	2398 + 1081 + 3008	_____ + _____ + _____ = _____	
⑮	5999 + 2198 + 991	_____ + _____ + _____ = _____	
⑯	12 345 – 1128	_____ – _____ = _____	
⑰	17 409 – 5280	_____ – _____ = _____	

Examples

Estimate the answers.

① 398 x 52 = _____
—— round to the nearest 100
—— round to the nearest 10

400 x 50 = 20 000
The product of 398 x 52 is close to 20 000.

② 6863 ÷ 33 = _____
—— round to the nearest 100
—— round to the nearest 10

6900 ÷ 30 = 230
The quotient of 6863 ÷ 33 is close to 230.

Estimate the products first by rounding the numbers to the nearest 10 or 100. Then find the exact answers.

⑱ 19 x 499 = _____   Estimate : _____ x _____ = _____

⑲ 208 x 21 = _____   Estimate : _____ x _____ = _____

⑳ 384 x 42 = _____   Estimate : _____ x _____ = _____

Estimate the quotients first by rounding the numbers to the nearest 10 or 1000. Then find the exact answers.

㉑ 5980 ÷ 52 = _____   Estimate : _____ ÷ _____ = _____

㉒ 2988 ÷ 19 = _____   Estimate : _____ ÷ _____ = _____

㉓ 4126 ÷ 38 = _____   Estimate : _____ ÷ _____ = _____

Estimate the following products and put a check mark ✔ in the circle for those products between 5000 and 6000.

㉔
A 498 x 15 ◯   B 198 x 19 ◯   C 501 x 11 ◯

D 230 x 34 ◯   E 292 x 18 ◯   F 149 x 38 ◯

G 21 x 251 ◯   H 98 x 59 ◯   I 61 x 103 ◯

Calculate. Use the correct order of operations.

㉕   51 + 92 − 2 x 12

     = 51 + 92 − _____

     = _____

㉖   123 + 51 ÷ 3 − 94

     = 123 + _____ − 94

     = _____

Quick Tip

For mixed operations, do x or ÷ first, and then do + or −.

㉗   15 x 20 + 17 x 2

     = _____

     = _____

㉘   32 x 16 − 28 ÷ 7

     = _____

     = _____

㉙   63 ÷ 9 + 45 x 8

     = _____

     = _____

See how many different kinds of coins each person has and help them solve the problems. Show your work.

	Ming	Susanna	Sam	Uncle Bill	Aunt Elaine
Quarter	12	108	56	458	0
Dime	15	0	0	0	192
Nickel	13	0	0	0	0

㉚   How much does Ming have?

     She has _____ ¢.

㉛   How much does Susanna have?

     She has _____ ¢.

㉜   Sam wants to change all his quarters into dimes. How many dimes can he get?

     He can get _____ dimes.

㉝   How much more money does Uncle Bill have than Aunt Elaine?

     Uncle Bill has _____ ¢ more than Aunt Elaine.

Keith loves to eat chocolate eggs. Help him solve the problems. Show your work.

㉞ Keith eats 12 chocolate eggs every day. How many chocolate eggs does he eat in a year with 365 days?

㉟ If one box contains 50 eggs, about how many boxes of chocolate eggs will Keith eat in a normal year?

㊱ Each small bag contains 58 chocolate eggs. Each big bag contains 96 chocolate eggs. Keith has 3 small bags and 2 big bags of chocolate eggs. How many chocolate eggs does he have in all?

㊲ Keith fills a jar with 2858 chocolate eggs for his friends to guess the number of chocolate eggs in it. Carol guesses 2732, Sarah guesses 2586, Oscar guesses 3726, Dave guesses 2866, and Stan guesses 3277. Whose guess is the closest?

㊳ The winner of the game divides the chocolate eggs into 30 bags. About how many chocolate eggs does each bag contain?

MIND BOGGLER

See how heavy a jar of chocolate eggs is . Answer the question.

The jar weighs 448 g and each chocolate egg weighs 24 g. How many chocolate eggs does the jar contain?

1 kg
1 kg
1 kg
1 kg

The jar contains _____ chocolate eggs.

Decimals

 Example

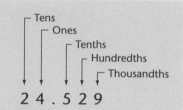

Standard form   Expanded form

24.529   = 20 + 4 + 0.5 + 0.02 + 0.009

In words : Twenty-four and five hundred twenty-nine thousandths   2 4 . 5 2 9

Tens — Ones — Tenths — Hundredths — Thousandths

Write each decimal number in expanded form and in words.

① 257.128   Expanded form : _____

              Words : _____

② 351.082   Expanded form : _____

              Words : _____

For the numbers given in expanded form, write them in standard form.

③ 5000 + 400 + 6 + 0.9 + 0.003   = _____

④ 600 + 20 + 0.5 + 0.08   = _____

Put each group of numbers in order from least to greatest using <.

⑤ 59.01   59.15   59.1   59.05   _____

⑥ 15.238   15.304   15.224   15.322   _____

Place the following decimal numbers on the number line below.

⑦ 0.42   0.4   0.05   0.35   0.18   0.29   0.09

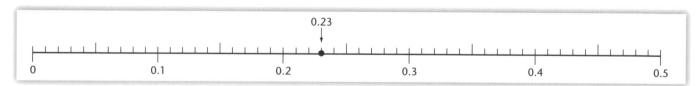

Write the value for each of the numbers on the number line below.

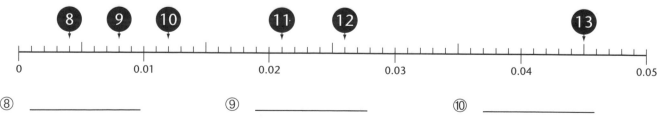

⑧ _____   ⑨ _____   ⑩ _____

⑪ _____   ⑫ _____   ⑬ _____

Add or subtract.

⑭ 28.46 + 21.59 = _____

⑮ 8.63 – 2.47 = _____

⑯ 12.95 – 1.08 = _____

⑰ 6.4 + 4.73 = _____

⑱ 3.745 – 2.339 = _____

⑲ 0.895 + 3.277 = _____

⑳ 4.26 – 3.954 = _____

㉑ 4.815 + 9.69 = _____

Examples

① 159.63 x 10 = 1596.3 ← Move the decimal point 1 place to the right.

↑
1 zero

159.63 x 100 = 15963 ← Move the decimal point 2 places to the right.

↑
2 zeros

② 12.3 x 200
= 12.3 x 100 x 2 ← Write 200 as 100x2.
= 1230 x 2 ← Multiply the decimal number by 100.
= 2460

Find the products mentally.

㉒ 29.36 x 100 = _____

㉓ 58.73 x 100 = _____

㉔ 139.05 x 10 = _____

㉕ 91.64 x 1000 = _____

㉖ 25.11 x 1000 = _____

㉗ 40.23 x 10 = _____

Find the products. Show your work.

㉘ 5.4 x 200 = 5.4 x 100 x _____

= _____

㉙ 8.5 x 90 = 8.5 x 10 x _____

= _____

㉚ 2.35 x 800 = _____

= _____

㉛ 12.4 x 60 = _____

= _____

Find the products.

㉜ 63.27 x 9 = _____

㉝ 4.53 x 6 = _____

㉞ 270.63 x 6 = _____

㉟ 162.59 x 4 = _____

㊱ 500.092 x 5 = _____

㊲ 327.461 x 7 = _____

㊳ 45.631 x 8 = _____

㊴ 88.64 x 3 = _____

Examples

① $392.6 \div 10 = 39.26$ ← Move the decimal point 1 place to the left.
↑
1 zero

$392.6 \div 100 = 3.926$ ← Move the decimal point 2 places to the left.
↑
2 zeros

②
Put a decimal point in the quotient above the one in the dividend.

$$\begin{array}{r} 98.09 \\ 4\overline{)392.36} \\ \underline{36} \\ 32 \\ \underline{32} \\ 36 \\ \underline{36} \end{array}$$

Don't forget to put a zero in the quotient as a place holder.

Find the quotients mentally.

④⓪ $58.23 \div 10$ = _____

④① $251.3 \div 100$ = _____

④② $246.5 \div 100$ = _____

④③ $425 \div 100$ = _____

④④ $285.9 \div 10$ = _____

④⑤ $239.4 \div 10$ = _____

Find the quotients.

④⑥
$$6\overline{)23.22}$$
_____
_____

④⑦
$$9\overline{)427.5}$$

④⑧
$$7\overline{)211.26}$$

④⑨
$$8\overline{)96.64}$$

⑤⓪ $9.232 \div 8$ = _____

⑤① $37.41 \div 5$ = _____

⑤② $30.092 \div 4$ = _____

⑤③ $20.64 \div 3$ = _____

⑤④ $28.609 \div 7$ = _____

⑤⑤ $38.506 \div 2$ = _____

Estimate the answers in the shaded boxes. Put a check mark ✔ in the circle if the answer is reasonable; otherwise put a cross X.

⑤⑥ 5.8×7 = **406.0** ◯

⑤⑦ $83.7 \div 6$ = **13.95** ◯

⑤⑧ $30.9 \div 6$ = **51.5** ◯

⑤⑨ $10.4 \div 4$ = **20.6** ◯

⑥⓪ 53.8×3 = **161.4** ◯

⑥① $100.3 \div 10$ = **10.03** ◯

Quick Tip

Round the numbers to the nearest whole number in order to estimate the answers.

Look at the flyer. Help Aunt Ann solve the problems.

62 2 boxes of shortcake weigh _____ kg.

63 3 boxes of shredded wheat weigh _____ kg.

64 6 kg of sausages cost $ _____ .

65 4 bags of apples cost $ _____ .

66 A pack of corned beef has 5 slices. 1 slice of corned beef costs $ _____ .

67 Aunt Ann pays 9 quarters for 1 bag of apples. How much more does she need to pay?

68 Aunt Ann wants to buy 3 kg of sausages and 2 kg of grapes. How much does she need to pay?

69 Aunt Ann buys 1 box of shredded wheat and divides the wheat equally into 3 portions. How many kg of shredded wheat are there in each portion?

 MIND BOGGLER

There are 2 boxes of shortcake and 3 packs of corned beef in the basket. If the total weight of the basket and the food is 3.085 kg, how many kilograms does the basket weigh?

The basket weighs _____ kg.

3 Integers and Number Theory

Examples

① Negative integers are used commonly:
- -20°C ← 20°C below 0°C
- -100 m ← 100 m below sea level
- -$200 ← $200 withdrawn

② If the temperature changes from 4°C to -2°C, it drops 6°C in all.

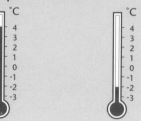

Write the value for each of the letters on the number line below.

①

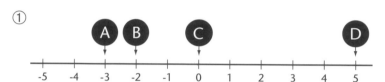

A _____   B _____

C _____   D _____

Circle the larger number in each pair of integers.

②		③		④		⑤	
-4	3	-3	-5	2	-2	0	-1
⑥		⑦		⑧		⑨	
-3	1	-2	-3	0	-5	-4	4

Record the temperature for each day. Then answer the questions.

⑩

SUN	MON	TUE	WED	THU	FRI	SAT
°C 4 3 2 1 0 -1 -2 -3 -4	°C 4 3 2 1 0 -1 -2 -3 -4	°C 4 3 2 1 0 -1 -2 -3 -4	°C 4 3 2 1 0 -1 -2 -3 -4	°C 4 3 2 1 0 -1 -2 -3 -4	°C 4 3 2 1 0 -1 -2 -3 -4	°C 4 3 2 1 0 -1 -2 -3 -4

⑪ Which day was colder, Sunday or Thursday? _____

⑫ Which day was the warmest? _____

⑬ In how many days was the temperature above 1°C? _____ days

⑭ On which day was the temperature 2°C higher than that on Monday? _____

Look at the 50-square chart and complete the following questions.

1	2	3	4	5	6	7	8	9	10
11	12	13	14	15	16	17	18	19	20
21	22	23	24	25	26	27	28	29	30
31	32	33	34	35	36	37	38	39	40
41	42	43	44	45	46	47	48	49	50

⑮ Circle the multiples of 4.

⑯ Cross the multiples of 6.

⑰ Colour the mutiples of 5 grey.

⑱ Numbers with ◯ are common multiples of 4 and _____ . They are _____ .

⑲ Numbers with ⊗ are common multiples of 4 and _____ . They are _____

_____ .

⑳ The least common multiple (L.C.M.) of 4 and 5 is _____ .

㉑ The least common multiple (L.C.M.) of 4 and 6 is _____ .

Write the first 10 multiples of each number.

㉒ 3 _____

㉓ 5 _____

㉔ 8 _____

㉕ 10 _____

Multiples of a number can be obtained by multiplying the number by 1, 2, 3, ... and so on. The smallest common multiple of a group of numbers is their least common multiple (L.C.M.).

Refer to question ㉒ to ㉕, list the first three common multiples of each group of numbers and write their least common multiple (L.C.M.).

		3 and 5	3 and 8	5 and 8	5 and 10
㉖	Common multiples				
㉗	L.C.M.				

Find the factors of each number and complete the sentences.

㉘ 12 = 1 x _____   ㉙ 20 ÷ 1 = _____

= 2 x _____   20 ÷ 2 = _____

= 3 x _____   20 ÷ 4 = _____

The factors of 12 :   The factors of 20 :

_____   _____

Numbers multiplied to form a product are called factors of the product.

You can use multiplication or division to find the factors of a number.

㉚ The common factors of 12 and 20 are _____ .

The greatest common factor of 12 and 20 is _____ .

COMPLETE MATHSMART (GRADE 6)   93

Find the factors of each number. List the common factors of each group of numbers and write their greatest common factor (G.C.F.).

			Common factors	G.C.F.
31	16 _____	18 _____		
32	15 _____	30 _____		
33	10 _____	24 _____		

Circle the prime numbers.

34

2	3	63	29	16	25	97
19	87	73	77	51	23	46
32	31	11	24	67	13	81

> **Quick Tip**
>
> Any number with only 1 and itself as factors is called a prime number. Numbers which are not prime are called composite numbers. 1 is neither a prime nor a composite number.

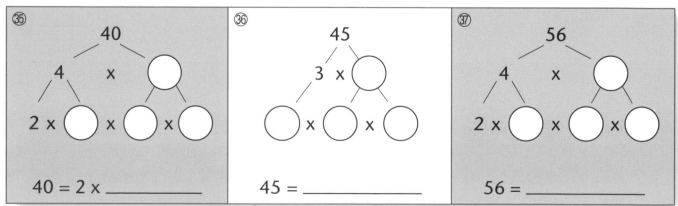

Example

Write 36 as a product of prime factors.

Factor tree

```
         36
        /  \
      4  x  9
     / \   / \
   2 x 2 x 3 x 3   ← prime numbers
```

36 = 2 x 2 x 3 x 3

> **Quick Tip**
>
> The number "1" is not used in factor trees.

Complete the factor trees and write each number as a product of prime factors.

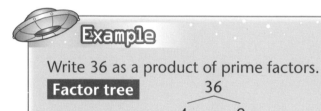

35
```
        40
       /  \
      4  x  ◯
     / \   / \
   2 x ◯ x ◯ x ◯
```
40 = 2 x _____

36
```
        45
       /  \
     3  x  ◯
          / \
   ◯ x ◯ x ◯
```
45 = _____

37
```
        56
       /  \
      4  x  ◯
     / \   / \
   2 x ◯ x ◯ x ◯
```
56 = _____

38 72 = _____

39 32 = _____

40 60 = _____

41 50 = _____

42 54 = _____

43 80 = _____

Example

Determine the G.C.F. and L.C.M. of 30 and 50.

30
2 x 15
2 x 3 x 5

50
2 x 25
2 x 5 x 5

```
common
factors

30 = [2] x 3 x [5]       product of
50 = [2]      x [5] x 5  common factors

G.C.F. = 2      x 5    = 10 ←   product of
L.C.M. = 2 x 3 x 5 x 5 = 150 ← common factors
                                and other factors
```

Write each number as a product of prime factors. Then determine the G.C.F. and L.C.M. of each group of numbers.

㊹ 21 = _____

28 = _____

G.C.F. = _____ L.C.M. = _____

㊺ 16 = _____

24 = _____

G.C.F. = _____ L.C.M. = _____

Complete the calculation.

㊻   7 x (3 + 4)

= 7 x ___ + 7 x ___

= ___ + ___

= ___

㊼   12 x (7 – 2)

= 12 x ___ – 12 x ___

= ___ – ___

= ___

 **Quick Tip**

Distributive property of multiplication:

5 x (10 + 6) = 5 x 10 + 5 x 6
              = 50 + 30
              = 80

㊽   9 x 27

= 9 x (20 + 7)

= 9 x ___ + 9 x ___

= ___ + ___

= ___

㊾   8 x 49

= 8 x (50 – 1)

= 8 x ___ – 8 x ___

= ___ – ___

= ___

㊿   5 x 98

= 5 x (100 – ___)

= 5 x ___ – 5 x ___

= ___ – ___

= ___

 MIND BOGGLER

Add or subtract. Then write even or odd to complete the sentences.

① 10 + 24 = ___   The sum of 2 even numbers is _____ .

② 37 – 15 = ___   The difference between 2 odd numbers is _____ .

③ 36 – 11 = ___   The difference between an even and an odd number is

_____ .

4 Percent

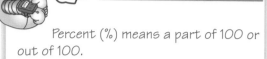
Rewrite the following percents using %.

① sixty-nine percent = _____

② one hundred percent = _____

③ 8 out of 100 = _____

④ 26 out of 100 = _____

⑤ $\frac{42}{100}$ = _____

⑥ $\frac{7}{100}$ = _____

⑦ $\frac{83}{100}$ = _____

⑧ $\frac{98}{100}$ = _____

Write the percent that represents the shaded part of each 100-square grid.

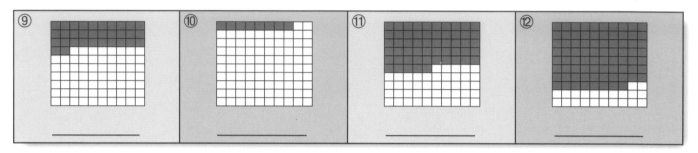

⑨ _____ ⑩ _____ ⑪ _____ ⑫ _____

Colour each 100-square grid according to the given percent.

⑬ 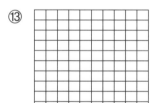   ⑭ 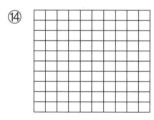   ⑮ 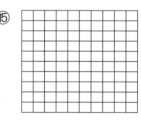   ⑯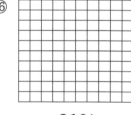

62%   24%   7%   91%

Look at the shapes. Then fill in the blanks.

⑰ There are _____ stars. _____ out of 100 shapes are stars. _____ % of the shapes are stars.

⑱ There are _____ circles. _____ out of 100 shapes are circles. _____ % of the shapes are circles.

⑲ There are _____ hearts. _____ out of 100 shapes are hearts. _____ % of the shapes are hearts.

Estimate the percent of the line segment represented by each mark.

⑳

0% _____ % _____ % _____ % 100%

㉑

0% _____ % _____ % _____ % 100%

Complete the following fractions and find the percents. Fill in the boxes.

Joshi gets 37 out of 50 on a test. What is his test percentage?

37 out of 50 = $\frac{37}{50}$ = $\frac{37 \times 2}{50 \times 2}$ = $\frac{74}{100}$ = 74% ← Write an equivalent fraction with 100 in the denominator.

㉒ $\frac{43}{50}$ = $\frac{}{100}$ = ☐ %   ㉓ $\frac{17}{20}$ = $\frac{}{100}$ = ☐ %

㉔ $\frac{9}{10}$ = $\frac{}{100}$ = ☐ %   ㉕ $\frac{130}{200}$ = $\frac{}{100}$ = ☐ %

㉖ $\frac{23}{25}$ = $\frac{}{100}$ = ☐ %   ㉗ $\frac{340}{400}$ = $\frac{}{100}$ = ☐ %

Write each percent as fraction in lowest terms.

㉘ 20% = _____   ㉙ 25% = _____   ㉚ 50% = _____

㉛ 75% = _____   ㉜ 82% = _____   ㉝ 8% = _____

㉞ 16% = _____   ㉟ 33% = _____   ㊱ 200% = _____

Rewrite the following percents as decimals.

㊲ 26% = _____   ㊳ 37% = _____

㊴ 95% = _____   ㊵ 66% = _____

㊶ 9% = _____   ㊷ 74% = _____

Write percents as fractions with 100 in the denominator first. Then write the fractions as decimals.

Circle the fraction closest in value to each percent.

㊸ 10% $\frac{1}{5}$ $\frac{1}{8}$ ㊹ 80% $\frac{19}{25}$ $\frac{3}{4}$

㊺ 66% $\frac{7}{10}$ $\frac{3}{5}$ ㊻ 43% $\frac{1}{2}$ $\frac{9}{20}$

COMPLETE MATHSMART (GRADE 6)   **97**

Complete the table.

	Percent	Decimal	Fraction with 100 as denominator	Fraction in lowest terms
㊼	70%			
㊽		0.6		
㊾			$\frac{45}{100}$	
㊿				$\frac{1}{20}$

Choose and write the percent that comes between each pair of numbers.

7%	78%	26%	52%	86%	11%

(51) 0.13 ______ $\frac{2}{5}$

(52) 0.8 ______ $\frac{3}{4}$

(53) $\frac{4}{5}$ ______ 0.92

(54) $\frac{2}{3}$ ______ 0.45

(55) $\frac{1}{20}$ ______ 0.2

(56) $\frac{1}{20}$ ______ 0.09

Write each group of numbers in order from least to greatest.

(57) $\frac{19}{50}$ 0.27 59% ____________________

(58) 0.93 64% $\frac{18}{25}$ ____________________

(59) 71% $\frac{3}{4}$ 0.73 ____________________

Complete the following fractions and statements.

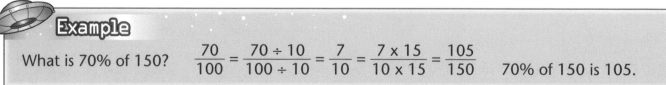

Example

What is 70% of 150? $\frac{70}{100} = \frac{70 \div 10}{100 \div 10} = \frac{7}{10} = \frac{7 \times 15}{10 \times 15} = \frac{105}{150}$ 70% of 150 is 105.

(60) $\frac{25}{100} = \frac{\quad}{300}$

25% of 300 is ______.

(61) $\frac{70}{100} = \frac{\quad}{50}$

70% of 50 is ______.

(62) $\frac{93}{100} = \frac{\quad}{200}$

93% of 200 is ______.

(63) $\frac{55}{100} = \frac{\quad}{20}$

55% of 20 is ______.

See how many cookies are in each group or each child has. Use % to complete each sentence and answer the questions.

⑥④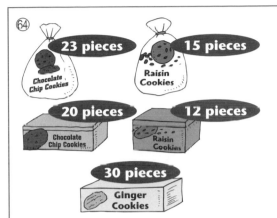

a. _____ of the cookies are chocolate chip cookies.

b. _____ of the cookies are raisin cookies.

c. _____ of the cookies are ginger cookies.

d. _____ of the cookies are in bags.

e. _____ of the cookies are in boxes.

⑥⑤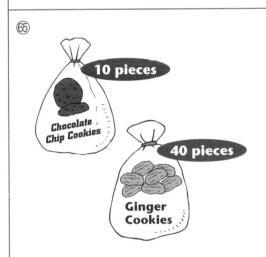

a. _____ of the cookies are chocolate chip cookies.

b. _____ of the cookies are ginger cookies.

c. Uncle Sam has a bag of ginger cookies and he eats 20 of them. He eats _____ of the ginger cookies.

d. Sue has a bag of chocolate chip cookies and she eats 4 of them. She eats _____ of the chocolate chip cookies.

⑥⑥ Tim has a box of 30 cookies; he eats 18 cookies. Ray has a box of 25 cookies; he eats 16 cookies. What percent of the cookies does each child eat? Who has eaten the higher percent of cookies?

 MIND BOGGLER

Read what Edmond says. Then tell why he is incorrect.

I have 100 marbles. There are the same number of marbles in each of the 4 colours. Each colour makes up 26% of the marbles.

_____

5 Fractions

Change each of the following improper fractions to mixed numbers and then find the message below by matching the letters with the mixed numbers.

① $\frac{3}{2}$ I ➤ _____ ② $\frac{9}{5}$ E ➤ _____

③ $\frac{17}{6}$ M ➤ _____ ④ $\frac{13}{6}$ K ➤ _____

⑤ $\frac{5}{4}$ F ➤ _____ ⑥ $\frac{13}{2}$ P ➤ _____

⑦ $\frac{29}{18}$ C ➤ _____ ⑧ $\frac{11}{5}$ R ➤ _____ ⑨ $\frac{7}{3}$ T ➤ _____

⑩ $\frac{7}{6}$ D ➤ _____ ⑪ $\frac{25}{18}$ S ➤ _____ ⑫ $\frac{23}{18}$ A ➤ _____

Quick Tip

Use division to convert an improper fraction to a mixed number.

e.g. $\frac{9}{5} = 1\frac{4}{5}$ $5\overline{)9}$ ... $\frac{5}{4}$

⑬

$6\frac{1}{2}$ _ $2\frac{1}{5}$ _ $1\frac{5}{18}$ _ $1\frac{11}{18}$ _ $2\frac{1}{3}$ _ $1\frac{1}{2}$ _ $1\frac{11}{18}$ _ $1\frac{4}{5}$ _ $2\frac{5}{6}$ _ $1\frac{5}{18}$ _ $2\frac{1}{6}$ _ $1\frac{4}{5}$ _ $1\frac{7}{18}$ _

$6\frac{1}{2}$ _ $1\frac{4}{5}$ _ $2\frac{1}{5}$ _ $1\frac{1}{4}$ _ $1\frac{4}{5}$ _ $1\frac{11}{18}$ _ $2\frac{1}{3}$ _ !

Put the following fractions in order from least to greatest using <.

⑭ $\frac{5}{8}$ $\frac{7}{8}$ $\frac{4}{8}$ _____

⑮ $\frac{9}{10}$ $\frac{9}{7}$ $\frac{9}{4}$ _____

⑯ $2\frac{4}{5}$ $3\frac{1}{5}$ $2\frac{3}{5}$ _____

⑰ $1\frac{5}{6}$ $1\frac{1}{6}$ $2\frac{5}{6}$ _____

Quick Tip

Fractions with the same denominator
The larger the numerator, the greater the value,

e.g. $\frac{2}{8} < \frac{5}{8}$

Fractions with the same numerator
The larger the denominator, the smaller the value,

e.g. $\frac{5}{9} < \frac{5}{4}$

Circle the smaller fraction in each pair.

⑱ $\frac{5}{2}$ $\frac{17}{6}$ ⑲ $\frac{7}{3}$ $\frac{8}{5}$ ⑳ $1\frac{1}{8}$ $\frac{13}{12}$

㉑ $\frac{13}{4}$ $\frac{17}{5}$ ㉒ $\frac{8}{3}$ $\frac{15}{6}$ ㉓ $\frac{12}{5}$ $\frac{5}{2}$

㉔ $\frac{23}{8}$ $\frac{16}{6}$ ㉕ $\frac{17}{4}$ $\frac{9}{2}$ ㉖ $\frac{11}{3}$ $\frac{16}{7}$

Quick Tip

Steps to compare fractions :

1st: Write the fractions as mixed numbers.

2nd: Compare the whole numbers. If they are the same, go to 3rd step.

3rd: Compare the fractions. Write the fractions with the same denominator and then compare their numerators.

Use fractions to write each addition or subtraction sentence. Write the answer in lowest terms.

Examples

① ⊕ + ⊕ = ⊕ = ◑

$$\frac{3}{8} + \frac{1}{8} = \frac{4}{8} = \frac{1}{2}$$

② ▦ − ▦ = ▦ = ▢

$$\frac{7}{8} - \frac{3}{8} - \frac{4}{8} = \frac{1}{2}$$

㉗ ▦ + ▦ = ▦

_____ + _____ = _____

㉘ ▦ + ▦ = ▦ = ▦

_____ + _____ = _____ = _____

㉙ ▦ − ▦ = ▦

_____ − _____ = _____

㉚ ⊕ − ⊕ = ⊕ = ◑

_____ − _____ = _____ = _____

Find the sums or differences. Reduce the answers to lowest terms.

㉛ $\dfrac{17}{18} - \dfrac{11}{18}$ = _____ = _____

㉜ $\dfrac{11}{20} + \dfrac{3}{20}$ = _____ = _____

㉝ $\dfrac{23}{30} + \dfrac{7}{30}$ = _____ = _____

㉞ $\dfrac{2}{15} + \dfrac{4}{15}$ = _____ = _____

㉟ $\dfrac{11}{25} + \dfrac{9}{25}$ = _____ = _____

㊱ $\dfrac{25}{42} - \dfrac{13}{42}$ = _____ = _____

㊲ $\dfrac{7}{12} - \dfrac{5}{12}$ = _____ = _____

Quick Tip

When adding or subtracting fractions with the same denominator, add or subtract the numerators. Remember to reduce the answers to lowest terms.

Use fractions to write each addition or subtraction sentence. Write each answer in lowest terms.

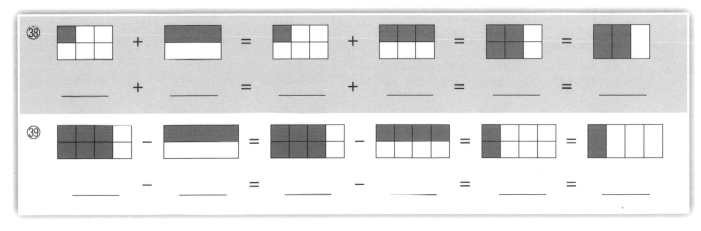

㊳ ▦ + ▦ = ▦ + ▦ = ▦ = ▦

_____ + _____ = _____ + _____ = _____ = _____

㊴ ▦ − ▦ = ▦ − ▦ = ▦ = ▦

_____ − _____ = _____ − _____ = _____ = _____

Write the numbers. Reduce your answers to lowest terms.

Quick Tip

Change the mixed numbers to improper fractions first. Then write equivalent fractions with a common denominator before adding or subtracting fractions with unlike denominators.

40 $\dfrac{1}{3} + \dfrac{1}{6}$ = $\dfrac{}{6}$ + $\dfrac{1}{6}$

= $\dfrac{}{6}$

= _____

41 $\dfrac{9}{10} - \dfrac{1}{2}$ = $\dfrac{9}{10}$ - $\dfrac{}{10}$

= $\dfrac{}{10}$

= _____

42 $1\dfrac{3}{4} - \dfrac{5}{8}$ = $\dfrac{}{4}$ - $\dfrac{5}{8}$

= $\dfrac{}{8}$ - $\dfrac{5}{8}$

= $\dfrac{}{8}$

= _____

43 $\dfrac{7}{12} + 1\dfrac{2}{3}$ = $\dfrac{7}{12}$ + $\dfrac{}{3}$

= $\dfrac{7}{12}$ + $\dfrac{}{12}$

= $\dfrac{}{12}$

= _____

Add or subtract. Reduce your answers to lowest terms. Show your work.

44 $\dfrac{1}{2} + \dfrac{1}{3} =$

45 $\dfrac{3}{5} - \dfrac{1}{3} =$

46 $2\dfrac{1}{3} - \dfrac{7}{15} =$

47 $3\dfrac{5}{6} - 1\dfrac{1}{4} =$

48 $1\dfrac{2}{5} + 2\dfrac{1}{10} =$

49 $1\dfrac{7}{8} + 2\dfrac{3}{4} =$

50 $1\dfrac{3}{4} - \dfrac{5}{8} =$

51 $3\dfrac{1}{3} - 2\dfrac{1}{4} =$

Look at the kinds of nuts the children have and answer the questions. Write all the fractions in lowest terms.

Steve

pistachios	$\frac{4}{5}$ kg
walnuts	$1\frac{3}{8}$ kg
pecans	$2\frac{2}{3}$ kg

Stan

pistachios	$1\frac{1}{2}$ kg
walnuts	$3\frac{1}{6}$ kg
pecans	$\frac{7}{12}$ kg

Bob

walnuts	$\frac{7}{8}$ kg
peanuts	$1\frac{1}{6}$ kg
pecans	$1\frac{1}{3}$ kg

㉒ How many kilograms of walnuts do Steve and Bob have? _____ kg

㉓ How many kilograms of pecans do Steve and Bob have? _____ kg

㉔ How many more kilograms of walnuts does Steve have than Bob? _____ kg

㉕ How many kilograms of pistachios do Steve and Stan have? _____ kg

㉖ How many kilograms of pecans do Stan and Bob have? _____ kg

㉗ How many more kilograms of pecans does Steve have than Stan? _____ kg

㉘ How many kilograms of nuts does Stan have? _____ kg

㉙ How many kilograms of nuts does Bob have? _____ kg

㉚ How many more kilograms of nuts does Stan have than Bob? _____ kg

㉛ Steve puts his pistachios into 2 bags. 1 bag weighs $\frac{2}{15}$ kg. How heavy is the other bag? _____ kg

MIND BOGGLER

See how Stan and Bob trade their nuts.

> Every $\frac{1}{3}$ kg of pecans can be traded for $\frac{1}{4}$ kg of pistachios. How many kilograms of pistachios can I get if I trade all my pecans to Stan?

Bob

Bob can get _____ kg of pistachios if he trades all his pecans to Stan.

6 Rate and Ratio

Example

Jim runs 14 km in 2 hours. At what rate does he run?

Rate: $14 \div 2 = 7$

His rate is 7 km/h (7 km per hour).

Quick Tip

Rate is a comparison between 2 quantities of different units.

Find the rates.

① 50 words in 20 min   _____ words/min

② 80 km in 4 h   _____ km/h

③ 300 words in 5 min   _____ words/min

④ 48 km in 8 h   _____ km/h

⑤ 25 boxes for $75.00 $ _____ /box

⑥ $24 for 6 h $ _____ /h

⑦ 5 boxes for $12.50 $ _____ /box

⑧ $126 for 9 h $ _____ /h

⑨
$ 2.00

$ _____ /orange

⑩
SOUP $ 9.60
8

$ _____ /can

⑪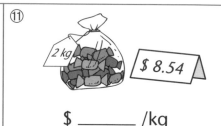
2 kg $ 8.54

$ _____ /kg

Find the unit price for each item sold in each store. Then tell which store offers the best buy.

		Store A	Store B	Store C	Best buy
⑫	Chicken breast	$19.80 for 3 kg $ ____ /kg	$25.80 for 4 kg $ ____ /kg	$34.25 for 5 kg $ ____ /kg	Store
⑬	Spring Water	3 bottles for $3.57 $ ____ /bottle	4 bottles for $5.00 $ ____ /bottle	2 bottles for $2.84 $ ____ /bottle	Store
⑭	Cup Noodles	5 cups for $3.95 $ ____ /cup	2 cups for $1.36 $ ____ /cup	3 cups for $2.67 $ ____ /cup	Store

Example

There are 4 girls and 6 boys. What is the ratio of the number of girls to the number of boys?

No. of girls : No. of boys = 4 : 6 $(4:6 = \frac{4}{6} = \frac{4 \div 2}{6 \div 2} = \frac{2}{3} = 2:3)$

= 2 : 3   (4:6 and 2:3 are equivalent ratios.)

The ratio of the number of girls to the number of boys is 2 : 3.

Quick Tip

Ratio is a comparison between 2 or more quantities of the same unit. A ratio can be written in fraction form,

e.g. $2 : 3 = \frac{2}{3}$

Write 2 equivalent ratios for each ratio.

⑮ 5 : 7   _____ _____   ⑯ 4 : 9   _____ _____

⑰ 10 : 15   _____ _____   ⑱ 12 : 20   _____ _____

Write each ratio in lowest terms.

⑲ 75 : 25   _____   ⑳ 20 : 80   _____   ㉑ 85 : 15   _____

㉒ 28 : 72   _____   ㉓ 32 : 48   _____   ㉔ 30 : 25   _____

Look at the fruits. Write each ratio in lowest terms.

㉕ apples to bananas   = _____

㉖ bananas to oranges = _____

㉗ apples to fruits   = _____

㉘ oranges to fruits   = _____

Complete the table.

	Ratio	Fraction	Decimal	Percent
㉙	9 : 25			
㉚		$\frac{2}{5}$		
㉛			0.82	
㉜				65%
㉝			0.15	

Quick Tip

Use division to convert a fraction to a decimal.

To convert a decimal to a percent, multiply the decimal by 100 and add %,

e.g.   0.17 = 0.17 × 100%
                = 17%

Lucy has a sheet of stickers. Look at Lucy's stickers and answer the questions. Write the ratios in lowest terms.

㉞ polar bears : teddy bears = _____

㉟ parrots : eagles = _____

㊱ polar bears : eagles = _____

㊲ teddy bears : bears = _____

㊳ polar bears : bears = _____

㊴ parrots : birds = _____

㊵ eagles : birds = _____

㊶ bears : all stickers = _____

㊷ birds : all stickers = _____

㊸ 2 sheets of stickers cost $3.24. What is the cost of 1 sheet of stickers?

_____

㊹ How much do 4 sheets of stickers cost?

_____

㊺ Lucy sells her stickers at the price of 6¢/sticker. If Amanda buys 8 stickers from Lucy, how much does she need to pay?

_____

㊻ Randy pays $0.90 to buy some stickers from Lucy. How many stickers does he buy?

_____

㊼ What is the ratio of the number of stickers sold to the number of stickers left?

_____

㊽ Lucy sells all her stickers in 3 days. What is the selling rate?

_____

Solve the problems. Reduce the answers to lowest terms.

㊾ In a bag, there are 8 red balloons, 4 green balloons and 12 blue balloons.

   a. What is the ratio of red balloons to green balloons?   _____

   b. What is the ratio of green balloons to blue balloons?   _____

   c. If it takes 48 minutes to inflate all the balloons, what is the rate of inflating the balloons?   _____

㊿ Sergi takes 2 years to collect 70 hockey cards and 28 baseball cards.

   a. What is the ratio of hockey cards to baseball cards?   _____

   b. What is the rate in cards/year at which Sergi collects his hockey cards?   _____

   c. If Sergi continues to collect hockey cards at the same rate, how many hockey cards will he have in 5 years?   _____

   d. What is the rate in cards/year at which Sergi collects his cards?   _____

   e. If Sergi continues to collect cards at the same rate, how many more cards will he collect over the next 10 years?   _____

MIND BOGGLER

Aunt Janet earns $4800 in 2 months. Look at her expenditure. Answer the questions.

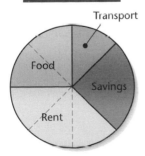

Aunt Janet's Expenditure

Transport

Food

Savings

Rent

① What is Aunt Janet's earning rate?   _____

② How much does Aunt Janet spend on rent each month?   _____

③ How much does Aunt Janet spend on food each month?   _____

④ What is the ratio of the money spent on transport to savings?   _____

7 Time, Distance and Speed

Write the 24-hour clock times.

① 4:35 p.m.   _____

② 6:12 a.m.   _____

③ 11:25:46 a.m.   _____

④ 10:42:11 p.m.   _____

⑤ 4:27:53 p.m.   _____

Quick Tip

- a.m. - from midnight to noon
- p.m. - from noon to midnight

Digital clock		Analog clock
12-h clock	24-h clock	
2:43:55 a.m.	02:43:55	
2:43:55 p.m.	14:43:55	

Write the 12-hour clock times in the boxes and draw the clock hands to show the times.

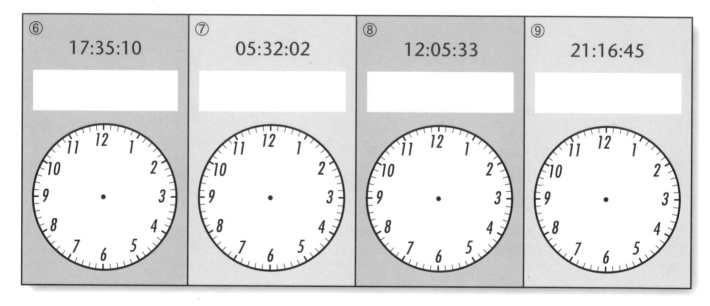

| ⑥ 17:35:10 | ⑦ 05:32:02 | ⑧ 12:05:33 | ⑨ 21:16:45 |

Write the 24-hour clock times.

⑩ 3 h before 02:11:20   _____

⑪ 1 h 15 s after 06:30:50   _____

⑫ 2 h 30 s before 15:38:20   _____

Answer the questions.

⑬ Movie A starts at 2:45:16 p.m. and ends at 4:55:51 p.m. How long does it last?   _____

⑭ Joshua goes to bed at 23:15:40 and gets up at 08:00:23 the next morning. How long does he sleep?   _____

Fill in the blanks to show the equivalent lengths.

⑮ 12 cm = _____ mm   ⑯ 50 mm = _____ cm

⑰ 8 m = _____ cm   ⑱ 900 cm = _____ m

⑲ 4 km = _____ m   ⑳ 2500 m = _____ km

㉑ 8.4 m = _____ cm   ㉒ 66 cm = _____ m   ㉓ 25 mm = _____ cm

㉔ 7500 m = _____ km   ㉕ 3.72 cm = _____ mm   ㉖ 452 cm = _____ m

Fill in the blanks.

(30 cm)   (560 km)   (9 mm)   (28 m)

㉗ The distance between 2 boys standing at 2 corners of a basketball court is about _____ .

㉘ The distance a cricket can leap is about _____ .

㉙ The distance between the eyes of a snail is about _____ .

㉚ The distance between Toronto and Montreal is about _____ .

Find the closest distance between the places. Then answer the questions.

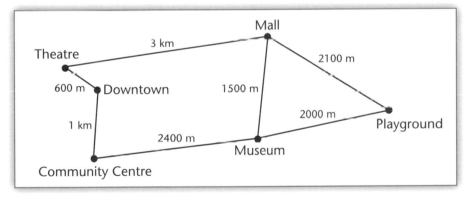

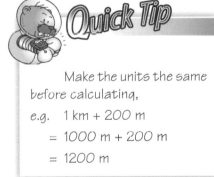

㉛ Theatre to mall : _____ m   ㉜ Museum to playground : _____ km

㉝ Theatre to downtown : _____ km   ㉞ Mall to museum : _____ km

㉟ Playground to community centre passing museum : _____ km

㊱ Museum to theatre via community centre and downtown : _____ km

㊲ Which is the shortest route to travel from downtown to playground? What is the distance?

_____

Examples

① Uncle Ron drives 90 km in 2 hours. At what speed does he drive?
Speed : 90 ÷ 2 = 45
He drives at 45 km/h.

② How far can Ted drive in 3 hours at 40 km/h?
Distance : 40 x 3 = 120
He can drive 120 km.

③ How long does Pat take to drive 50 km at 20 km/h?
Time : 50 ÷ 20 = 2.5
He takes 2.5 hours.

Complete the table.

	Distance	Time	Speed
㊳	100 km	4 h	
㊴	320 km	5 h	
㊵	25 m	10 s	
㊶		2 h	46 km/h
㊷		3.5 h	20 km/h
㊸	120 m		60 m/s
㊹	125 m		5 m/s

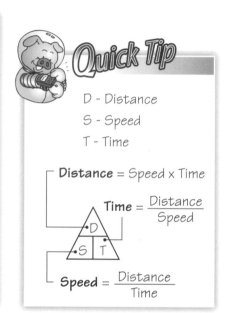

Quick Tip

D - Distance
S - Speed
T - Time

$\text{Distance} = \text{Speed} \times \text{Time}$

$\text{Time} = \dfrac{\text{Distance}}{\text{Speed}}$

$\text{Speed} = \dfrac{\text{Distance}}{\text{Time}}$

Solve the problems.

㊺ The Singh family drives 560 km from Toronto to Montreal in 7 h. At what speed do they drive?   _____

㊻ How long does the Singh family take to drive from Montreal to Toronto at 56 km/h?   _____

㊼ Lucy cycles 23 km in 2 h. What is her speed?   _____

㊽ How far can Lucy cycle in 4.5 h?   _____

㊾ How long does Lucy take to cycle 80.5 km?   _____

㊿ Paul cycles 7 km in $\frac{1}{2}$ h and Pat cycles 24 km in 2 h. Who cycles faster? Show your work.

_____ cycles faster.

Look at the records for the Track and Field Day at Riverview School. Complete the tables and solve the problems.

㉚ a.

Place	100-m Race		
	Start	Finish	Time taken
1st			15 s
2nd			20 s
3rd	10:20:35		25 s
4th			29 s
5th			30 s

b.

Place	1500-m Race		
	Start	Finish	Time taken
1st			6 min
2nd			6 min 30 s
3rd	12:05:45		6 min 45 s
4th			6 min 55 s
5th			7 min 10 s

㉜ What was the difference in time between the 1st and the 5th place runners in the 100-m race? _____

㉝ What was the difference in time between the start of the 100-m race and the start of the 1500-m race? _____

㉞ Ben can run 100 m in 18 s. How long will it take him to run 200 m at the same speed? _____

㉟ Ben can run 1500 m at half his 100-m speed. How long would he take to run 1500 m? _____

㊱ Sarah can run at a speed of 5 m/s. How far can she run in 20 s? _____

㊲ Pete can run 200 m in 100 s. What is his speed in m/s? _____

㊳ How far in m can Pete run in 1 min at this speed? _____

MIND BOGGLER

How many metres more will a car travel in 12 min at a speed of 50 km/h than at a speed of 40 km/h?

It will travel _____ m more.

Circle the letter which represents the correct answer in each problem.

① How many prime numbers are there between 1 and 30?

  A. 7   B. 9   C. 10   D. 11

② Which of the following is equal to 5 x (7 + 9)?

  A. 5 x 7 + 9   B. 5 + 7 x 9   C. 5 + 5 x 9   D. 35 + 45

③ The time on a digital clock reads 23:53:50. How long is it till midnight?

  A. 6 min 10 s   B. 6 min 50 s   C. 7 min 10 s   D. 7 min 5 s

④ The greatest common factor (G.C.F.) of 12 and 18 is _____ .

  A. 6   B. 12   C. 18   D. 36

⑤ The least common multiple (L.C.M.) of 12 and 15 is _____ .

  A. 30   B. 60   C. 120   D. 180

⑥ The temperature was -8°C and it increased by 3°C to _____ .

  A. -11°C   B. -5°C   C. 5°C   D. 11°C

⑦ What is the sum of $\frac{5}{6}$ and $\frac{1}{9}$ in lowest terms?

  A. $\frac{6}{15}$ B. $\frac{5}{54}$ C. $\frac{17}{18}$ D. $\frac{51}{54}$

⑧ Which number, when divided by 100, equals 152.3?

  A. 1.523   B. 15.23   C. 1523   D. 15 230

⑨ How many km can you travel in 20 min at 60 km/h?

  A. 12   B. 20   C. 30   D. 80

⑩ What is 15% of $150?

  A. $20   B. $22.50   C. $23   D. $25

⑪ There are 8 boys and 10 girls. What is the ratio of boys to girls?

  A. 8:18   B. 10:18   C. 5:4   D. 4:5

Do the following calculation without a calculator. Show your work.

⑫
$$\begin{array}{r} 123 \\ \times \quad 47 \\ \hline \end{array}$$

⑬
$$\begin{array}{r} 342.95 \\ \times \qquad 7 \\ \hline \end{array}$$

⑭
$$29\,\overline{)1566}$$

⑮
$$3\,\overline{)25.92}$$

⑯ $4 \times 5.2 \times 25$

⑰ $52 + 3 \times 15$

⑱ 15×53

⑲ $12 \times 50 + 52 \div 4$

⑳ $5\frac{1}{4} - 2\frac{1}{2}$

㉑ $\frac{7}{15} - \frac{1}{6}$

㉒ $3\frac{1}{4} + 1\frac{7}{8}$

㉓ $12.3 \div 100$

㉔ Write $\frac{3}{4}$ as a %.

㉕ Which is bigger, $1\frac{3}{4}$ or $1\frac{2}{3}$?

㉖ Find the G.C.F. of 21 and 35.

㉗ Find the L.C.M. of 25 and 40.

Mrs. Saura goes shopping. Look at the map and help her solve the problems.

㉘ Use 24-h clock time to write the opening and closing times for the convenience stores.

㉙ How long is Ben's convenience store open every day? _____

㉚ How long is Lucy's convenience store open every day? _____

㉛ Mrs. Saura can cycle 55.8 m in 9 s. What is her speed? _____

㉜ Mrs. Saura cycles at a speed of 6 m/s. How long will it take her to go to Ben's convenience store? _____

㉝ How long will it take her to go to Lucy's convenience store? _____

㉞ Mrs. Saura leaves her home at 21:58:02. Which convenience store should she go to ? Why?

㉟ Mrs. Saura has 15 $20 bills and 12 $5 bills. How much does she have in all?

㊱ What fraction of Mrs. Saura's money is in $20 bills?

Look at the flyer. Answer Mrs. Saura's questions.

③⑦ What fraction of the popsicles in the box are lemon flavoured? _____

③⑧ What fraction of the popsicles in the box are blueberry flavoured? _____

③⑨ What percent of the popsicles in the box are lime flavoured? _____

④⓪ What percent of the popsicles in the box are strawberry flavoured? _____

④① What is the ratio of strawberry flavoured popsicles to the total number of popsicles in a box? _____

④② I bought 3 boxes of popsicles. I gave 9 lemon flavoured and 12 lime flavoured to my neighbours. How many popsicles do I have now? _____

④③ How much do 5 boxes of popsicles cost? _____

④④ How much does each roll of paper towel cost? _____

④⑤ I have bought 7 toy cars. Each toy car needs 3 batteries to move. What is the minimum number of packs of batteries should I buy? _____

④⑥ How much do I need to pay for 32 batteries? _____

④⑦ I want 5 kg of ham and pay with 3 $20 bills. How much change will I get? _____

④⑧ I cut the ham into slices. Each slice weighs 25 g. How many slices of ham will I get from 5 kg of ham? _____

8 Perimeter and Area

Determine the perimeter and area of each shape.

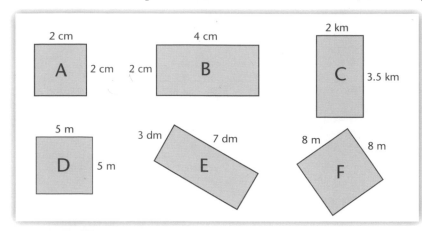

Quick Tip

Perimeter is the distance around the outside of a shape. It is measured in linear units, e.g. m, km.

Area is the space within a shape. It is measured in square units, e.g. cm^2, km^2.

Shape	A	B	C	D	E	F
① Perimeter	cm	cm	km	m	dm	m
② Area	cm^2	cm^2	km^2	m^2	dm^2	m^2

Find the perimeters (P) and areas (A) of the parallelograms. Show your work.

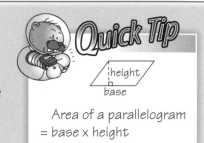

Example

Cut a right triangle from the left. Move it to the right to form a rectangle together with the unshaded part.

height: 5 cm

base: 10 cm

Area of parallelogram
= area of rectangle
= 5 x 10
= 50 cm^2

Quick Tip

height
base

Area of a parallelogram
= base x height

③
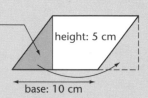
7 cm
5 cm
6 cm

P = _____ = _____ cm

A = _____ = _____ cm^2

④
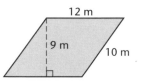
12 m
9 m
10 m

P = _____ = _____ m

A = _____ = _____ m^2

⑤
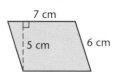
60 cm
20 cm
25 cm

P = _____ = _____ cm

A = _____ = _____ cm^2

⑥
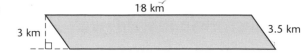
18 km
3 km
3.5 km

P = _____ = _____ km

A = _____ = _____ km^2

Find the perimeters (P) and areas (A) of the triangles. Show your work.

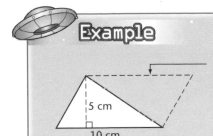

Example

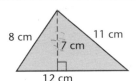

A parallelogram can be formed by 2 congruent triangles.

Area of a triangle — half of the area of a parallelogram

Area of the triangle
= area of the parallelogram ÷ 2
= base x height ÷ 2
= 10 x 5 ÷ 2
= 25 cm^2

⑦

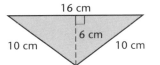

P = _____ = _____ cm

A = _____ = _____ cm^2

⑧

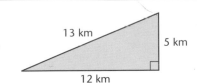

P = _____ = _____ km

A = _____ = _____ km^2

⑨

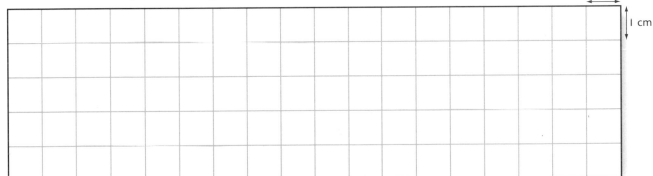

P = _____ = _____ cm

A = _____ = _____ cm^2

⑩

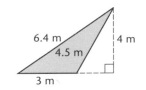

P = _____ = _____ m

A = _____ = _____ m^2

Draw 3 different parallelograms, each having an area of 12 cm^2.

⑪

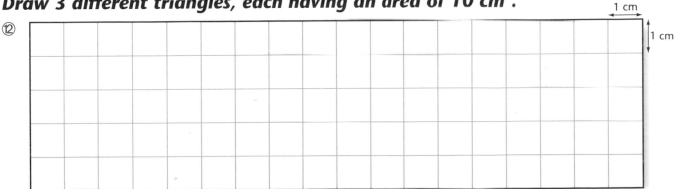

1 cm

1 cm

Draw 3 different triangles, each having an area of 10 cm^2.

⑫

1 cm

1 cm

Draw the possible shapes. Label their dimensions and give the correct answers.

⑬ Draw 3 different rectangles, each having an area of 12 cm². Colour the rectangle which has the greatest perimeter.

a.

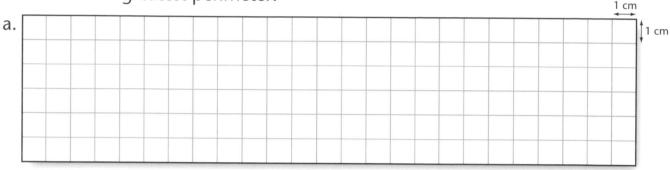

b. The greatest perimeter is _____ cm.

⑭ Draw 3 different rectangles, each having a perimeter of 18 m. Colour the rectangle which has the greatest area.

a.

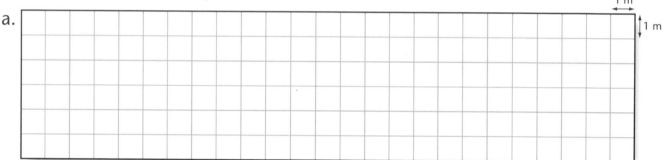

b. The greatest area is _____ m².

⑮ Draw an isosceles triangle, a right triangle and a scalene triangle, each having a base of 6 cm and a height of 4 cm.

a.

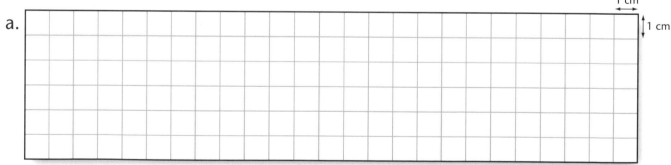

b. Are the areas of the triangles the same or different? _____

c. Are the perimeters of the triangles the same or different? _____

d. If the height and base of triangles are the same, are their areas the same or different? _____

Solve the problems. Show your work.

⑯ A rectangular field measures 8.5 m by 6 m.

  a. How many metres of fencing are needed to enclose the field?

  b. How many m² of turf must be laid to cover the whole field?

⑰ Sean has a poster with dimensions of 27 cm by 21 cm and a baseball card with dimensions of 9 cm by 7 cm. How many times is the poster larger than the card?

⑱ a. Calculate the area of the door.

  b. Calculate the area of the wall.

⑲ Antville is 13 km north of Beetown and Capeview is 20 km east of Beetown. What is the area enclosed by Antville, Beetown and Capeview?

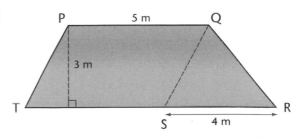

MIND BOGGLER

PQRT is a trapezoid. Determine its area if PQST is a parallelogram.

Its area is _____ .

Volume and Mass

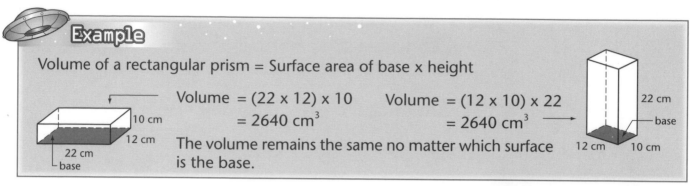

Example

Volume of a rectangular prism = Surface area of base x height

Volume = (22 x 12) x 10 = 2640 cm³

Volume = (12 x 10) x 22 = 2640 cm³

The volume remains the same no matter which surface is the base.

10 cm
12 cm
22 cm
base

22 cm
base
12 cm 10 cm

Find the volume of each of the following rectangular prisms.

Quick Tip

height
base

Volume of a rectangular prism

= surface area of base × height

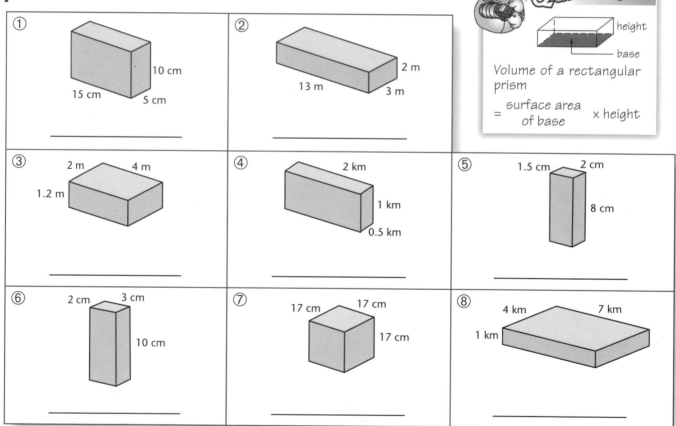

① 10 cm
15 cm
5 cm

_____

② 2 m
13 m
3 m

_____

③ 2 m 4 m
1.2 m

_____

④ 2 km
1 km
0.5 km

_____

⑤ 1.5 cm 2 cm
8 cm

_____

⑥ 2 cm 3 cm
10 cm

_____

⑦ 17 cm 17 cm
17 cm

_____

⑧ 4 km 7 km
1 km

_____

A set of Canadian Encyclopedias has 20 books. Each book cover measures 24 cm by 16 cm. The thickness of each book is 4 cm. Answer the questions.

⑨ What is the area of each book cover? _____

⑩ What is the volume of each book in cm³? _____

⑪ What is the total volume of the 20 books in cm³? _____

⑫ Would all the books fit on a 1-m bookshelf of depth 20 cm? Explain.

_____

Sam and Jack use 1-cm³ blocks to build a tower having dimensions 7 cm by 4 cm by 3 cm. Check ✔ the tower they built and answer the questions.

⑬

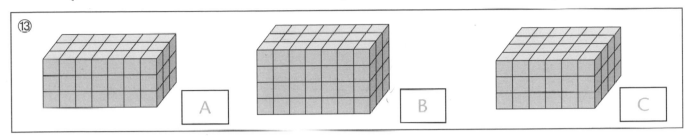

A   B   C

⑭ How many 1-cm³ blocks do they need? _____

⑮ If they add more 1-cm³ blocks to build a new tower measuring 9 cm x 4 cm x 3 cm, how many additional blocks do they need? _____

Look at the following items in Ann's cupboard. Round all the dimensions to the nearest cm and use the rounded figures to find the volume of each item.

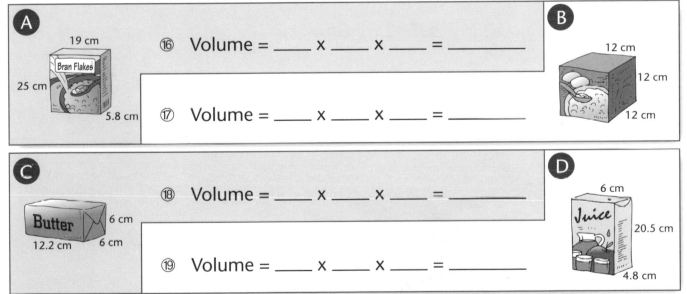

A   19 cm
Bran Flakes
25 cm
5.8 cm

⑯ Volume = ____ x ____ x ____ = _____

⑰ Volume = ____ x ____ x ____ = _____

B   12 cm
12 cm
12 cm

C
Butter   6 cm
12.2 cm   6 cm

⑱ Volume = ____ x ____ x ____ = _____

⑲ Volume = ____ x ____ x ____ = _____

D   6 cm
Juice   20.5 cm
4.8 cm

E   22.3 cm
3 cm
Tea Bags   5 cm

⑳ Volume = ____ x ____ x ____ = _____

㉑ Volume = ____ x ____ x ____ = _____

F   15 cm
Cracker   22.8 cm
3.6 cm

㉒ List the items in order from the one with the smallest volume to the one with the largest. Write the letters only.

_____

Fill in the missing information for each rectangular prism.

Volume (cm³)	㉓	㉔	147	320
Surface area of base (cm²)	25	12.5	㉕	16
Height (cm)	40	3	21	㉖

Find the volume of each solid.

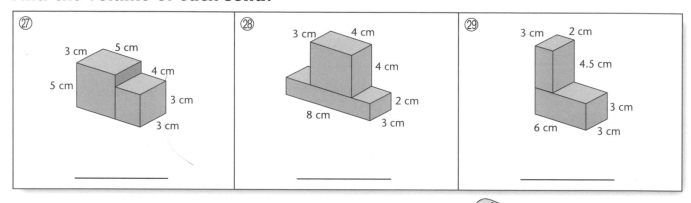

㉗ 3 cm, 5 cm, 5 cm, 4 cm, 3 cm, 3 cm

㉘ 3 cm, 4 cm, 4 cm, 8 cm, 2 cm, 3 cm

㉙ 3 cm, 2 cm, 4.5 cm, 6 cm, 3 cm, 3 cm

Look at Tim's aquarium. Help Tim solve the problems. Show your work.

60 cm   30 cm

Quick Tip

1 mL = 1 cm³
1 L = 1000 mL

㉚ If the aquarium is filled to a depth of 15 cm, how many litres of water does it contain?

㉛ How many litres of water must be added if the depth of the water is increased to 16 cm?

㉜ If 18 litres of water is poured into the empty aquarium, what will the depth of the water be in the aquarium?

㉝ If the depth of the aquarium is 25 cm, what is the capacity of the aquarium in litres?

Kay is in a drugstore. Help her solve the problems.

 Bottle weighs 40 g.
Each tablet weighs 500 mg.

 Bottle weighs 50 g.
Each tablet weighs 500 mg.

 Bottle weighs 35 g.
Each tablet weighs 250 mg.

 Bottle weighs 45 g.
Each tablet weighs 300 mg.

Quick Tip

1 kg = 1000 g
1 g = 1000 mg

㉞ What is the mass of a bottle of Vitamin C in g? _____

㉟ What is the mass of a bottle of Vitamin E in g? _____

㊱ What is the mass of a bottle of Aspirin in g? _____

㊲ What is the mass of a bottle of calcium in g? _____

㊳ There are 40 bottles of Vitamin C. How heavy are they in kg? _____

㊴ There are 50 bottles of calcium. How heavy are they in kg? _____

㊵ Kay's doctor recommends that she take about 1 g of calcium daily. How many tablets should she take daily? _____

㊶ The pharmacist advises against taking more than 4 aspirin tablets daily. What is the maximum mass of aspirin Kay should take daily? _____

 **MIND BOGGLER**

The total mass of the calcium tablets in the bottle is 50 g. Answer the questions.

① What is the mass in g of each tablet? _____

② If you take one tablet daily, how many grams of calcium will you take in May? _____

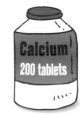

10 Symmetry, 2-D and 3-D Figures

Draw all the lines of symmetry for each shape. Write the number of lines of symmetry in the circle.

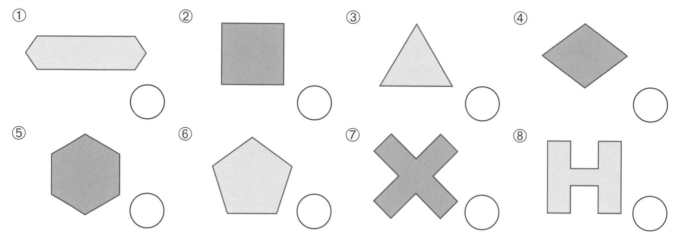

Use the lines of symmetry (dotted lines) to complete each shape.

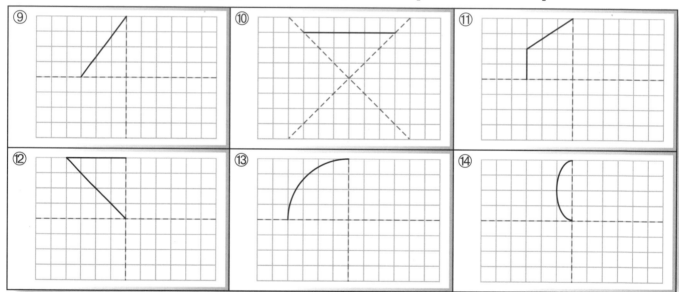

Add the minimum number of squares to each shape to make it symmetrical. Draw the square(s) and write the number.

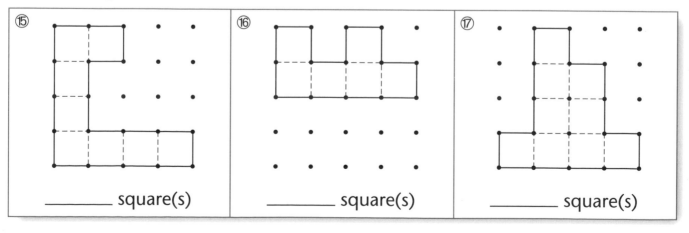

⑮ _____ square(s)   ⑯ _____ square(s)   ⑰ _____ square(s)

Write the order of rotational symmetry for the following shapes in the circles.

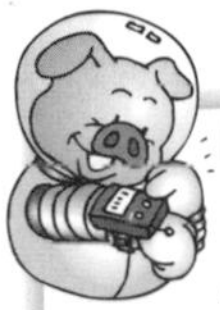

Quick Tip

A figure has rotational symmetry if it fits on itself within a complete rotation. The order of rotational symmetry is the number of times the figure fits on itself in one complete rotation.

e.g. This figure has rotational symmetry of order 3.

⑱

⑲

⑳

㉑

㉒

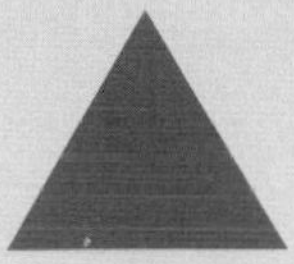

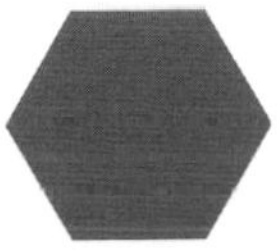

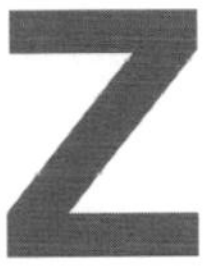

㉓

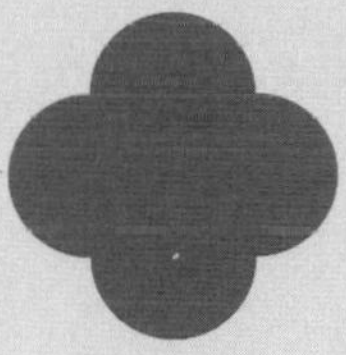

Use your protractor and ruler to construct the shapes.

㉔ Draw a triangle with only 1 line of symmetry.

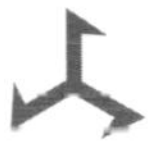

㉕ Draw a right triangle with sides 3 cm, 4 cm and 5 cm.

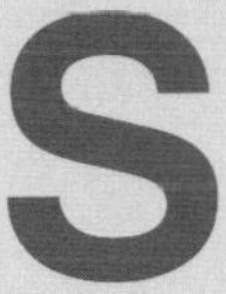

㉖ Draw a triangle with angles 30°, 60°and 90°.

㉗ Draw a parallelogram with sides 3 cm and 5 cm, angles 60°and 120°.

㉘ Draw a rectangle with sides 12 cm and 2 cm. Then cut it into 8 identical triangles.

Draw one congruent and one similar figure for each shape.

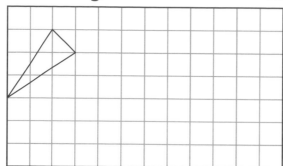 ㉙

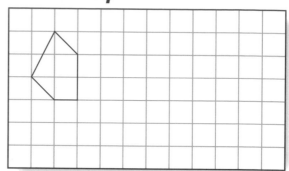 ㉚

Complete the net for each solid and write the number of faces in the circle.

㉛
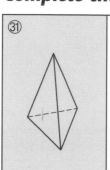 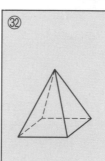 ◯

㉜
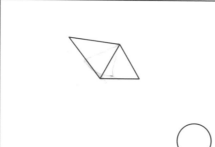 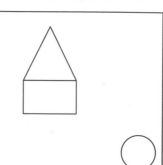 ◯

㉝
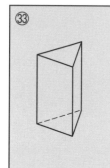 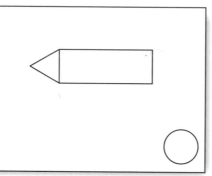 ◯

㉞
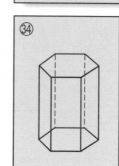 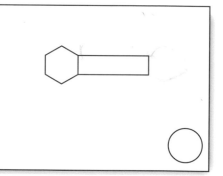 ◯

Tom has built some models with interlocking cubes. Help him draw the models on the isometric dot paper.

㉟
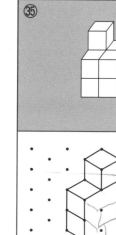

㊱
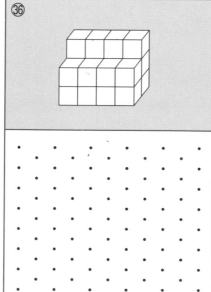

㊲
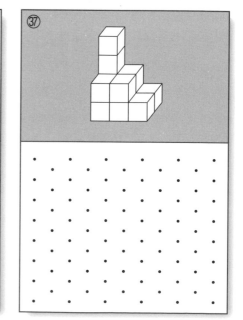

Write the names of the quadrilaterals.

㊳

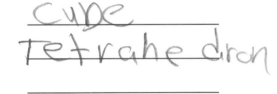

A _square_

B _rh_

C _trapizooce_

D _____

E _____

F _____

Check ✔ the boxes to show the properties of the shapes.

Property \ Quadrilateral	Rectangle	Rhombus	Parallelogram	Square
㊴ opposite sides parallel				
㊵ all sides equal				
㊶ 2 pairs of opposite sides equal				
㊷ all angles 90°				
㊸ 2 pairs of opposite angles equal				

Read the clues. Write the names of the geometric figures.

㊹ I am a solid with 6 congruent faces.

Cube

㊺ I am a solid with 4 faces.

Tetrahedron

㊻ I am a solid with 5 faces.

_____

㊼ I am a 2-D figure with 4 lines of symmetry
and rotational symmetry of order 4.

_____

MIND BOGGLER

Look at the views of the model and draw it out.

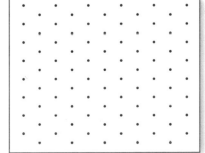

Top	Front	Side

11 Transformations and Coordinates

Each picture undergoes two transformations. Draw the images of the pictures.

① Reflection and rotation

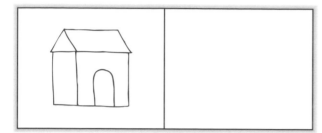

② Rotation and translation

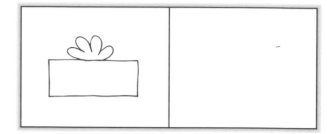

③ Reflection and translation

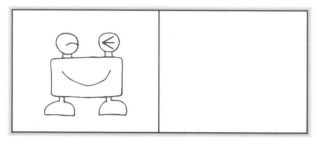

④ Rotation and reflection

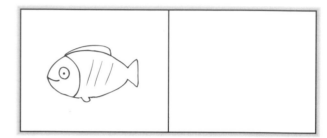

Complete the tiling using each shape.

⑤

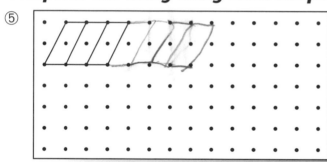

Quick Tip

Complete a tiling pattern using a shape by translating, reflecting or rotating the shape.

⑥

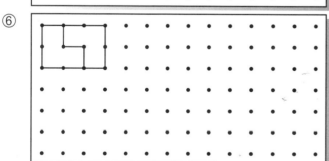

⑦

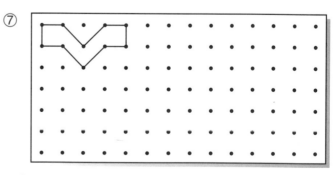

Check ✔ the figures which do not tile a plane.

⑧

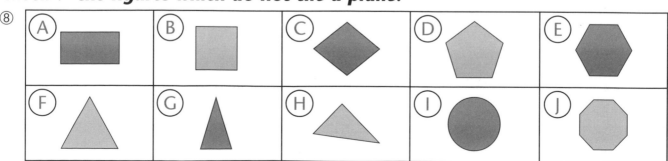

Draw the transformed images and answer the questions.

⑨ Reflect △ ABC in ℓ₁ and label it ★.

⑩ Reflect ★ in ℓ₂ and label it ♥.

⑪ Would the result be the same if you reflected △ ABC in ℓ₂ first and then ℓ₁?

_____

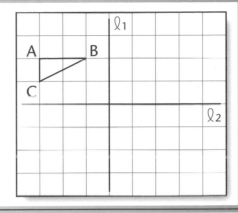

⑫ Translate trapezoid ABCD 3 units right and 1 unit down and label it ★.

⑬ Reflect ★ in ℓ and label it ♥.

⑭ Would the result be the same if you did the reflection before the translation?

_____

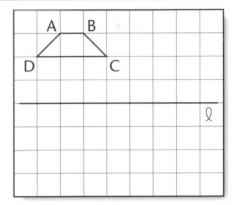

⑮ Reflect rectangle ABCD in ℓ and label it ★.

⑯ Rotate ★ a $\frac{1}{4}$ turn clockwise about point P and label it ♥.

⑰ Would the result be the same if you did the rotation before the reflection?

_____

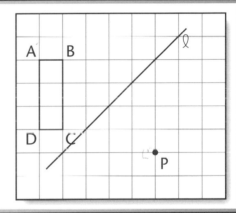

⑱ Rotate the shaded figure a $\frac{1}{4}$ turn clockwise about point P and label it ★.

⑲ Translate ★ 4 units down and 2 units left. Label it ♥.

⑳ What transformations could you do to the final image to get back to the original position?

_____

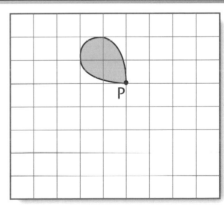

Write ordered pairs to represent each of the points plotted on the grid and answer the questions.

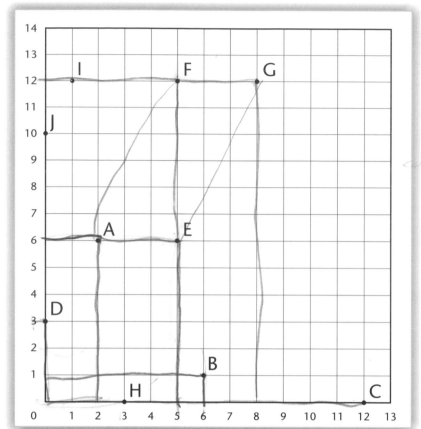

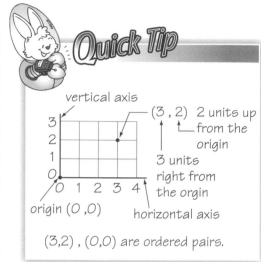

㉑

A (2 , 6)   B (6 , 1)

C (12 , 0)   D (0 , 3)

E (5 , 6)   F (5 , 12)

G (8 , 12)   H (3 , 0)

I (1 , 12)   J (0 , 10)

㉒ Join the points A, E, G and F. What shape is AEGF ? _____

㉓ Which points have a horizontal distance of 5 units from the origin? E F _____

㉔ Which points are vertically 12 units from the origin? _____

㉕ Which points lie on the horizontal axis? _____

㉖ Which points lie on the vertical axis? _____

㉗ Join the point A, E and F. What is the area of △ AEF? _____

㉘ Join the point D, A and J. What is the area of △ DAJ? _____

㉙ Translate E 3 units up and 2 units right. What is the ordered pair of the translated image? _____

㉚ How do you translate F to A? _____

㉛ How do you translate H to C? _____

Plot and join the points to see what shapes they are. Then label them and answer the questions.

- A (3 , 5) , B (2 , 2) , C (6 , 2)

- P (5 , 10) , Q (9 , 10) , R (9 , 6) , S (5 , 6)

- E (15 , 10) , F (19 , 10) , G (17 , 6) , H (13 , 6)

- L (11 , 5) , M (14 , 5) , N (14 , 0) , O (11 , 0)

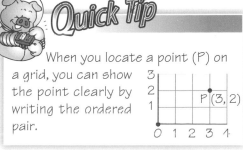

Quick Tip

When you locate a point (P) on a grid, you can show the point clearly by writing the ordered pair.

③②

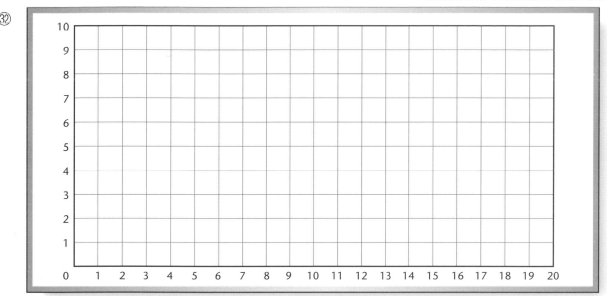

③③ If A is moved 1 unit up and 1 unit right, what will its ordered pair be? After the translation, what kind of triangle is △ ABC?

_____

③④ If H is moved 2 units right, what will its ordered pair be? After the translation, what shape is EFGH?

_____

MIND BOGGLER

What are the coordinates of point P?

If A (2, 8) is rotated $\frac{1}{2}$ turn about P, its image is at (4, 0).

The coordinates of point P are _____ .

12 Patterns and Simple Equations

Sarah writes some patterns and asks Sunita to describe the rules and give the next 3 terms in each pattern. Help Sunita with her task.

Examples

① Continue the pattern 5 , 6 , 8 , 11 , ...

5 , 6 , 8 , 11 , 15 , 20 , 25
+1 +2 +3 +4 +5 +6

Rule : The numbers increase by 1 more each time.

② Continue the pattern 4 , 9 , 19 , 39 , ...

4 , 9 , 19 , 39 , 79 , 159
4x2+1 9x2+1 19x2+1 39x2+1 79x2+1

Rule : Double the previous term and add 1.

① 100 , 98 , 94 , 88 , _____ , _____ , _____ , ...

Rule : _____

② 1 , 2 , 6 , 24 , _____ , _____ , _____ , ...

Rule : _____

③ 50 , 48 , 51 , 49 , _____ , _____ , _____ , ...

Rule : _____

④ 5 , 9 , 17 , 33 , _____ , _____ , _____ , ...

Rule : _____

⑤ 1 , 4 , 9 , 16 , _____ , _____ , _____ , ...

Rule : _____

For each set of numbers, write the rule that relates the first two columns to the third. Then follow the rule to write another set of numbers in the boxes.

⑥

5	9	13
8	4	11
7	10	16

_____

⑦

18	3	7
20	4	6
15	5	4

_____

⑧

4	3	10
5	6	17
7	4	15

_____

The data in each table follow a pattern. Complete the tables and answer the questions.

⑨ Population of Markville

a.

Year	1980	1985	1990	1995		
Population in thousands	69	77	89	105		

b. In which year will the population be 177 000? _____

⑩ Cost of a movie ticket

a.

Year	1995	1996	1997	1998		
Amount ($)	6.00	6.50	7.50	8.00		

b. How much was a movie ticket in 2001? _____

⑪ Mass of a new born baby

a.

Age (month)	0	1	2	3			
Mass (kg)	3.2	3.4	3.7	4.1			

b. When will the baby weigh 7.6 kg? _____

John saves money according to a pattern. Complete the graph to show the pattern and answer the questions.

⑫ a.

Money Saved by John

b. How much will he save by Week 12? _____

c. After how many weeks will there be $20 in savings? _____

d. Describe John's saving pattern. _____

The movement of gas price follows a pattern. Follow the pattern to complete the graph and answer the questions.

⑬ a.

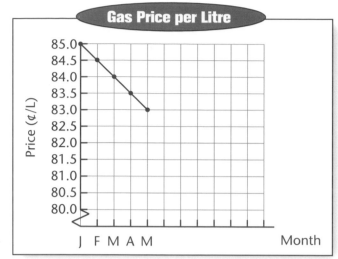

b. What will the gas price be in June?

_____

c. When will the gas price reach 80¢?

_____

Draw the next 2 diagrams in each pattern. Describe the changing rules for each figure.

⑭   a.

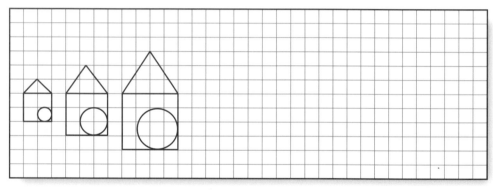

b. Triangle   : _____

c. Square   : _____

d. Circle   : _____

⑮   a.

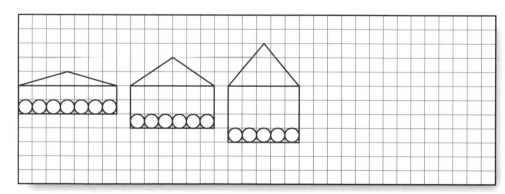

b. Triangle   : _____

c. Rectangle : _____

d. Circle   : _____

Read the number puzzles and find the numbers using the guess-and-test method.

⑯ Increase this number by 7 and then double it. The result is 70.

This number is ☐ .

⑰ The number is halved and then reduced by 20. The result is 30.

This number is ☐ .

⑱ Divide this number by 2 and then reduce it by 3. The result is 11.

This number is ☐ .

⑲ Add 25 to this number. Then multiply it by 3. The result is 120.

This number is ☐ .

⑳ This number is 7 more than half of 30.

This number is ☐ .

㉑ Half of this number is 7 more than 37.

This number is ☐ .

Determine the value of the missing number in each of the following equations.

㉒ _____ − 17 = 98

㉓ _____ + 23 = 170

㉔ 39 x _____ = 156

㉕ _____ x 13 = 117

㉖ 85 ÷ _____ = 17

㉗ _____ ÷ 12 = 8

㉘ 2 x _____ = 31 − 1

㉙ 5 x _____ = 8 + 92

㉚ 59 − 5 = _____ x 9

㉛ 30 − 9 = _____ x 3

㉜ 520 ÷ _____ = 13 + 7

㉝ 13 + _____ = 220 ÷ 11

Quick Tip

Do the part without missing terms first. Then 'guess and test' the missing numbers.

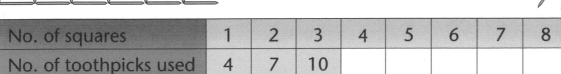

MIND BOGGLER

Stan uses toothpicks to make the following pattern. Complete the table and the statement.

No. of squares	1	2	3	4	5	6	7	8
No. of toothpicks used	4	7	10					

To make 10 squares, Stan needs _____ toothpicks.

13 Data and Graphs

Choose the type of graph that best represents each of the following sets of data. Write the letters in the circles.

Quick Tip

Circle graph - To show the relationship between individual data and the whole data set

Bar graph - To show the relationship between individual data pairs

Line graph - To show the tendency of data to change

C - circle graph   **B - bar graph**   **L - line graph**

① Maximum daily temperature in Toronto each day in June ◯

② Gas prices at different gas stations on a particular day ◯

③ Percentage of money spent on different items (food, housing, etc) ◯

④ Total number of goals scored by different hockey teams in a season ◯

⑤ Changes in gas price over a 1-month period ◯

⑥ Percentage of students with different Math grades (A to E) in a Grade 6 class ◯

⑦ Number of students in a school with different hair colours ◯

⑧ Changes in weight of Baby Sam during the first year ◯

⑨ Comparison of masses of different types of dogs ◯

⑩ Size of family among Grade 6 students ◯

Melissa conducted a survey among 30 classmates in her Grade 6 class to find out their favourite snacks. Help her complete the tally chart and present the data in a bar graph and a circle graph.

⑪

Snack	Chips	Nuts	Chocolate	Candy	Ice cream
Tally	ⵗⵗ‖	ⵗⵗ	ⵗⵗ‖‖‖	‖‖‖	ⵗⵗ‖
No. of Students	7				
Fraction of the Whole	$\frac{7}{30}$				

⑫

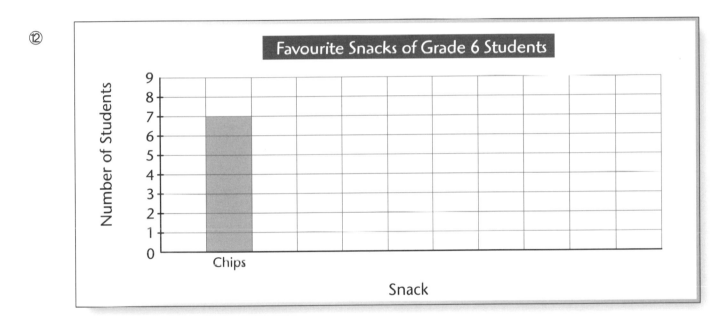

Favourite Snacks of Grade 6 Students

⑬

Favourite Snacks of Grade 6 Students

Chips

Quick Tip

Don't forget to label each axis in a bar graph and each sector in a circle graph.

Find the mean, median and mode of each set of data.

Example

Number of stickers collected by Sarah in the last 6 weeks: 10 , 2 , 5 , 9 , 12 , 10
Mean (average) = (10 + 2 + 5 + 9 + 12 + 10) ÷ 6 = 48 ÷ 6 = 8
Median (middle value) = (9 + 10) ÷ 2 = 9.5 ◄— Put the numbers in order. There are 6 numbers. The median
is the average of the 2 middle terms.
Mode (most common value) = 10

2 5 ⑨ ⑩ 10 12

⑭ Gas price (¢/litre) over a 2-week period:

| 87.5 | 78.2 | 76.9 | 76.9 | 79.2 | 80.1 | 81.9 |

a. mean = _____ b. median = _____ c. mode = _____

⑮ Number of children in 10 families:

| 5 | 1 | 2 | 2 | 3 | 4 | 6 | 2 | 2 | 3 |

a. mean = _____ b. median = _____ c. mode = _____

⑯ Number of candies in 9 different bags:

| 15 | 18 | 27 | 30 | 14 | 15 | 12 | 10 | 21 |

a. mean = _____ b. median = _____ c. mode = _____

⑰ Math test percentages: 3 students get 50%, 2 students get 60%, and 5 students get 80%

a. List the percentages of all 10 students in order from lowest to highest:

_____

b. mean = _____ c. median = _____ d. mode = _____

36 students were asked to choose their favourite colour. Look at the circle graph and write fractions in lowest terms to complete the statements below.

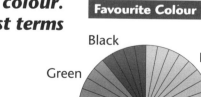

Favourite Colour

⑱ _____ of the students chose blue.

⑲ _____ of the students chose red.

⑳ _____ of the students did not choose blue.

Diane did a survey of the reading and TV watching habits of 15 friends. Look at the results and complete the table and the bar graph for each set of data. Answer the questions.

㉑

Reading Time (minutes / week)	20	25	60	30	40	50	55	80	100
	70	10	15	30	35	65			

a.

Time in Minutes	Tally	No. of Students
1 - 20		
21 - 40		
41 - 60		
61 - 80		
81 -100		

b.

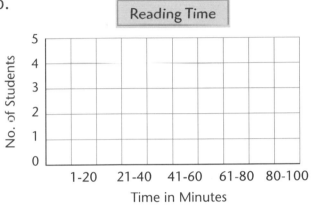

c. How many students read for more than 1 h a week? _____

㉒

TV watching time (hours / week)	2	3	8	10	5	6	7	9	5	8	10
	9	2	1	5							

a.

Time in Hours	Tally	No. of Students
1 - 2		
3 - 4		
5 - 6		
7 - 8		
9 - 10		

b.

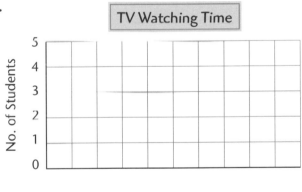

c. How many students watch TV for more than 6 h a week? _____

MIND BOGGLER

Find 3 numbers which are all positive integers with a mean of 10 and a median of 8.

There are many possible answers.

The 3 numbers are _____ .

14 Probability

Janice picks a marble from the box. Write the probability in fractions in lowest terms. Label each part of the circle graph to show the probability of picking marbles of different colours.

20 marbles

Black - 5	White - 4
Green - 2	Blue - 6
Red - the rest	

Quick Tip

Probability = $\dfrac{\text{No. of times a particular event occurs}}{\text{No. of all possible events}}$

= fraction of times for a particular event to occur

Probability can also be written as a decimal or in %.

① The probability of picking a marble in

    a. black   _____

    b. blue   _____

    c. white   _____

    d. green   _____

    e. red   _____

    f. blue or red _____

② **Probability of Picking Marbles in Different Colours**

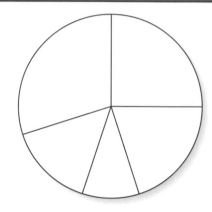

③ How can you increase the probability of picking a red marble?

_____

On a certain day in April the probability of rain is $\dfrac{3}{10}$, the probability of sun is $\dfrac{1}{5}$, the probability of mist is $\dfrac{1}{6}$ and the probability of cloud is $\dfrac{1}{3}$.

④ Is it more likely to be sunny or cloudy?   _____

⑤ Is it more likely to be rainy or sunny?   _____

⑥ What is the probability of not raining?   _____

⑦ List all the fractions representing the probabilities from least to greatest.

_____

⑧ List all the weather conditions from least likely to most likely.

_____

Sarah spins 2 identical spinners and multiplies the numbers that the arrows have landed on each time.

⑨ Complete the table to show all the possible outcomes.

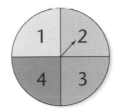

X	1	2	3	4
1				
2				
3				
4				

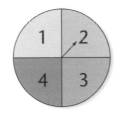

⑩ How many possible outcomes are there? _____

⑪ Which outcome is the most likely ? _____

⑫ What is the probability of getting the most likely outcome? _____

⑬ How many outcomes are greater than 10? _____

⑭ What is the probability of getting outcomes which are greater than 10? _____

⑮ What is the probability of getting outcomes which are not an even number? _____

Mr. and Mrs. Ling have 2 children. Complete the tree diagram to show all the possible combinations of boys (B) and girls (G). Then fill in the blanks.

⑯

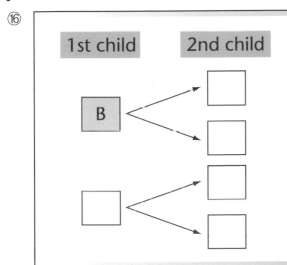

⑰ There are _____ combinations.

They are _____ .

⑱ The probability that the Lings have 2 girls is _____ .

⑲ The probability that they have 1 boy and 1 girl is _____ .

Look at the menu. Choose one item from each category and use a tree diagram to show all the possible combinations. Answer the questions.

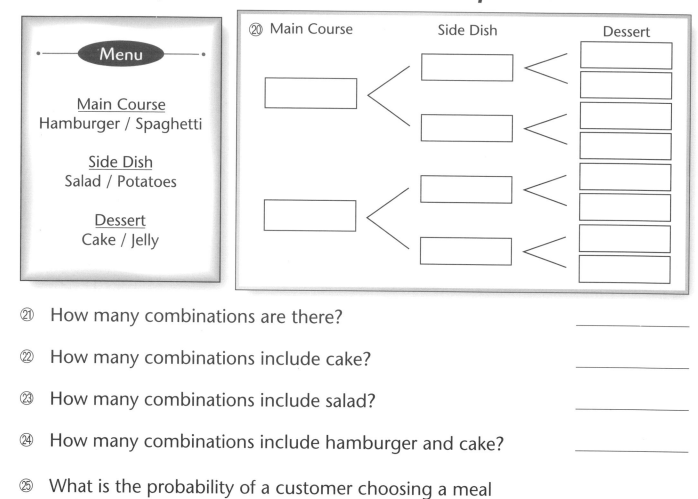

Menu

Main Course
Hamburger / Spaghetti

Side Dish
Salad / Potatoes

Dessert
Cake / Jelly

㉑ How many combinations are there? _____

㉒ How many combinations include cake? _____

㉓ How many combinations include salad? _____

㉔ How many combinations include hamburger and cake? _____

㉕ What is the probability of a customer choosing a meal with hamburger, salad and jelly? _____

㉖ What is the probability of a customer choosing a meal with hamburger, potatoes and cake? _____

Look at the food and drinks you can choose for tea time. Choose one item from each category and answer the questions.

Food   Sandwich (S)   Hog dog (H)
Doughnut (D)   Muffin (M)   Cookies (C)

Drinks
Coffee (CO)   Tea (T)

㉗ How many combinations are there? What are they?

_____

_____

㉘ What is the probability of getting a sandwich and coffee? _____

Sarah spins each spinner once to see what outfits she will put on. Draw a tree diagram to show all the combinations.

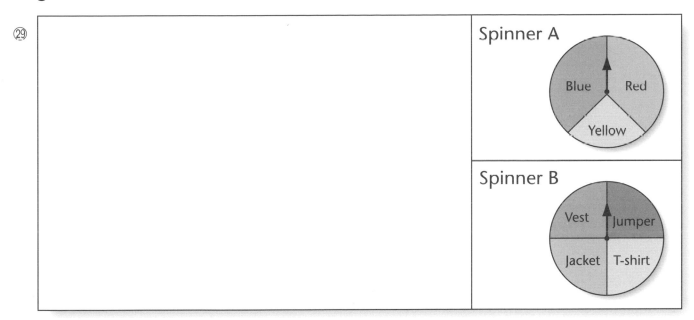

㉙

Spinner A

Blue Red Yellow

Spinner B

Vest Jumper Jacket T-shirt

㉚ What is the probability that Sarah will put on a blue vest? _____

㉛ What is the probability that Sarah will put on yellow clothes? _____

㉜ What is the probability that she will put on a jumper? _____

㉝ Sarah changes the word 'Vest' in Spinner B to 'Jacket'.

a. How many combinations will there be then? _____

b. What kind of clothes is Sarah more likely to wear? _____

c. What is the probability that Sarah will put on a blue jumper? _____

d. What is the probability that she will put on a red jacket? _____

e. What is the probability that she will put on a red or yellow T-shirt? _____

MIND BOGGLER

Jennifer has 3 hooks and 3 coats of different colours. If each hook holds only 1 coat, what is the probability that the red coat is on the 2nd hook?

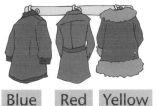

Blue Red Yellow

The probability is _____ .

Circle the letter which represents the best answer to each question.

① The area of the triangle is _____ cm² .

4 cm
3 cm
5 cm

A. 6   B. 12

C. 20   D. 60

② A rectangular pool is 5 m long, 2 m wide, and 1.5 m deep. If 1 m³ = 1000 L, how many L of water will fill up the pool?

A. 30 000 L   B. 8500 L   C. 41 000 L   D. 15 000 L

③ A bottle contains 500 vitamin tablets of 325 mg each. The total mass of the tablets in the bottle is _____ g.

A. 162.5   B. 1625   C. 16 250   D. 162 500

④ Which of the following letters has rotational symmetry of order 2?

A. A   B. P   C. S   D. T

⑤ How many lines of symmetry does a parallelogram have?

A. 0   B. 1   C. 2   D. 3

⑥ A net with 5 faces can be used to make a _____ .

A. cube   B. rectangular prism   C. square pyramid   D. triangular pyramid

⑦ A/An _____ triangle has 3 equal angles.

A. right   B. equilateral   C. isosceles   D. scalene

⑧ 20 identical books fill a shelf of width 0.5 m. How thick is each book?

A. 10 mm   B. 20 mm   C. 25 mm   D. 30 mm

⑨ Which of the following figures can tile a plane?

A. Circles   B. Regular pentagons   C. Regular hexagons   D. Regular octagons

⑩ The coordinates of point A are _____ .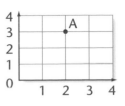

A. (3,4)   B. (4,3)

C. (3,2)   D. (2,3)

⑪ The translation of a point on a grid from (0,5) to (4,1) is 4 units _____ and 4 units _____ .

A. right, down   B. right, up   C. left, up   D. left, down

⑫ The next 2 terms in the pattern 5, 1, 7, 2, ... are _____ .

A. 3, 9   B. 9, 3   C. 3, 4   D. 9, 8

⑬ Look at the changes in gas price.

Month	January	February	March	April
Gas price (¢/L)	88.2	88.0	87.6	87.0

If the trend continues, the gas price in June will be _____ ¢/L.

A. 85.2   B. 86   C. 86.2   D. 86.8

⑭ A number when doubled and then reduced by 2 gives 14. The number is _____ .

A. 4   B. 6   C. 8   D. 9

⑮ Join the points A, C and D. What kind of triangles do you get?

Graph for ⑮ - ⑰.

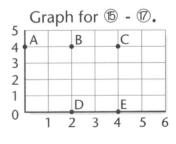

A. Right triangle   B. Isosceles triangle

C. Equilateral triangle   D. Scalene triangle

⑯ Which points are horizontally 2 units from the origin?

A. A and B   B. B and C   C. B and D   D. C and E

⑰ What is the area of rectangle BCED?

A. 8 square units   B. 6 square units   C. 4 square units   D. 10 square units

 What fraction of a day does Dan spend at school?

Circle Graph for ⑱ - ⑳.

Dan's Daily Activities

School
Sleep
Other
Homework   TV

A. $\frac{1}{9}$ B. $\frac{1}{5}$

C. $\frac{1}{4}$ D. $\frac{1}{3}$

⑲ What fraction of a day does Dan spend on 'Other' activities?

A. $\frac{1}{2}$ B. $\frac{1}{4}$ C. $\frac{1}{8}$ D. $\frac{1}{10}$

⑳ What fraction of a day does Dan spend sleeping?

A. $\frac{1}{2}$ B. $\frac{3}{8}$ C. $\frac{3}{4}$ D. $\frac{1}{8}$

㉑ Find the median of 9, 5, 7, 11, 12.

A. 6   B. 7   C. 8.8   D. 9

㉒ Find the mean of 9, 16, 3, 9, 7.

A. 6   B. 7   C. 8.8   D. 9

㉓ Find the mode(s) of 5, 8, 2, 2, 8, 5, 5.

A. 2   B. 5   C. 2, 5   D. 2, 5, 8

㉔ The mean of 3 numbers is 10. Two of the numbers are 2 and 5. What is the 3rd number?

A. 3   B. 23   C. 17   D. 7

㉕ A family has 2 children. What is the probability that they are both girls?

A. $\frac{1}{2}$ B. $\frac{1}{3}$ C. $\frac{1}{4}$ D. $\frac{2}{3}$

㉖ A family has 3 children. What is the probability that all 3 children are boys?

A. $\frac{1}{9}$ B. $\frac{1}{8}$ C. $\frac{1}{4}$ D. $\frac{1}{3}$

Find the answers.

㉗ 324.9 ÷ 100 = ________

㉘ 0.0984 x 100 = ________

㉙ 5.982 x 3 = ________

㉚ 324.9 ÷ 3 = ________

㉛ 116 – 28 x 2 ÷ 7 = ________

㉜ 56 x 3 – 16 ÷ 4 = ________

㉝ 15 + 30 ÷ 6 = ________

㉞ 40 x 5 – 1 + 12 = ________

Complete the number sentences.

㉟ 15 x (7 – 2) = 15 x ______

= ______

㊱ 7 x (3 + 4) = 7 x 3 + 7 x ______

= ______

㊲ 7 + 9 x 2 = 7 + ______

= ______

㊳ (7 + 9) x 2 = ______ x ______

= ______

Write each number as a product of prime factors. Then determine the greatest common factor (G.C.F.) and the least common multiple (L.C.M.) of each pair of numbers.

㊴ a. 18 = ____________

24 = ____________

b. G.C.F. of 18 and 24 : ________

L.C.M. of 18 and 24 : ________

㊵ a. 36 = ____________

44 = ____________

b. G.C.F. of 36 and 44 : ________

L.C.M. of 36 and 44 : ________

Find the answers and write the fractions in lowest terms.

㊶ $\frac{2}{3} + \frac{3}{4}$ = ______

㊷ $\frac{7}{8} - \frac{3}{4}$ = ______

㊸ $1\frac{3}{5} - 1\frac{1}{4}$ = ______

㊹ $\frac{1}{6} + \frac{3}{8}$ = ______

㊺ $\frac{3}{4} - \frac{3}{8}$ = ______

㊻ $\frac{5}{6} - \frac{3}{4}$ = ______

㊼ $1\frac{3}{4} - 1\frac{1}{4}$ = ______

㊽ $\frac{1}{2} - \frac{1}{5}$ = ______

㊾ $2 - 1\frac{1}{8}$ = ______

㊿ $\frac{5}{4} - \frac{4}{5}$ = ______

(51) $\frac{2}{3} + \frac{5}{9}$ = ______

(52) $1\frac{4}{5} + \frac{5}{6}$ = ______

Final Test

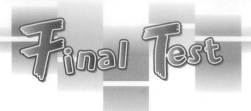

Find the volume of each solid. Then answer the question.

(53)

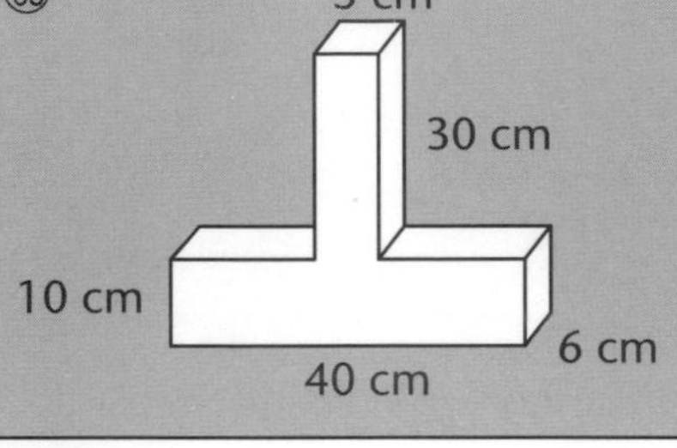
5 cm
30 cm
10 cm
40 cm
6 cm

A

(54)

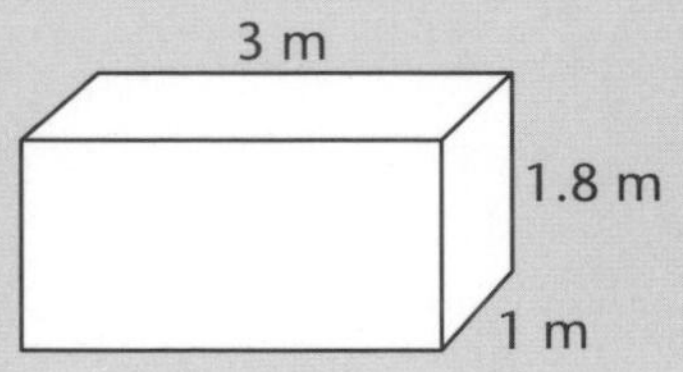
3 m
1.8 m
1 m

B

(55)

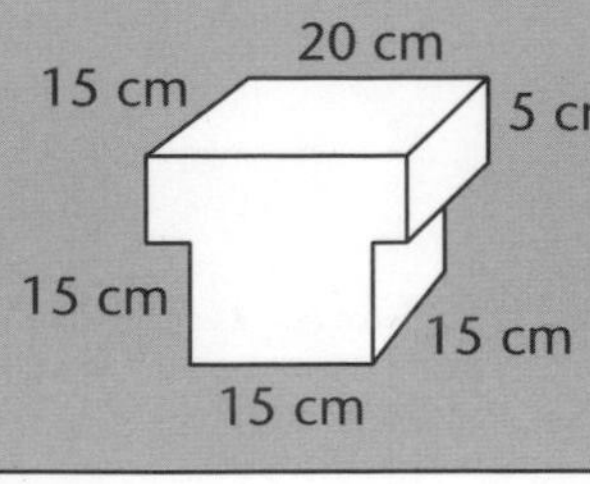
20 cm
15 cm
5 cm
15 cm
15 cm
15 cm

C

(56) Which solid has the largest volume? ________

Draw all the lines of symmetry and write the order of rotational symmetry for each shape in the circle.

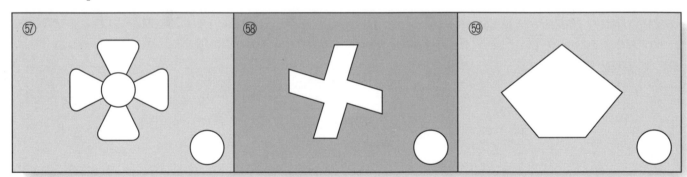

(57)

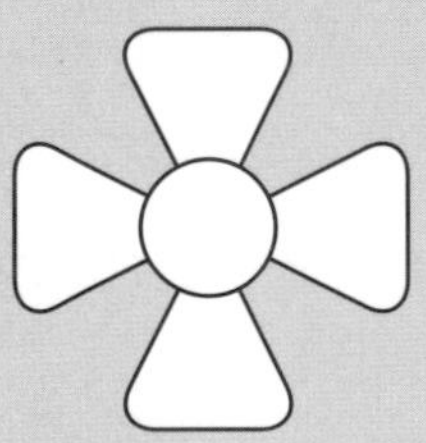

(58)

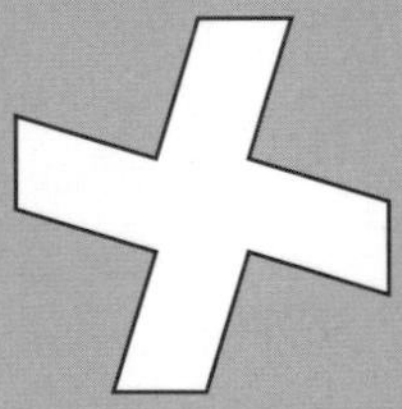

(59)

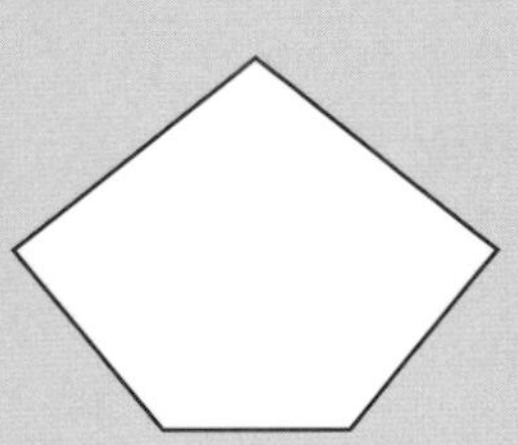

Find the next 3 terms for each pattern. Then write the rules.

(60) 5, 9, 17, 33, 65, ______ , ______ , ______

Rule : ________________________________

(61) 500, 260, 140, 80, ______ , ______ , ______

Rule : ________________________________

Determine the value of the missing numbers.

(62) 25 ÷ ______ = 12.5 (63) ______ x 4 = 108 (64) 26.5 – ______ = 14

(65) 15 + ______ = 20.3 (66) ______ ÷ 5 = 52.5 (67) 14 x 6 – ______ = 28

Sami eats $\frac{3}{4}$ of a chocolate bar. Fred eats $\frac{2}{3}$ of a chocolate bar, and Steve eats $\frac{3}{2}$ of a chocolate bar. Help them solve the problems.

68 Who eats the most?   _____

69 Who eats the least?   _____

70 How many chocolate bars do they eat altogether?   _____ bars

71 If they have 4 chocolate bars, how much is left over? _____ bars

72 Each chocolate bar costs $0.98. If they want to buy 4 chocolate bars, how much change do they get from $5?   _____

73 If each chocolate bar weighs 225 g, how many kilograms do 50 chocolate bars weigh?   _____

Mary is cycling from Georgetown to Rosehill via Huttonville. She records her times at each location using a digital watch. Help her solve the problems.

74 How long does Mary take to cycle from Georgetown to Huttonville?   _____ min

75 How long does Mary take to cycle from Huttonville to Rosehill?   _____ min

76 What is her speed from Georgetown to Huttonville?   _____ km/h

77 What is her speed from Huttonville to Rosehill?   _____ km/h

78 What is her average speed over the whole journey from Georgetown to Rosehill?   _____ km/h

Final Test

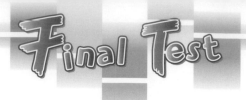

A teacher measures the heights of 20 students in cm. Complete the table and the graphs using the data. Then answer the questions.

152	158	165	169	172	174	175	180	175	162
165	162	168	175	176	152	160	165	158	162

(79)

Range of Height (cm)	Tally	No. of Students	Fraction of the Whole
150 - 159			
160 - 169			
170 - 179			
180 - 189			

(80)

Height of Students

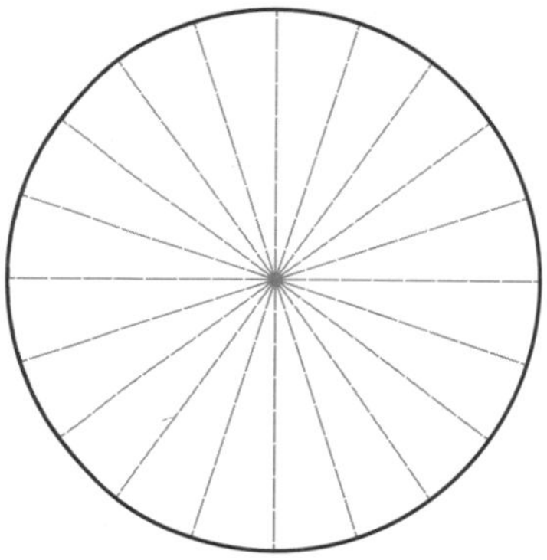

(81)

Height of Students

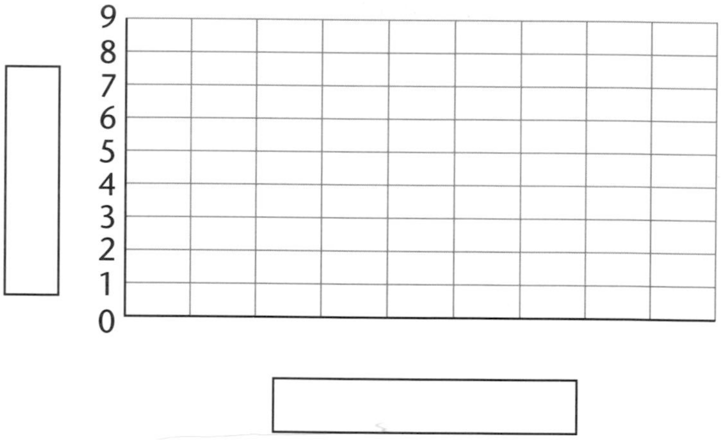

(82) A student is picked by the teacher to clean the blackboard. What is the probability that a student between 150 cm and 159 cm is picked ? __________

(83) What is the most likely height range among the students? __________

(84) There are 5 girls between170 cm and 179 cm. The teacher wants to pick a student between 170 cm and 179 cm. What is the probability that the teacher will pick a girl? __________

(85) Use your calculator to find the mean height of the students. Write your answer to the nearest tenth. __________

Section III

Overview

In Section II, number skills were practised and developed. In this section, these skills are applied in order to solve word problems in Number Sense and Numeration as well as Patterning and Algebra strands.

Solving problems in Number Sense and Numeration involves applying all four arithmetic operations to fractions and decimals as well as whole numbers. Percent, rate and ratio applications are also included.

In Patterning and Algebra, line graphs are used to show patterns in numbers. In the Equations unit, students practise writing equations to represent problem situations and solving them by the guess-and-test method.

Mixed Operations with Whole Numbers

EXAMPLE

After a closing sale, Mr Quinn still had 1334 clear bulbs and 195 white bulbs left in his shop. If each box could hold 16 bulbs, how many boxes would he need to pack away all the bulbs?

Think : First find the total number of bulbs. Then divide it by 16.

Write : No. of boxes : $(1334 + 195) \div 16$
$$= 1529 \div 16$$
$$= 95 \ldots 9$$

1st	
	1 3 3 4
+	1 9 5
	1 5 2 9

2nd
9 5
16 ⟌ 1 5 2 9
1 4 4
8 9
8 0
9

Answer : He would need 96 boxes.

Solve the problems. Show your work.

Francis and Philip are helping out in the library. The library has a collection of 2492 hardcover books, 4716 paperback books and 378 magazines.

① How many books are there in the library?

Answer : There are _____ books.

② How many more paperback books are there than hardcover ones?

Answer : _____

③ If a book shelf holds 16 hardcover books, how many shelves will the library need to hold all the hardcover books?

Answer : _____

④ If each wire rack holds 48 magazines, how many wire racks will the library need to hold all the magazines?

Answer : _____

⑤ The library receives 17 magazines each month. How many magazines will the library have after 8 months?

Answer : _____

⑥ If there are 1296 fictional paperback books, how many non-fictional paperback books are there?

Answer : _____

Kelly has a collection of CDs. She has 142 Rock and Roll, 57 Rhythm and Blue and 86 Country.

⑦ If the average price of a Rock and Roll CD was $14, how much did Kelly spend on these CDs?

Answer : _____

⑧ If the average price of a Rhythm and Blue CD was $11, how much did Kelly spend on these CDs?

Answer : _____

⑨ Kelly was told that her collection of Country CDs was worth $1892. What was each Country CD worth?

Answer : _____

⑩ On average, a CD plays for 53 minutes. How long would it take Kelly to listen to all of her CDs?

Answer : _____

⑪ On average, a CD has 12 songs. How many songs are there in Kelly's collection?

Answer : _____

⑫ On average, a CD weighs 89 grams. What is the total weight of Kelly's CDs?

Answer : _____

⑬ Kelly's goal is to own 1000 CDs. How many more CDs must she buy to meet her goal?

Answer : _____

⑭ If each CD holder stores 16 CDs, how many CD holders does Kelly need for all her CDs?

Answer : _____

Candies are sold in bags of 128, 72 and 48. Loni recorded the sales of candies from yesterday. Use the table to solve the problems.

Bag	Big (128)	Regular (72)	Small (48)
No. of bags sold	18	32	56

⑮ How many candies in bags of 128 were sold yesterday?

Answer : _____

⑯ How many candies were sold in all?

Answer : _____

⑰ The cost of a bag of 128 candies was $42. How much money did Loni collect from the sales of the big bags?

Answer : _____

⑱ The weight of the candies in a regular bag was 1 kg 584 g. What was the average weight of 1 candy?

Answer : _____

⑲ How heavy were the candies in 1 big bag?

Answer : _____

⑳ Which contained more candies, 60 big bags or 102 regular bags?

Answer : _____

㉑ Loni tried to put 9504 candies into regular bags. How many regular bags did she need?

Answer : _____

㉒ Loni tried to put 4872 candies into 25 small bags and the rest into regular bags. How many regular bags did she need?

Answer : _____

㉓ Loni sold 18 big bags of candies and some small bags of candies. If she sold 3600 candies, how many small bags did she sell?

Answer : _____

Don't forget: ← Read this first.
1 kg = 1000 g

e.g.   1 kg 125 g
      = 1000 g + 125 g
      = 1125 g

• For Question 18, write the weight of the candies in grams first.

Solve the problems. Show your work.

Mr Neilson works in a factory that makes fancy pencils and rollerball pens.

㉔ The factory produces 10 320 pencils a day. If 6144 pencils are put in packages of 64 and the rest in packages of 36, how many pencils will there be in packages of 36?

Answer : _____

㉕ How many packages of 64 pencils are produced each day?

Answer : _____

㉖ How many packages of 36 pencils are produced each day?

Answer : _____

㉗ The factory produces 44 000 rollerball pens in 25 days. On average, how many rollerball pens are produced in one day?

Answer : _____

㉘ 2816 cartons of pens are being delivered to Vancouver and 3844 cartons of pens to Montreal. How many cartons of pens are being delivered?

Answer : _____

㉙ If the delivery charge for 32 cartons is $148.00, how much will be the cost of delivering the pens to Vancouver?

Answer : _____

CHALLENGE

A total of 4448 paper clips and push pins were shared equally among 32 students. Each student got 64 paper clips. How many push pins did each student get?

Answer : _____

Multiples and Factors

EXAMPLE

Mario has a collection of 175 coins. He wants to put them in boxes so that each box has the same number of coins in it. What is the least number of boxes he needs? How many coins will there be in each box?

Think : Since 175 ends in 5, 175 is a multiple of 5.

Write : 175 ÷ 5 = 35

Answer : The least number of boxes Mario needs is 5. There will be 35 coins in each box.

Use the 100-chart on the right to solve the problems.

① Circle every multiple of 2.

② Colour all the multiples of 4 yellow.

③ Put a \ over every multiple of 5.

④ Put a / over every multiple of 10.

⑤ What are the first 5 multiples of 2?

The first 5 multiples of 2 are

Answer : _____ .

⑥ What are the first 5 multiples of 4?

Answer : _____

⑦ What are the first 5 multiples of 5?

Answer : _____

⑧ What are the first 5 multiples of 10?

Answer : _____

⑨ What are the ones digits of the multiples of 2?

Answer : _____

1	2	3	4	5	6	7	8	9	10
11	12	13	14	15	16	17	18	19	20
21	22	23	24	25	26	27	28	29	30
31	32	33	34	35	36	37	38	39	40
41	42	43	44	45	46	47	48	49	50
51	52	53	54	55	56	57	58	59	60
61	62	63	64	65	66	67	68	69	70
71	72	73	74	75	76	77	78	79	80
81	82	83	84	85	86	87	88	89	90
91	92	93	94	95	96	97	98	99	100

⑩ What are the ones digits of the multiples of 5?

Answer : _____

⑪ Are the multiples of 4 also the multiples of 2?

Answer : _____

⑫ Are the multiples of 10 also the multiples of 5?

Answer : _____

⑬ Write 3 numbers which are the multiples of 4 and 5.

Answer : _____

⑭ Write 3 numbers which are the multiples of 2 and 10.

Answer : _____

Solve the problems.

To make a long walk interesting, Ken and James played a game called multiples. If Ken said '2' and James said '3', then Ken would have to say '2, 4, 6' because they are the first 3 multiples of 2.

⑮ If James said '6' and Ken said '4', what would James have to say?

Answer : _____

⑯ If Ken said '8' and James said '5', what would Ken have to say?

Answer : _____

⑰ If James said '3' and Ken said '4', what would James have to say?

Answer : _____

⑱ If Ken said '4' and James said '2', what would Ken have to say?

Answer : _____

⑲ If James said '7' and replied with '7, 14, 21, 28 and 35', what would Ken have said?

Answer : _____

⑳ If Ken replied with '11, 22, 33, 44 and 55', what would each of them have said?

Answer : _____

㉑ James started to say '9, 18', then coughed twice and said '45, 54'. What were the two missing numbers and what did each of them say to produce these numbers?

Answer : _____

㉒ Which of the following numbers are the multiples of 3: 127, 849, 243, 239, 552?

Answer : _____

㉓ Which of the following numbers are the multiples of 4: 392, 686, 473, 684, 118?

Answer : _____

- For Question 22:
  A number is a **Read this first.** multiple of 3 if the sum of its digits is divisible by 3.

- For Question 23:
  A number is a multiple of 4 if its last 2 digits form a number that is divisible by 4.

Mr Norad divided his class into groups. Each group used different materials to make handicrafts.

㉔ Mr Norad's class had 24 students. If each group had the same number of students and there were no more than 5 groups, how could the students be divided? How many students would be in each group?

• *Numbers multiplied to get a product are called factors.*

e.g. $4 \times 6 = 24$
      factors   product

• *For Question 24, make use of the multiplication facts with a product of 24.*

Read this first.

Answer : _____

㉕ What are the factors of 24?

Answer : _____

㉖ Students in group A made their handicrafts with ribbons. They cut an 18 m piece of ribbon into strips of equal lengths. If the length of each strip had to be more than 4 m, how could the ribbon be cut? How long would each strip be?

Answer : _____

㉗ What are the factors of 18?

Answer : _____

㉘ Students in group C put 20 beads into rows. If each row had the same number of beads and there were fewer than 5 rows, how could the beads be put? How many beads would be in each row?

Answer : _____

㉙ What are the factors of 20?

Answer : _____

㉚ What are the common factors of 18, 20 and 24?

Answer : _____

Mrs Majic has invented a machine that can generate numbers at random. Use the numbers to solve the problems. Show your work.

28   3 10   24   147   27   409
8   64   280   394   573   72
540   382   85   97   51   89
151   116   406

③¹ Which numbers on the screen are the multiples of 5?

Answer : _____

③² Write a rule to explain how to tell that a number is divisible by 5.

Answer : _____

③³ Which numbers on the screen are the multiples of 10?

Answer : _____

③⁴ Write a rule to explain how to tell that a number is divisible by 10.

Answer : _____

③⁵ Which numbers on the screen are the multiples of 4?

Answer : _____

③⁶ Are all the multiples of 2 also the multiples of 4?

Answer : _____

③⁷ Which numbers on the screen are the multiples of 3?

Answer : _____

③⁸ Which numbers on the screen are the multiples of 3 and 4?

Answer : _____

③⁹ What are the first 4 common multiples of 3 and 4?

Answer : _____

④⁰ 280 is the second multiple of a number. What is that number?

Answer : _____

④¹ 51 is the third multiple of a number. What is that number?

Answer : _____

④² 28 is the second common multiple of 2 and a number. What is that number?

Answer : _____

Solve the problems. Show your work.

㊸ Chris and Judy bought some packs of lollipops. Chris bought 12 lollipops and Judy bought 16 lollipops. Each pack had the same number of lollipops. How many different ways could the lollipops be packed?

- For Questions 43 and 45: Follow these steps to find the answers: ← Read this first.

  1st List the factors of each number.

  2nd Circle the factors that they have in common.

Answer : _____

㊹ What could be the ways of packaging the lollipops?

Answer: _____

㊺ If Chris and Judy put their lollipops together and divide them equally into groups, how many different ways could the lollipops be divided?

Answer: _____

㊻ What could be the ways of dividing the lollipops?

Answer: _____

㊼ Chris said, 'The greater a number is, the more factors it has.' Is he correct? Explain and give an example to support your answer.

Answer: _____

㊽ The number of chocolate bars that Judy wants to buy is between 14 and 19. If the number has 6 factors, how many chocolate bars will Judy buy?

Answer: _____

㊾ Chris bought 216 g of candies. He said that he could pack them equally into 9 bags. Is he correct? Explain.

Answer: _____

Complete the tables and solve the problems.

50)

Number	7	8	9	10
Factor				

• Any number with only 2 factors (1 and itself) is a prime number. Otherwise, it is a composite number.
e.g. The factors of 13 are 1 and 13, so 13 is a prime number. The factors of 10 are 1, 2, 5 and 10, so 10 is a composite number.

Read this first.

51) Write all the prime numbers up to 10.

Answer : _____

52)

Number	Factor	Prime / Composite
16		
25		
11		
39		

Number	Factor	Prime / Composite
29		
51		
36		
47		

53) Write all the prime numbers up to 50.

Answer : _____

54) What is the sum of all the composite numbers between 20 and 30?

Answer : _____

55) What is the sum of all the prime numbers between 50 and 60?

Answer : _____

CHALLENGE

Write True or False.

① The product of 2 prime numbers is a prime number. _____

② 1 is neither composite nor prime. _____

③ All the prime numbers are odd numbers. _____

④ The product of 1 prime number and 1 composite number is a composite number. _____

Addition and Subtraction of Fractions

EXAMPLE

There were $2\frac{5}{8}$ L of orange juice in a jug. For breakfast, Dora drank $\frac{1}{2}$ L of orange juice and for lunch she drank $\frac{3}{4}$ L. How many litres of orange juice did Dora drink? How many litres of orange juice were left in the jug?

Orange juice drunk : $\frac{1}{2}+\frac{3}{4}=\frac{2}{4}+\frac{3}{4}=\frac{5}{4}=1\frac{1}{4}$

Orange juice left : $2\frac{5}{8}-1\frac{1}{4}=2\frac{5}{8}-1\frac{2}{8}=1\frac{3}{8}$

Answer : Dora drank $1\frac{1}{4}$ L of orange juice; $1\frac{3}{8}$ L of orange juice were left.

Solve the problems. Show your work. Write the answers in simplest form.

Sara and her friends are buying remnants of cloth at a fabric store to make costumes for the school play.

① Sara needs $2\frac{1}{2}$ m of green velvet to make a special costume. She has $1\frac{1}{4}$ m of green velvet at school. How much more green velvet does she need to buy?

Answer : She needs to buy _____ of green velvet. _____

② Milly buys $2\frac{3}{4}$ m of yellow velvet and $\frac{1}{8}$ m of blue velvet. How much velvet does she buy?

Answer : _____

③ Sara needs some cloth to make togas. She needs $2\frac{1}{5}$ m of blue cloth, $\frac{3}{5}$ m of yellow cloth and $\frac{7}{10}$ m of red cloth. How much cloth does she need to buy?

Answer : _____

④ Freda finds $3\frac{7}{10}$ m of lace in 2 pieces. One piece is $1\frac{3}{5}$ m. How long is the other one?

• To add or subtract fractions ← **Read this first.** with different denominators:

1. Find the common denominator.
2. Add or subtract the numerators.
3. Write the fraction in simplest form.

Answer : _____

Mr Stim's class was filling an aquarium with water for some experiments. The students were carrying water to fill the aquarium in large pails.

⑤ Mary and Peter went first. Mary carried $\frac{2}{5}$ pail of water and Peter carried $\frac{3}{4}$ pail of water. How many pails of water did they carry in all?

Answer : _____

⑥ If Mary and Peter were required to carry $1\frac{1}{2}$ pails of water between them, how much more water would they have to carry?

Answer : _____

⑦ Perry and Wayne went second. They carried $2\frac{2}{3}$ pails of water in all. If Perry carried $1\frac{1}{2}$ pails of water, how many pails of water did Wayne carry?

Answer : _____

⑧ How much more water did Perry carry than Wayne?

Answer : _____

⑨ Jack carried $\frac{9}{10}$ pail at the beginning. He tripped and spilled $\frac{1}{5}$ pail of water. How much water did he carry to the aquarium?

Answer : _____

⑩ Joseph found a small wagon and delivered 3 pails of water to the aquarium. Each pail was $\frac{3}{4}$ full. How much water did Joseph carry to the aquarium?

Answer : _____

⑪ The length of the aquarium was $1\frac{1}{5}$ m long and its width was $\frac{1}{2}$ m shorter than its length. What was the width of the aquarium?

Answer : _____

⑫ At the beginning, the water level in the aquarium was $\frac{3}{10}$ m. After Mr Stim put 1 bag of pebbles into the aquarium, the water level rose to $\frac{2}{5}$ m. How much did the water level rise?

Answer : _____

⑬ Mr Stim kept putting pebbles into the aquarium until the water level rose by $\frac{3}{5}$ m. How many bags of pebbles did he put into the aquarium?

Answer : _____

Glenda's school was having a charity food fair. Glenda and her friends brought a lot of food to school.

⑭ Glenda brought $1\frac{7}{10}$ boxes of banana muffins and $\frac{1}{5}$ box of chocolate muffins. How many boxes of muffins did Glenda bring to school?

Answer : _____

⑮ Glenda sold $1\frac{1}{2}$ boxes of muffins. How many boxes of muffins were left over?

Answer : _____

⑯ Linda brought $2\frac{4}{5}$ kg of chocolate cookies and $1\frac{1}{2}$ kg of oat cookies to school. How many kilograms of cookies did Linda bring to school?

Answer : _____

⑰ Linda sold $3\frac{1}{10}$ kg of cookies. How many kilograms of cookies were left over?

Answer : _____

⑱ Jessica bought $1\frac{1}{4}$ boxes of sesame crackers and $\frac{3}{8}$ box of cheese crackers. How many boxes of crackers did Jessica buy in all?

Answer : _____

⑲ Raymond brought 2 bags of jellybeans to school. Bag A weighed $1\frac{5}{12}$ kg and Bag B weighed $\frac{1}{6}$ kg. How many kilograms of jellybeans did Raymond bring to school?

Answer : _____

⑳ How much heavier was Bag A than Bag B?

Answer : _____

㉑ Elaine brought 2 pies of the same size to school. One of the pies had 12 slices and 5 slices were sold. The other pie had 4 slices and 3 slices were sold. What fraction of the pies were sold?

Answer : _____

㉒ What fraction of the pies were left over?

Answer : _____

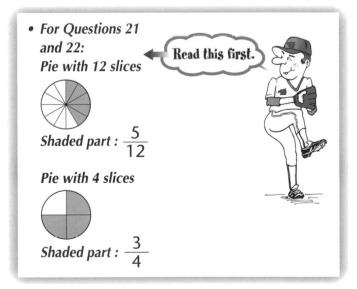

• For Questions 21 and 22:
Pie with 12 slices

Read this first.

Shaded part : $\frac{5}{12}$

Pie with 4 slices

Shaded part : $\frac{3}{4}$

A group of children were making some handicrafts with cardboard, ribbons, beans and paint.

㉓ The width of a piece of cardboard was $35\frac{1}{10}$ cm. Its length was $4\frac{1}{5}$ cm longer than its width. What was the length of the cardboard?

Answer : _____

㉔ Grace had a roll of ribbon $4\frac{1}{2}$ m long. She used $1\frac{1}{8}$ m to make some flowers. How many metres of ribbon were left?

Answer : _____

㉕ Grace used $1\frac{1}{4}$ m of the remaining ribbon to decorate a box. How many metres of ribbon were left?

Answer : _____

㉖ Shirley had $3\frac{3}{4}$ boxes of beans. She used $1\frac{1}{2}$ boxes of beans for her handicraft. How many boxes of beans were left?

Answer : _____

㉗ After that, Shirley gave $1\frac{1}{5}$ boxes of beans to Ryan. How many boxes of beans did she still have?

Answer : _____

㉘ Ryan painted his model with $5\frac{1}{3}$ mL of green paint. $3\frac{1}{6}$ mL of green paint were left. How many millilitres of green paint had Ryan got at the beginning?

Answer : _____

CHALLENGE

Tammy had a $2\frac{3}{5}$ m long ribbon. She cut it into strips of $\frac{2}{5}$ m each.

① How many strips did she get?

No. of strips	1	2	
Total length of strips	$\frac{2}{5}$ m	$\frac{4}{5}$ m	

Answer : _____

② How much ribbon was left?

Answer : _____

Addition and Subtraction of Decimals

EXAMPLE

Doris was making cocktail juice. She put 0.375 L of strawberry juice , 0.428 L of pineapple juice and 0.24 L of orange juice into the blender. How much juice did she put in and how much more juice could Doris add if the blender could hold 1.5 L of juice?

Amount of juice : 0.375 + 0.428 + 0.24 = 1.043

Space : 1.5 – 1.043 = 0.457

Answer : Doris put in 1.043 L of juice; she could add 0.457 L more.

Solve the problems. Show your work.

Frank and Mindy were shopping for groceries. They bought some vegetables and fruits.

① Mindy bought 2 bags of apples. 1 bag weighed 1.465 kg and the other 1.389 kg. What was the total weight of the apples?

The total weight of the apples
Answer : was _____ .

② The prices of the 2 bags of apples were $1.45 and $1.38. What was the total cost of the apples?

Answer : _____

③ Frank bought some grapes. The total weight of 2 bags of grapes was 2.15 kg. If one bag weighed 1.309 kg, what would the weight of the other bag be?

Answer : _____

④ Mindy bought a bag of red onions at $3.27 and a bag of white onions at $4.69. How much did Mindy spend on onions?

Answer : _____

⑤ The total cost of Mindy's purchases was $18.27. How much change would she receive from a $20 bill?

Answer : _____

⑥ The total cost of Frank's purchases was $23.19. If he had $4.58 left, how much had Frank got at the start?

Answer : _____

Frank lives 2.544 km from the grocery store and Mindy lives 3.068 km from the grocery store but in the opposite direction.

⑦ How much farther from the grocery store is Mindy than Frank?

Answer : _____

⑧ If Frank decided to help Mindy take the groceries home and then walk back to his house, how far would he travel?

Answer : _____

⑨ Mindy forgot to buy milk. Frank was at her home and said that he would go back for the milk. How far would Frank have walked in all to get the milk for Mindy?

Answer : _____

⑩ Mindy's mother gave Frank a $5 bill to buy the milk that was on sale for $2.29. How much change did Frank get?

Answer : _____

⑪ If Mindy's mother told Frank that he could buy a 79-cent candy bar for helping out, how much change would she get?

Answer : _____

⑫ Frank bought a $0.56 lollipop instead. How much more change would Mindy's mother get?

Answer : _____

⑬ It would take Frank 15.5 minutes to walk to the grocery store and 11.27 minutes to run to the grocery store. How much time could he save if he ran to the grocery store and back to Mindy's house instead of walking?

Answer : _____

CHALLENGE

Mario was a young figure skater. He performed well but fell once and used music that was too short. He lost 0.25 point for falling and 0.36 point for his music.

① Mario got a score of 4.7. What would have been his score if he had not fallen and his music had been suitable?

Answer : _____

② For his next turn, Mario hoped he would not fall, but it was too late to change his music. If a perfect score was 6, what would be the highest score Mario could get?

Answer : _____

Multiplication and Division of Decimals

EXAMPLE

Jerome saved $96.55 in 5 months and Susanne saved $74.88 in 4 months. How much more did Jerome save than Susanne each month?

Money Jerome saved each month : 96.55 ÷ 5 = 19.31

Money Susanne saved each month : 74.88 ÷ 4 = 18.72

Difference : 19.31 − 18.72 = 0.59

Answer : Jerome saved $0.59 more than Susanne each month.

Solve the problems. Show your work.

Jim went on a driving trip with his family. They drove 321.75 km on the first day, 297.54 km on the second day and 306.72 km on the third day.

① What was the mean distance they travelled?

Answer : The mean distance was _____ .

② They drove 3 hours on the first day. What was the average speed?

Answer : _____

③ They also drove 3 hours on the second day. What was the average speed?

Answer : _____

④ They averaged 90 km/h on the third day. How many hours did they drive?

Answer : _____

⑤ If their car consumed 1 L of gasoline for every 12 km driven, how much gasoline did they use on the second day?

Answer : _____

⑥ On the fourth day, they were still 210.72 km from their destination. How much more gasoline would they need to reach there?

Answer : _____

⑦ If they took 4 hours to travel the remaining distance, what would their average speed be?

Answer : _____

⑧ They used 94.68 L of gasoline for the trip. If 1 L of gasoline cost 57¢, how much did they pay for the gasoline?

Answer : _____

Theresa went shopping with her friends at Sweetie Candy Store. All the prices in the store included taxes.

⑨ The average weight of 3 bags of candies was 1.19 kg. What was the total weight?

Answer : _____

⑩ If Theresa bought 1.45 kg of jellybeans at the special price of $9.00 per kg, how much would she pay?

Answer : _____

⑪ Elaine bought 9 packs of chewing gum for $7.74. How much did 1 pack of chewing gum cost?

Answer : _____

⑫ 6 boxes of chocolates cost $25.53. 8 boxes of chocolates cost $32.12. Which were a better buy?

Answer : _____

⑬ Fruit gums were $7.90 per kg. If David wanted to buy 2.4 kg, how much would he pay?

Answer : _____

⑭ Chocolates with almonds were $23.71 per kg. If Theresa bought 0.5 kg, how much would she pay?

Answer : _____

- **For Questions 13 & 14 :**

  Don't forget the number of decimal places in the product is equal to the total number of decimal places in the two numerals.

  e.g.

  $$
  \begin{array}{r}
  4.6 \quad \textit{1 decimal place} \\
  \times \quad 5.3 \quad \textit{1 decimal place} \\
  \hline
  1\,3\,8 \\
  2\,3\,0\,0 \\
  \hline
  2\,4.3\,8 \quad \textit{2 decimal places}
  \end{array}
  $$

 Read this first.

Kirby went on a camping vacation with his family. Kirby's parents prepared everything for the camp.

⑮ They bought two new tents for $375.06. How much did 1 tent cost?

Answer : _____

⑯ They hoped to hike for 28.25 km each day for 5 days. How far could they go?

Answer : _____

⑰ Kirby hiked 16.1 km in 1.4 h. What was his average speed?

Answer : _____

⑱ Food costs were estimated at $32.78 per day. How much did the family spend on food for 5 days?

Answer : _____

⑲ There were 5 members in Kirby's family, what was the food cost per person per day?

Answer : _____

⑳ If they consumed 8.25 L of water per day, how much water would they need for 5 days?

Answer : _____

㉑ A bottle could hold 1.5 L of water. If they wanted to have 13.5 L of water, how many bottles would they need?

Answer : _____

㉒ Kirby's backpack was 1.4 times heavier than his sister's. If his sister's backpack weighed 12.45 kg, how heavy was Kirby's?

Answer : _____

㉓ Kirby's backpack weighed 0.7 of his father's. How heavy was his father's backpack?

Answer : _____

㉔ The first-aid box was 12.8 cm long, 8.4 cm wide and 6 cm high. What was its volume?

Answer : _____

- *To divide a decimal by another decimal, multiply the divisor and the dividend by 10, 100 or 1000 to make the divisor a whole number.*

Read this first.

e.g. 7.5 ÷ 1.5 = 5

$$1.5\overline{)7.5} \rightarrow 15\overline{)75}$$
$$\begin{array}{r} 5 \\ 15\overline{)75} \\ 75 \end{array}$$

Miss Prem's class and Mr Holly's class were locked in a bitter basketball rivalry.

㉕ The school basketball court is 28 m long and 15.56 m wide. What is the area of the court?

Answer : _____

㉖ Mr Holly's team practised 1.35 hours each day to get ready for the game. If the big game was 8 days away, how many hours of practice would his team have?

Answer : _____

㉗ Miss Prem's team ran a total of 26 km in the 8 days before the big game. How many kilometres did they run each day?

Answer : _____

㉘ In the first 4 games of the season, Miss Prem's team scored 277 points. How many points per game were scored by her team on average?

Answer : _____

㉙ In the first 4 games of the season, Mr Holly's team scored an average of 68.25 points per game. How many points did his team get in all?

Answer : _____

CHALLENGE

A tie costs 1.6 times more than a belt. A belt costs 1.8 times less than a scarf. If the scarf costs $35.01, how much does the belt cost? How much does the tie cost? How many times more does the scarf cost than the tie?

Answer : _____

Solve the problems. Show your work.

In Gary's school auditorium, there are 1252 seats in 35 rows. The average class size in Gary's school is 33 students.

① The number of seats in each row is the same except the last one, which has 28 seats only. How many seats are there in each row?

Answer : _____

② There are 35 classes in Gary's school. If 632 students are girls, how many boys are there in all?

Answer : _____

③ If all the students are in the auditorium, how many seats will be left for the teachers?

Answer : _____

④ If the chairs are stacked in piles of 12, how many piles will there be? How many chairs will be left?

Answer : _____

⑤ There are 32 students in Gary's class. Miss Sullivan wants them to line up in no more than 5 rows, with the same number of students in each row. How many ways can they form rows, and how many students will there be in each case?

Answer : _____

⑥ Mr Friedman wants his class of 36 students to line up in no more than 8 rows, and also with the same number of students in each row. How many ways can they form rows, and how many students will there be in each case?

Answer : _____

⑦ Miss Sullivan's class join Mr Friedman's class. The students have to line up in no more than 5 rows, with the same number of students in each row. How many ways can they form rows, and how many students will there be in each case?

Answer : _____

There was a sale at Jackie's popcorn store. The store decided to give a $1.95 discount for every 3 items bought. The popcorn was packed in boxes 10 cm long, 5 cm wide and 15.5 cm high.

⑧ What was the volume of each box?

Answer : _____

⑨ Jackie put the boxes on a shelf 1.5 m long and 0.18 m deep. She wanted to store the boxes as deep as she could without coming closer to the edge than 3 cm. How many boxes of popcorn could she put on the shelf side by side?

Answer : _____

⑩ If Jackie was to pack the boxes 3 rows high, how many boxes of popcorn could she put on the shelf?

Answer : _____

⑪ The weight of 1 box of popcorn was 0.128 kg. What was the total weight of all the popcorn on the shelf?

Answer : _____

⑫ If each box sold for $2.25, how much would all the popcorn on the shelf be worth?

Answer : _____

⑬ Elaine had a $20 bill. What was the maximum number of boxes of popcorn she could buy without the discount? How much was her change?

Answer : _____

⑭ If Elaine bought 9 boxes of popcorn, how much change would she receive from a $20 bill?

Answer : _____

⑮ If Mr Stanley bought 26 boxes of popcorn, how much discount would he get?

Answer : _____

⑯ How much change would Mr Stanley receive from a $50 bill?

Answer : _____

⑰ A carton holds 65 boxes of popcorn. Last month, Jackie sold 128 cartons and 16 boxes of popcorn. How many boxes of popcorn did she sell in all?

Answer : _____

The Annual Open Day is approaching, and the children are busy preparing for it. Dave and his classmates are making name tags and decorating the display boards.

⑱ What is the area of each piece of cardboard paper?

Answer :

⑲ What is the area of each card?

Answer :

⑳ If the children want to make 1280 name tags, how many pieces of cardboard paper do they need?

Answer :

㉑ 1280 is the 160th multiple of a number. What number is it?

Answer :

㉒ If Dave wants to put the cards in 12 stacks with 106 cards in each, how many cards will there be?

Answer :

㉓ Dave has a single-hole punch that can punch 6 cards at a time. If he wants to punch 2 holes in each card, how many times does he need to punch for his stacks of cards?

Answer :

21.2 cm

27.9 cm

Name tag

㉔ Elaine has 1 roll of $1\frac{4}{5}$ m-long ribbon. If she uses $1\frac{1}{2}$ m for the name tags for the guests, how many metres of ribbon will be left?

Answer :

㉕ 2 rolls of ribbon cost $9.25. If Elaine paid $27.75, how many rolls of ribbon did she buy?

Answer :

㉖ The children want to decorate the display boards with coloured paper. If each pack of coloured paper costs $5.29, how much do 12 packs cost?

Answer :

㉗ The children have $1\frac{1}{5}$ packs of red paper and $2\frac{2}{3}$ packs of yellow paper. How many packs of coloured paper are there?

Answer :

Circle the correct answer in each problem.

㉘ Which is a prime number?

A. 39   B. 49   C. 59   D. 69

㉙ If a number, A, is a factor of another number, B, then B is a _____ of A.

A. number   B. multiple   C. factor   D. fraction

㉚ Larry has a piece of wood $3\frac{3}{5}$ m long. He uses $1\frac{1}{10}$ m of it for a project. How many metres of wood are left?

A. $2\frac{1}{2}$ m   B. $1\frac{1}{2}$ m   C. $2\frac{1}{5}$ m   D. $1\frac{2}{5}$ m

㉛ Jenny needs 1.4 m of cloth to finish a dress. The cloth costs $6.75 per 0.5 m. How much does she pay?

A. $4.73   B. $6.08   C. $18.90   D. $9.45

㉜ 6 is not a factor of :

A. 32.   B. 48.   C. 60.   D. 120.

㉝ Mrs Kim bought 129 boxes of chocolates at $16 for 3 boxes. How much did she pay?

A. $654   B. $2064   C. $645   D. $688

㉞ Michael has 329 quarters, 215 dimes and 279 nickels. How many coins does Michael have in all?

A. 813 coins   B. 823 coins   C. 723 coins   D. 822 coins

㉟ How much does Michael have?

A. $857.95   B. $127.70   C. $243.25   D. $117.70

EXAMPLE

. . . .

Mrs Brown wanted to clean her 3.25 m × 4.6 m carpet. The cleaners said that the carpet would cost $5.20 a square metre to clean. How much would it cost Mrs Brown to have her carpet cleaned?

Area of the carpet : 3.25 × 4.6 = 14.95

Cost : 14.95 × 5.2 = 77.74

Answer : It would cost Mrs Brown $77.74 to have her carpet cleaned.

Solve the problems. Show your work.

Lori has just moved into a new apartment. She is measuring the dimensions of her living room, dining room and hallway.

① The area of her living room is 38.88 m². If the length of the room is 7.2 m, what is the width?

Answer : The width is _____ .

② The dining room has a fancy plaster border around the top of the walls. If the dining room is 5.5 m wide and 8.14 m long, what is the length of the border?

Answer : _____

③ What is the area of the dining room?

Answer : _____

④ The hallway is 2.4 m long and covered with square tiles. Each side of the tiles is 0.3 m. How many tiles are there in the length of the hallway?

Answer : _____

⑤ The hallway is 1.8 m wide. How many tiles are there in the entire hallway?

Answer : _____

Paul and Petula were going on a trip with their parents. They drove 259.79 km on the first day, 302.57 km on the second day and an average of 225.67 km on the next 2 days.

⑥ How far did they drive for the whole trip?

Answer : _____

⑦ If the average speed was 75 km/h, how many hours did they drive for the trip?

Answer : _____

⑧ They filled up their car 3 times – 46.37 L before the trip, 49.45 L on the second day, and 42.69 L on the fourth day. On average, how many litres of gasoline did they buy each time?

Answer : _____

⑨ If the average fill-up cost was $27.76, what would the total fill-up cost be?

Answer : _____

⑩ They spent $58.27 on food on the first day, $63.39 on the second day and $123.84 on the next 2 days. How much did they spend on food in all?

Answer : _____

⑪ How much did they spend on food per day?

Answer : _____

⑫ Paul's mother said, 'The cost we spent on food exceeded our budget by $25.50.' What was their budget for food?

Answer : _____

⑬ Paul's mother bought 3 kg of ham at $2.29 a kilogram, 4.6 kg of turkey at $3.40 a kilogram, 2.4 kg of potatoes at $0.60 a kilogram and 3.8 kg of beans at $1.40 a kilogram. How much more money did she spend on meat than on vegetables?

Answer : _____

⑭ The lodging cost an average of $26.69 per night per person. If they spent 3 nights there, what would be their total lodging bill?

Answer : _____

Fred was learning to make a cabinet in a carpentry class.

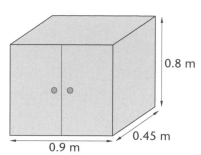

0.8 m

0.45 m

0.9 m

⑮ How many square metres of wood would Fred need for the top of the cabinet?

Answer : _____

⑯ The wood for the top of the cabinet was $57.90 per square metre. What was the cost of the wood for the top? (correct to the nearest cent)

Answer : _____

⑰ The sides of the cabinet were to be made of lighter wood that cost $42.99 per square metre. What was the cost of the wood for the sides? (correct to the nearest cent)

Answer : _____

⑱ The cost of the wood for the back and front of the cabinet was $60.84. What was the cost of the wood per square metre?

Answer : _____

⑲ Fred spent $153.27 in all for wood. What was the cost of the wood for the bottom of the cabinet?

Answer : _____

• 'Correct to the nearest cent' means 'correct to the nearest hundredth of a dollar.' To do this, you have to look at the thousandth digit. If it is 5 or more, round it up and add 1 to the hundredth digit. If it is 4 or less, leave it out.

Read this first.

e.g. $4.125 ⟶ $4.13 (round up)
       $4.124 ⟶ $4.12 (round down)

⑳ 2 hinges cost $8.27. How much did 1 hinge cost? (correct to the nearest cent)

Answer : _____

㉑ Fred bought 4 hinges with a $20 bill. What was his change?

Answer : _____

㉒ Fred needed 2 knobs. The knobs cost $3.09 each or $5.73 a pair. How much would Fred save by buying a pair instead of 2 separately?

Answer : _____

㉓ If one small can of paint can cover 0.5 m² and Fred wanted to paint the cabinet except the bottom and the back, how many small cans of paint would Fred need?

Answer : _____

Tony is the chairman of the Stamp Club. The club has 24 members, and each member pays $4.29 for his or her annual membership fee. Mr Knapp, the teacher, gives Tony $196.50 to run the club in this school year.

㉔ How much will the club collect from its members this year?

Answer : _____

㉕ How much money is available for the club each month in this school year, excluding the 2-month summer break?

Answer : _____

㉖ Tony wants to spend a quarter of the money on a newsletter to be published twice a year. How much money will there be for each issue? (correct to the nearest cent)

Answer : _____

㉗ After budgeting for the newsletter, how much money will be left for other activities?

Answer : _____

㉘ Everybody in the club needs a stamp album which costs $9.95. Can the club afford to give each member an album?

Answer : _____

CHALLENGE

Harry gets 2 doughnuts free for every 4 doughnuts he buys. If each doughnut costs $0.89, how much does he need to pay for 6 chocolate doughnuts and 48 strawberry doughnuts?

Answer : _____

Percent, Decimals and Fractions

EXAMPLE

Frank coloured 25 hundredths of his 100-square paper. What fraction or percent of his paper is coloured?

Think : 25 hundredths means 0.25 or 25 out of 100.

Write : $0.25 = \dfrac{25}{100} = \dfrac{1}{4}$ or $0.25 = \dfrac{1}{4} = 25\%$

Answer : $\dfrac{1}{4}$ or 25% of his paper is coloured.

Solve the problems. Show your work.

Henry and Molly were going shopping at the F & G Discount Department Store.

① Henry saw a big sign that read '$\dfrac{1}{2}$ off all shoes'. What percent discount were they offering?

Answer : They were offering _____ discount.

② All the suits were on sale at a 20% discount. What fraction of the price of a suit was reduced?

Answer : _____

③ Molly paid $\dfrac{4}{5}$ of the price of a dress that she liked. What percent of the price of the dress did Molly pay?

Answer : _____

④ The store manager said that 45 out of 50 items were on sale. What percent of the items were on sale?

Answer : _____

⑤ The store assistant said that 50 out of 200 pairs of shoes were sold. What percent of the shoes were sold?

Answer : _____

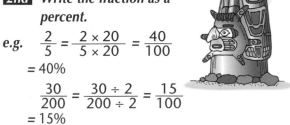

• To convert a fraction to a percent :
  Read this first.
  1st Change the fraction with 100 as the denominator.
  2nd Write the fraction as a percent.
  e.g. $\dfrac{2}{5} = \dfrac{2 \times 20}{5 \times 20} = \dfrac{40}{100}$
  $= 40\%$
  $\dfrac{30}{200} = \dfrac{30 \div 2}{200 \div 2} = \dfrac{15}{100}$
  $= 15\%$

Ron and Judy were trying to increase their fitness levels. They wanted to improve a bit each day.

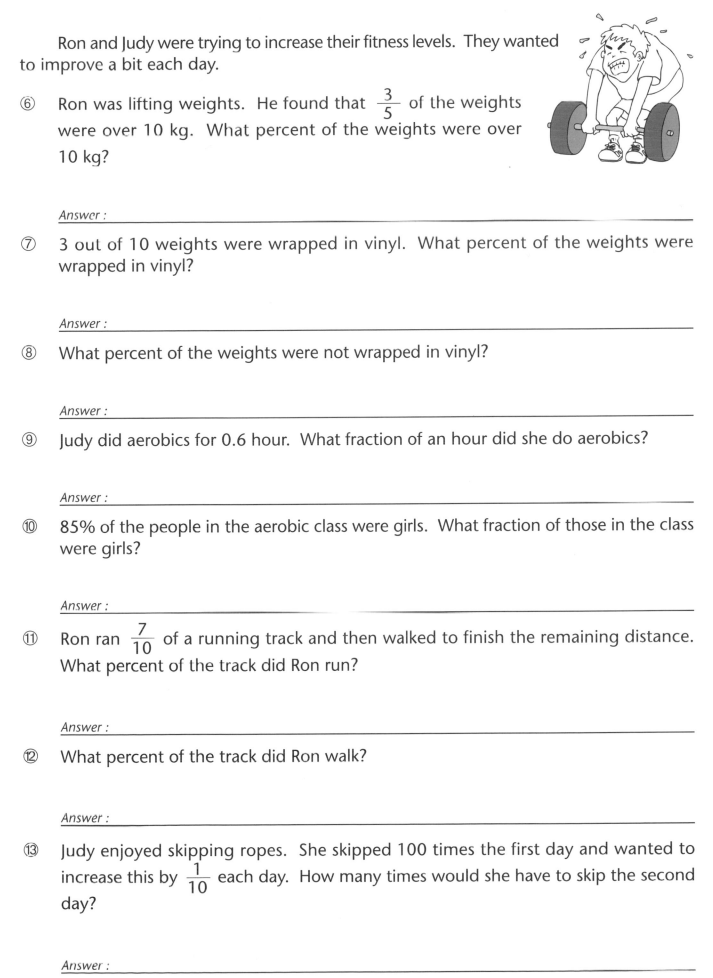

⑥ Ron was lifting weights. He found that $\frac{3}{5}$ of the weights were over 10 kg. What percent of the weights were over 10 kg?

Answer : _____

⑦ 3 out of 10 weights were wrapped in vinyl. What percent of the weights were wrapped in vinyl?

Answer : _____

⑧ What percent of the weights were not wrapped in vinyl?

Answer : _____

⑨ Judy did aerobics for 0.6 hour. What fraction of an hour did she do aerobics?

Answer : _____

⑩ 85% of the people in the aerobic class were girls. What fraction of those in the class were girls?

Answer : _____

⑪ Ron ran $\frac{7}{10}$ of a running track and then walked to finish the remaining distance. What percent of the track did Ron run?

Answer : _____

⑫ What percent of the track did Ron walk?

Answer : _____

⑬ Judy enjoyed skipping ropes. She skipped 100 times the first day and wanted to increase this by $\frac{1}{10}$ each day. How many times would she have to skip the second day?

Answer : _____

Look at Emily's stickers. Solve the problems. Show your work.

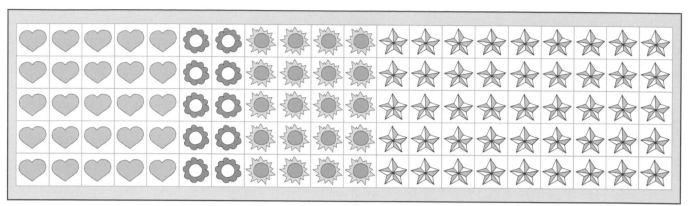

⑭ What percent of Emily's stickers are ❤ ?

Answer : _____

⑮ What percent of her stickers are ✿ ?

Answer : _____

⑯ What percent of her stickers are ✺ ?

Answer : _____

⑰ What percent of her stickers are ★ ?

Answer : _____

⑱ If Emily used 20 , what fraction of her stickers would be left?

Answer : _____

⑲ If Emily used 16 stickers, what percent of her stickers would be left?

Answer : _____

⑳ If Emily gave 0.35 of her stickers to her sister, what percent of her stickers would be left?

Answer : _____

㉑ If Emily used $\frac{3}{4}$ of her stickers, what percent of her stickers would be left?

Answer : _____

㉒ If Emily used 10 ❤ , what percent of her ❤ stickers would be left?

Answer : _____

㉓ If Emily had 12 ✺ left, what percent of her ✺ stickers would she have used?

Answer : _____

㉔ If Emily used 60% of her stickers, how many stickers would be left?

Answer : _____

Solve the problems. Show your work. Write your answers correct to 3 decimal places.

㉕ 5 out of 8 doughnuts in a box are chocolate flavour. Write a decimal for the doughnuts that are chocolate flavour.

Answer : _____

㉖ What percent of the doughnuts in the box are chocolate flavour?

Answer : _____

㉗ $\frac{11}{80}$ of the students in Amy's school like Math. Write a decimal for the students who like Math.

Answer : _____

㉘ What percent of the students in Amy's school like Math?

Answer : _____

• To write a fraction as a decimal number, you can divide the numerator by the denominator.

e.g. $\frac{3}{8} = 0.375$

```
    0.3 7 5
8 ) 3 0
    2 4
    ‾‾‾
      6 0
      5 6
    ‾‾‾
        4 0
        4 0
        ‾‾‾
```

Read this first.

㉙ 42.5% of the drinks are grape flavour. Write a decimal for the drinks that are grape flavour.

Answer : _____

㉚ What fraction of the drinks are grape flavour?

Answer : _____

㉛ What percent of the drinks are not grape flavour?

Answer : _____

CHALLENGE

Jenny had a bag of 100 g candies and Jeffrey had a bag of 50 g candies. If Jenny ate 30% of her candies and Jeffrey ate 50% of his candies, who ate more? How much more?

Answer : _____

UNIT 8 — Ratio and Rate

EXAMPLE

There are 12 boys and 16 girls in Sally's class. What is the ratio of boys to girls in Sally's class?

Ratio of boys to girls = 12:16 (divide each term by 4)
= 3:4

Answer : The ratio of boys to girls in Sally's class is 3:4.

Solve the problems. Show your work. Write your answers in simplest form.

There are 25 History books and 35 Geography books in the class library of 200 books.

① What is the ratio of History books to Geography books?

Answer : The ratio is _____ .

② What is the ratio of Geography books to the total number of books?

Answer : _____

③ What is the ratio of History books to the total number of books?

Answer : _____

④ If there were 100 fictions in the library, what would be the ratio of fictions to the total number of books?

Answer : _____

- The ratio is in simplest form when the only common factor of the terms is 1.
  e.g. 2:3 is in simplest form.

Read this first.

⑤ What would be the ratio of History books to fictions?

Answer : _____

⑥ If the library added 50 more History books, what would be the ratio of new books to old books?

Answer : _____

⑦ What would be the ratio of History books to the total number of books?

Answer : _____

In Molly's collection of 20 dolls, 5 dolls have porcelain faces, 4 wear lace dresses, 2 have leather boots and 12 are taller than 20 cm.

⑧ What is the ratio of dolls with porcelain faces to dolls with faces of other materials?

Answer : _____

⑨ What is the ratio of dolls with lace dresses to dolls with other types of dresses?

Answer : _____

⑩ What is the ratio of dolls that are taller than 20 cm to the total number of dolls?

Answer : _____

⑪ The dolls with leather boots are more valuable than the other dolls. What is the ratio of more valuable dolls to less valuable dolls?

Answer : _____

⑫ Daisy, Molly's friend, has 16 dolls. 6 of her dolls have leather boots. What is the ratio of Daisy's dolls that have leather boots to those without leather boots?

Answer : _____

⑬ What is the ratio of Daisy's dolls to Molly's dolls?

Answer : _____

⑭ If Daisy gives 4 of her dolls to Molly, what will be the ratio of Daisy's dolls to Molly's dolls?

Answer : _____

⑮ If Molly gives 4 of her dolls to Daisy, what will be the ratio of Daisy's dolls to Molly's dolls?

Answer : _____

Wanda went shopping with her friends. They were comparing the fruit prices.

⑯ The cost of 5 kg of apples was $6.45. How much did 1 kg of apples cost?

Answer : _____

⑰ If Wanda wanted to buy 3 kg of apples, how much would she need to pay?

Answer : _____

⑱ The cost of 4 kg of peaches was $6.76. How much did 1 kg of peaches cost?

Answer : _____

⑲ If Louis wanted to buy 3 kg of peaches, how much would he need to pay?

Answer : _____

⑳ Catherine paid $1.96 to buy 4 kg of bananas. How much did 1 kg of bananas cost?

Answer : _____

㉑ If Catherine bought 7 kg of bananas, how much would she need to pay?

Answer : _____

㉒ The cherries were sold in 3-kg and 5-kg baskets. A basket of 3 kg of cherries cost $14.97. A basket of 5 kg of cherries cost $25.80. Which was a better buy?

Answer : _____

- A rate is a relation between different kinds of quantities.

  Read this first.

  e.g. John earns $20 in 2 hours. Rate of earnings :

  $20 \div 2 = 10$

  John earns $10/h .
  (The second term of a rate is usually 1.)

㉓ A basket of 2 kg of plums cost $5.58. A basket of 3 kg of plums cost $8.07. Which was a better buy?

Answer : _____

㉔ If Wanda bought 2 baskets of 3 kg of plums, how much would she need to pay?

Answer : _____

㉕ If Wanda paid $32.28 to buy some baskets of 3 kg of plums, how many baskets of plums did she buy?

Answer : _____

㉖ The shopkeeper wanted to pack his 350 apples in bags of 5 or 7. Each bag of 5 apples would be sold for $1.35 and each bag of 7 apples for $1.75. Which way should the shopkeeper pack his apples to make more money? How much more?

Answer : _____

Solve the problems. Show your work.

㉗ Edwin travels 3 km in 20 minutes. What is his rate of speed in km/h?

Answer : _____

㉘ William can read 27 pages in 1.5 hours. What is his reading rate in pages per hour?

Answer : _____

㉙ Donny earned $77.00 in 8 hours. How much did Donny earn each hour? (correct to the nearest cent)

Answer : _____

㉚ Shirley reads 108 words in 10 min while Henry reads 147 words in 15 min. Who reads faster? Explain.

Answer : _____

㉛ Bright Lite bulbs are sold in packs of 4 for $1.49 while Supergood bulbs are sold in packs of 12 for $4.96. Which is a better buy?

Answer : _____

㉜ If Supergood bulbs last twice as long as Bright Lite bulbs, which brand offers a better value? Explain.

Answer : _____

What is the ratio of free muffins to paid muffins in each offer? Which one is the best buy?

> A. Buy 3 muffins for $2.45 and get 1 free.
> B. Buy 10 muffins for $8.95 and get 2 free.
> C. Buy 12 muffins for $8.99 and get 3 free.

Answer : _____

EXAMPLE

Darren is trying to increase the number of pages he has to read. He reads 2 pages on Monday, 4 pages on Tuesday, 8 pages on Wednesday, etc. How many pages will he have to read on Saturday?

Think : Each day, Darren has to read 2 times the number of pages he read the previous day.

Write :

Day	Mon	Tue	Wed	Thu	Fri	Sat
No. of pages	2	4	8	16	32	64

×2 ×2 ×2 ×2 ×2

Answer : Darren will have to read 64 pages on Saturday.

Complete the tables and solve the problems. Show your work.

Jimmy is making mixed nuts with peanuts, almonds, hazelnuts and Brazil nuts.

① Jimmy starts with peanuts and almonds. For every 5 peanuts, he adds 1 almond. How many peanuts will he have when he has added 10 almonds?

No. of almonds	1	2	3	4	5	6	7	8	9	10
No. of peanuts	5									

Answer : He will have _____ peanuts. _____

② For every 3 peanuts, he adds 2 hazelnuts. How many hazelnuts will he have when there are 27 peanuts?

Answer : _____

③ For the 1st 3 almonds, Jimmy adds 2 Brazil nuts. For the 2nd 3, he adds 3, for the 3rd 3, he adds 4 and so on. How many Brazil nuts will he add for the 9th 3 almonds?

Answer : _____

Gary kept track of the growth of his favourite vine in his greenhouse. Look at Gary's graph and solve the problems. Show your work.

④ How much did Gary's vine grow between September and October?

Length of Gary's Vine

Answer : _____

⑤ What was the growth pattern of Gary's vine between September and April?

Answer : _____

⑥ If the growth pattern stayed the same, when would the vine be 110 cm long?

Answer : _____

⑦ If the growth pattern stayed the same, how long would the vine be in the coming September?

Answer : _____

⑧ Gary decided to cut off 2.5 cm for every 10 cm it grew from April. If the growth pattern of his vine stayed the same, how long would it be in the coming August?

Answer : _____

⑨ Gary noticed that the number of leaves of his vine was also increasing. For every 5 cm the vine grew, the number of leaves increased by 4. How many new leaves grew between September and April?

Answer : _____

Solve the problems. Show your work.

Dennis won $5000 in a lottery. He decided to put it in a new bank account and only pay his $750 monthly rent from it.

⑩   What would be the balance in the bank account in the third month?

Answer : _____

⑪   For how many months could he pay his rent from his account?

Answer : _____

⑫   Describe the pattern of the balance in his account.

Answer : _____

⑬   If the bank gave him $8.80 interest on the second of the second month, $7.70 on the second of the third month and $6.60 on the second of the fourth month and so on, how much would he receive on the second of the sixth month?

Answer : _____

⑭   Describe the pattern of Dennis' interest.

Answer : _____

⑮   How much interest would Dennis receive over the 6 months?

Answer : _____

⑯   What would be his balance after 5 months of paying rent and receiving interest?

Answer : _____

Erin was having an interesting time financially. In the first month, she received $12.00 as a gift and spent $8.00 towards some books that she wanted. In the second month, she received $14.00 as a gift and spent $10.50. In the third month, she received $16.00 and spent $13.00.

⑰ Describe the pattern of the money that Erin received.

Answer : _____

⑱ If this pattern continued, how much would she receive on the sixth month?

Answer : _____

⑲ Describe the pattern of the money that Erin spent.

Answer : _____

⑳ If this pattern continued, how much would she spend in the sixth month?

Answer : _____

㉑ How much money would she save over the first 6 months?

Answer : _____

㉒ When would the amount Erin received be the same as the amount she spent?

Answer : _____

CHALLENGE

The numbers 1, 1, 2, 3, 5, 8, 13 ... form a pattern.

a.   Describe the pattern.   b.   Find the next 5 terms in the pattern.

Answer : _____   Answer : _____

EXAMPLE

The cost of 5 boxes of crackers is the same as the cost of 3 boxes of chocolates. If 1 box of chocolates costs $3.15, how much does 1 box of crackers cost?

$? \times 5 = 3.15 \times 3$ (? represents the cost of 1 box of crackers)

$? \times 5 = 9.45$

$? = 1.89$

Answer : 1 box of crackers costs $1.89.

Write an equation with a ? to solve each problem. Show your work.

Last weekend, there was a fun fair near Tim's house. 2 adult tickets cost the same as 3 children's tickets.

① If an adult ticket cost $9.75, what was the price of 1 children's ticket?

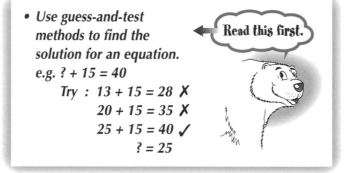

• *Use guess-and-test methods to find the solution for an equation.*
  e.g. $? + 15 = 40$
    Try : $13 + 15 = 28$ ✗
      $20 + 15 = 35$ ✗
      $25 + 15 = 40$ ✓
      $? = 25$

Read this first.

The price of 1 children's ticket
Answer : was _____ .

② Tim went to the fun fair with his friends. They shared a $4.86 box of popcorn and a $6.98 bag of candies. Each paid $2.96. How many children were there in all?

Answer : _____

③ Tim had $12.69 left after paying for his ticket and his share of snacks. How much money had Tim got at the beginning?

Answer : _____

④ Tim paid for his drink with 4 quarters and 2 dimes. He got $0.04 change. How much did the drink cost?

Answer : _____

⑤ Tim got a jar of 156 jellybeans from the batting game and shared it with 3 of his friends. Then he put his own share equally into 3 bags. How many jellybeans were there in each bag?

Answer : _____

⑥ There were 100 children in the fun fair. If 20% of the children were under 2 years old and 35% over 6 years old, how many of the children there were between 2 and 6 years old?

Answer : _____

⑦ Tokens came in packages of 6 and 12. A package of 12 tokens cost $0.75 less than 2 packages of 6 tokens. If a package of 6 tokens cost $2.25, how much did a package of 12 tokens cost?

Answer : _____

⑧ Elaine bought a package of 12 tokens and got $1.25 change. How much did she give to the cashier?

Answer : _____

⑨ Tim paid $18.75 for 2 packages of 12 tokens and some packages of 6 tokens. How many packages of 6 tokens did he buy?

Answer : _____

⑩ Elaine played 3 games. She got 136 points in the first game and 216 in the second one. The points she got in the third game was 59 points fewer than the total points she got in the first two games. How many points did Elaine get in the third game?

Answer : _____

⑪ Tim got a lot of coupons. He divided the coupons into 16 groups, each having 3 discount coupons and 4 coupons for games. How many coupons did Tim get in all?

Answer : _____

Harry and Anna went shopping at Super Discount Store where they took $5 off purchases $20.00 or under, and $8 off purchases $20.01 and over. All prices included taxes, too.

⑫ The cost of a handbag was $15 more than that of a wallet. If the wallet cost $12, how much did the handbag cost?

Answer : _____

⑬ The price difference between skirt A and skirt B was $7. Skirt A was less expensive than skirt B. If the cost of skirt A was $35, how much did skirt B cost?

Answer : _____

⑭ A sweater cost $25 less than a jacket. If the jacket cost $145, how much did the sweater cost?

Answer : _____

⑮ The total cost of 3 T-shirts and a pair of shorts was $54 before discount. If the cost of a T-shirt was $12, how much did a pair of shorts cost?

Answer : _____

⑯ If Anna paid for a pair of jeans with 2 $20 bills and got $5 change, how much did the jeans cost before discount?

Answer : _____

⑰ Anna bought a pair of earrings which cost $12 before discount. If she got $3 change, how much did she give to the cashier?

Answer : _____

⑱ Harry wanted to buy a coat which cost $56 before discount. If he got $12 change, how much did he give to the cashier?

Answer : _____

Write an equation with an $\boxed{n}$ for each problem and solve it.

⑲ A number divided by 2 is 5.

Answer : _____

⑳ 5 more than a number is 7.

Answer : _____

㉑ The sum of 3 and a number is 12.

Answer : _____

㉒ 4 less than a number is 15.

Answer : _____

㉓ 3 times a number is 21.

Answer : _____

㉔ The product of 4 and a number is 36.

Answer : _____

㉕ A number increased by 11 is 26.

Answer : _____

㉖ Half of a number is 12.

Answer : _____

㉗ 9 more than a number is 40.

Answer : _____

㉘ 75 divided by a number is 15.

Answer : _____

Match the equations with the problems. Write the letters.

A. $p \div 2 = q + 1$ C. $2x + 1 = y$ E. $(s \div 2) + 2 = t$

B. $2m - 1 = n$ D. $b \div 2 + 1 = a$ F. $c + 2 = d$

① 2 times Susan's age minus 1 is equal to Tim's age. ☐

② Mr Ryan's age is 1 year older than 2 times his son's age. ☐

③ Half of Raymond's age is equal to Elaine's age plus 1. ☐

④ Harry's age is 2 years older than half of Henry's age. ☐

⑤ Susan's age is 2 years older than Louis' age. ☐

⑥ Half of Raymond's age plus 1 is equal to Gary's age. ☐

Solve the problems. Show your work.

Miss Glink's class held a fundraising day last week. They wanted to raise money to help the homeless.

① There were 12 girls and 15 boys in Miss Glink's class. What was the ratio of girls to boys in the class?

Answer : _____

② What fraction of Miss Glink's students were girls?

Answer : _____

③ If the goal was to raise $20.75 per person, how much money would they want to raise?

Answer : _____

④ Betsy was at a booth selling raisins. She had 4635 grams of golden raisins and 6430 grams of sultana raisins. How many grams of raisins did Betsy have?

Answer : _____

⑤ How many bags would Betsy need for the golden raisins, if she wanted to put them in bags of 85 grams each? How many grams of golden raisins were left over?

Answer : _____

⑥ How many bags would Betsy need for the sultana raisins, if she wanted to put them in bags of 75 grams each? How many grams of sultana raisins were left over?

Answer : _____

⑦ Each bag of golden raisins cost $0.50 and each bag of sultana raisins cost $0.65. If Betsy sold 35 bags of golden raisins and 60 bags of sultana raisins, how much money would she raise?

Answer : _____

⑧ Betsy found that she sold an average of 18 bags of raisins per hour. How many bags of raisins could she sell in 6 hours?

Answer : _____

⑨ At the end of the day, Betsy found that $\frac{4}{5}$ of all her raisins had been sold. What percent of her raisins had been sold?

Answer : _____

⑩ Elaine was at another booth selling fresh juice. She sold 108 glasses of orange juice for $1.25 each, 88 glasses of apple juice for $1.75 each and 104 glasses of watermelon juice for $1.45 each. How much money did she raise?

Answer : _____

⑪ What was the ratio of orange juice sold to all the juice sold?

Answer : _____

⑫ What percent of the juice sold was orange juice?

Answer : _____

⑬ What fraction of the juice sold was apple juice?

Answer : _____

⑭ Mr Pratt bought 7 glasses of watermelon juice and got 1 loonie, 3 quarters and 1 dime back. How much did he give to Elaine? (Write an equation with a ⸤?⸥ to solve this problem.)

Answer : _____

⑮ The boys raised $60.00 more than the girls. The girls raised $255.00. How much money did the boys raise? (Write an equation with a ⸤?⸥ to solve this problem.)

Answer : _____

⑯ Could the students meet their goal? Explain.

Answer : _____

Gary and his family were going on a vacation. They were travelling to a vacation spot 1200 km from their home.

⑰ If the airplane travelled an average of 400 km/h, how long would the trip take?

Answer : _____

⑱ They lived 48 km from the airport and took 36 minutes to travel from their house to the airport. What was the average driving speed in km/h?

Answer : _____

⑲ There were 5 members in Gary's family. The air fare for the trip was $415.37 per person, but Gary's father redeemed some points for 1 free ticket. How much was the air fare for the whole family?

Answer : _____

⑳ They were going to spend 8 nights at a hotel. The hotel charged them the family rate of $239.45 per night. How much did they spend on accommodation?

Answer : _____

㉑ Each day, they spent an average of $125.75 on food. How much was their food bill for the 9-day vacation?

Answer : _____

㉒ How much did they spend on food and accommodation for the entire vacation?

Answer : _____

㉓ The hotel offered a package deal of $625 per person, all meals included. Would that be a good deal for Gary's family?

Answer : _____

㉔ During the vacation, Gary and his sister bought some souvenirs for their friends. Gary bought 16 key-rings and his sister bought 24. If they wanted to put the key-rings in small boxes, with each of their boxes containing the same number of key-rings, how many ways could they put the key-rings?

Answer : _____

㉕ What were the ways of putting the key-rings?

Answer : _____

㉖ Gary's brother bought 9 packs of bookmarks. Each pack had the same number of bookmarks. He said that he could put them equally into 3 piles. Is he correct? Explain.

Answer : _____

㉗ Gary's mother bought a straw hat for herself. The price of the hat was between $11.00 and $20.00. If the price was a factor of 24, how much did the hat cost?

Answer : _____

㉘ Gary's mother bought some T-shirts for her friends. The number of T-shirts she bought was between 10 and 19. If the number was a multiple of 8, how many T-shirts did Gary's mother buy?

Answer : _____

㉙ Gary's father likes collecting seashells. He picked 2 seashells from the beach on the third day of their vacation, 3 on the fourth day, 5 on the fifth day and 9 on the sixth day. Complete the table below and describe the pattern.

Day	3rd	4th	5th	6th	7th	8th	9th
No. of seashells picked	2	3	5	9			

Answer : _____

㉚ How many seashells would Gary's father collect during his vacation?

Answer : _____

㉛ What fraction of the seashells were picked on the 7th day?

Answer : _____

Circle the correct answer in each problem.

③② What is the smallest number that both 12 and 18 will divide into evenly?

A. 216   B. 261   C. 36   D. 48

③③ If Sari has 12 yellow flowers and 18 pink ones, what is the ratio of pink to yellow flowers?

A. 3:2   B. 2:3   C. 12:18   D. 12:30

③④ What decimal is equal to 27%?

A. 2.7   B. 0.27   C. 0.027   D. 27.0

③⑤ If Willy saves 25% of his allowance each week, what fraction of his allowance can he spend?

A. $\dfrac{1}{4}$ B. $\dfrac{2}{4}$ C. $1\dfrac{3}{4}$ D. $\dfrac{3}{4}$

③⑥ Peter, Paul and George are having a contest to see who can be the first to finish a 5 km run. Peter says that he has run 2.5 km. Paul says that he has completed 50% of the distance and George says that he still has $\dfrac{1}{2}$ the distance to go. Who has run the farthest?

A. Peter   B. Paul   C. George   D. None of the above

③⑦ Irving went shopping with 2 $10 bills in his pocket. If his first purchase was $7.38, how much money would he still have?

A. $2.26   B. $2.62   C. $12.62   D. $12.52

③⑧ If a car travels at 60 km/h for 4 hours and 18 minutes, how far will it have travelled?

A. 13.95 km   B. 258 km   C. 250.8 km   D. 6.97 km

③⑨ If Randy wants to make a pile of quarters worth $21.50, how many quarters will he need for the pile?

A. 86   B. 90   C. 96   D. 84

Section IV

Overview

Section III included problems in the Number Sense and Numeration as well as Patterning and Algebra strands.

In Section IV, word problems cover Measurement, Geometry and Spatial Sense, and Data Management and Probability strands.

Measurement applications include money, speed, distance, time, perimeter, area and volume.

The Geometry strand includes 2- and 3-D figures, coordinates and transformations.

Data Management involves reading circle graphs, line graphs and bar graphs, and finding the median of a set of data. Tree diagrams are included in the Probability unit.

EXAMPLE

Bill is painting a box which is 130 mm long, 5 cm wide and 1 dm high. How many square metres does he have to paint?

Think : 130 mm = 13 cm = 0.13 m ; 5 cm = 0.05 m ; 1dm = 0.1 m

Write : Areas of 2 sides : $0.13 \times 0.1 \times 2 = 0.026$

Areas of 2 ends : $0.1 \times 0.05 \times 2 = 0.01$

Areas of top and bottom : $0.13 \times 0.05 \times 2 = 0.013$

Total areas : $0.026 + 0.01 + 0.013 = 0.049$

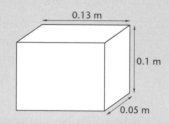

Answer : He has to paint 0.049 m^2.

Complete the tables and solve the problems. Show your work.

①

m	40				950	
cm		200		80 000		
km			4.5			0.7

②

g	900		50		60 000	
kg		8.3		0.29		3.44

③

mL		450		52 000		9
L	2.05		0.11		32.4	

④ State True or False for each of the following.

a. 40 cm + 8 dm = 840 cm

b. 500 mm + 6 m = 650 cm

c. 8.2 kg + 200 g = 8400 g

d. 0.5 L + 400 mL = 0.54 L

> • **Length :** 1 km = 1000 m ← **Read this first.**
> 1 m = 10 dm
> 1 dm = 10 cm
> 1 cm = 10 mm
>
> • **Weight :** 1 kg = 1000 g
>
> • **Capacity :** 1 L = 1000 mL

Answer : a.　　　　b.　　　　c.　　　　d.

Kelly and Milly were buying candies and drinks for their party.

⑤ Kelly bought 1.3 kg of jellybeans and 250 g of cinnamon hearts. How many grams of candies did she buy in all?

Answer : _____

⑥ Milly wanted to buy some licorice that was priced per 100g. If she wanted to buy 0.75 kg of licorice, how many times the price per 100 g would she pay?

Answer : _____

⑦ They wanted to buy some small bags to put the candies in and ribbons to tie them up. If they bought 14 cm of red ribbon, 0.8 m of blue ribbon and 1200 mm of white ribbon, how many metres of ribbon did they buy?

Answer : _____

⑧ How many centimetres of ribbon did they buy?

Answer : _____

⑨ Milly bought 2 bags of candies. They weighed 1.03 kg and 800 g. How many kilograms of candies did she buy in all?

Answer : _____

⑩ On average, each bag weighed 600 g. If the total weight of bags was 2.4 kg, how many bags of candies did they buy in all?

Answer : _____

⑪ If the total amount of juice in 5 containers was 2.25 L, how many millilitres of juice did 1 container hold on average?

Answer : _____

⑫ Container A could hold 0.89 L of juice and container B could hold 450 mL of juice. How much more juice in litres could container A hold than container B?

Answer : _____

CHALLENGE

Freda was piling tiles. Each tile was 8 mm thick and weighed 18 g.

① How many tiles were there in a pile of 6.4 m high?

Answer : _____

② How many kilograms did the 6.4 m high pile of tiles weigh?

Answer : _____

Operations with Money

EXAMPLE

Billy bought 2 boxes of chocolates for $12.70 each. The cashier charged him an additional $3.81 for taxes. What was his change from a $50 bill?

Total cost : $12.7 \times 2 + 3.81 = 29.21$

Change : $50 - 29.21 = 20.79$

Answer :   His change was $20.79.

Solve the problems. Show your work.

Milly and Jeffrey went shopping at their favourite mall. All the purchases were tax free that day.

① Milly was looking for a blouse. Store A had the blouse on sale for $35.98. Store B had the same blouse on sale for $41.52, but offered her a $5.25 discount. Which store had the lower price?

Answer : Store _____ had the lower price. _____

② If Milly bought the cheaper blouse and the cashier gave the change to her with the fewest coins or bills, what was her change from a $50 bill? What were the coins or bills?

Answer : _____

③ Milly wanted to buy some candies. She saw her favourite candy on sale for $1.49 per 100 g. How much would it cost her for 0.7 kg?

Answer : _____

④ If the cashier gave the change to her with the fewest coins, what was her change from a $10 bill and a toonie? What were the coins?

Answer : _____

⑤ Jeffrey wanted to buy some shoe polish for his old boots. Store C had it on sale for $3.95 for a 125-g tube, but store D sold it for $2.99 for a 100-g jar. Which was a better buy?

Answer : _____

⑥ Jeffrey wanted to call his friend, but he did not have any quarters. If he changed his $10 bill into quarters, how many quarters would he get?

Answer : _____

⑦ In the food court, hamburgers were sold for $2.49 each, French Fries for $1.39 each and soft drinks for $1.25 each. If Jeffrey bought 2 hamburgers and 1 soft drink and paid with the fewest number of coins, what coins would he pay for his food?

Answer : _____

⑧ Milly used one-eighth of her money to buy 1 hamburger, 1 order of French Fries and 1 soft drink. How much money did Milly have at the beginning?

Answer : _____

⑨ Milly bought 4 boxes of chocolates for $11.16. She opened 1 box and found that the chocolates did not taste good. Then Milly returned 3 boxes of chocolates. How much money did Milly get back?

Answer : _____

⑩ The average cost of 2 bags of popcorn and a jumbo soft drink was $4.32. If the average cost of 2 bags of popcorn was $4.59, how much did the jumbo soft drink cost?

Answer : _____

⑪ Jeffrey had 4 quarters, 24 dimes and 16 nickels left. Did he have enough money to buy a jumbo soft drink? Explain.

Answer : _____

Jerry got a part-time job in Alco Parking Lot. He wanted to save some money for a trip in summer.

⑫ If he got paid $7.05 per hour and worked 18 hours a week, how much could he earn per week?

Answer : _____

⑬ Jerry worked 6 days a week and took a bus to and from work. If the bus fare was $1.85 per trip, how much did he earn each week after paying for the transportation?

Answer : _____

⑭ Jerry's employer deducted $25.38 of his weekly earnings for income tax. How much did he earn after paying for transportation and the deduction?

Answer : _____

⑮ Jerry wanted to save up at least $600.00 for the trip. How many weeks would he have to work to save this amount?

Answer : _____

⑯ In the parking lot, the parking fee for the 1st half hour was $1.75 and $3.00 for every extra half hour. How much was the parking fee for 2 hours and 25 minutes?

Answer : _____

⑰ Mr Keller parked his car for 1 hour and 46 minutes. Jerry gave $1.25 change to him. How much did Mr Keller give to Jerry for his parking fee?

Answer : _____

⑱ Jerry had to prepare some coins for change. If he traded a $5 bill for nickels, how many nickels would he get?

Answer : _____

Jerry recorded the money collected in the past 6 days. Use his table to write the amount of money in words to complete what he said.

Day	Mon	Tue	Wed	Thu	Fri	Sat
Money Collected ($)	5975.45	6094.00	4210.30	3981.95	5700.40	9008.10

• It is easier to know the values of decimal numbers if we place them on a place value chart.

e.g. 2736.54

Read this first.

Thousands			H	T	O	Tenths	Hun-dredths
H	T	O					
			2	7	3	6. 5	4

It's busy working here. Last week, I collected :

⑲ _____ on Monday,

⑳ _____ on Tuesday,

㉑ _____ on Wednesday,

㉒ _____ on Thursday,

㉓ _____ on Friday, and

㉔ _____ on Saturday.

CHALLENGE

Gary had 50 coins. $\frac{1}{2}$ of his coins were toonies, $\frac{1}{10}$ loonies, $\frac{1}{5}$ quarters, $\frac{1}{10}$ dimes and the rest nickels. How much did Gary have? Did he have enough money to trade for a $50 bill?

	Toonie	Loonie	Quarter	Dime	Nickel
No. of coins					

Answer : _____

Time, Distance and Speed

Tommy left home at 10:42 a.m. and walked to the mall, a distance of 2 km. If Tommy arrived at the mall at 11:07 a.m., how long did he take to walk there? What was his walking speed?

Time taken :   11 h 07 min – 10 h 42 min = 25 min

Speed :   2 ÷ 25 = 0.08

Answer :   He took 25 min to walk to the mall.
His walking speed was 0.08 km/min.

Solve the problems. Show your work.

Sandy, Elaine and Matthew were going on a car trip. They were going to meet at Elaine's house. Sandy's house was 1040 m from Elaine's house and Matthew's house was 2160 m from Elaine's house.

① If Sandy walked at an average speed of 0.08 km/min, how long would it take her to reach Elaine's house?

Answer : It would take her _____.

② Matthew had to arrive at Elaine's house at 11:00 a.m. If Matthew left his house at 10:42 a.m., at what speed should he walk so as to reach Elaine's house on time?

Answer : _____

③ If Matthew's speed was also 0.08 km/min, at what time would he reach Elaine's house?

Answer : _____

④ The first part of their trip was 506 km long. It took them 9.2 hours to drive there. What was their average speed?

Answer : _____

⑤ The three friends took turns driving. If Sandy drove 2 hours 45 minutes and Elaine drove 3 hours 30 minutes, how long did Matthew drive?

Answer : _____

⑥ The next day, they drove at an average speed of 72 km/h for 6 hours and 50 km/h for 1 hour 33 minutes. How far did they drive in all?

Answer : _____

⑦ On the third day, they drove 300 km in 3 hours 12 minutes. What was their average speed in kilometres per hour?

Answer : _____

⑧ Sandy drove at 60 km/h to the convenience store 36 km away and returned to the motel at 40 km/h. If she left the motel at 12:44 p.m., at what time did she return?

Answer : _____

⑨ On the fourth day, they visited a museum which was 138.92 km from the motel. They left the motel at 2:45 p.m. and took 2 hours and 18 minutes to reach there. At what time did they reach the museum?

Answer : _____

⑩ What was their average speed in kilometres per hour?

Answer : _____

⑪ If they wanted to reach the museum 16 min earlier than their actual arrival time, what time would it be?

Answer : _____

⑫ At what speed would they have to drive then? (correct to 2 decimal places)

Answer : _____

CHALLENGE

A car started from Townville at an average speed of 80 km/h towards Littleton. A truck started from Littleton at an average speed of 50 km/h towards Townville. If both the car and the truck started at 2:45 p.m. and passed each other at 6:15 p.m., what was the distance between Townville and Littleton?

Answer : _____

EXAMPLE

Rose wanted to plant a herb garden in the shape of a triangle as shown. How much edging would she need to go all the way around the garden? What was the area of the garden?

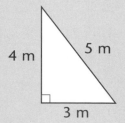

Perimeter : $5 + 4 + 3 = 12$

Area : $3 \times 4 \div 2 = 6$

Answer : Rose would need 12 m of edging. The area of the garden was 6 m^2.

Look at the pieces of cardboard and solve the problems. Show your work.

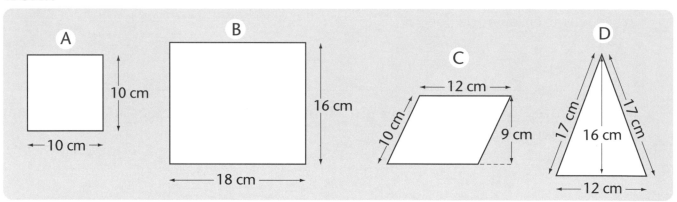

① Olive wanted to decorate the edges of each piece of cardboard with a braid border. How long would the braid border be for A?

Answer : The braid border would be _____ long.

② How long would the braid border be for B?

Answer : _____

③ How long would the braid border be for C?

Answer : _____

④ How long would the braid border be for D?

Answer : _____

⑤ What was the area of A?

Answer : _____

⑥ What was the area of B?

Answer : _____

⑦ What was the area of C?

Answer : _____

⑧ What was the area of D?

Answer : _____

⑨ Olive cut out a square from the middle of A, leaving 2 cm on each side. What was the area of the cardboard left?

Answer : _____

⑩ Olive cut out a rectangle from the middle of B, again leaving 2 cm on each side. What was the area of the cardboard left?

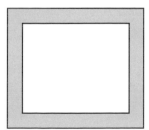

Answer : _____

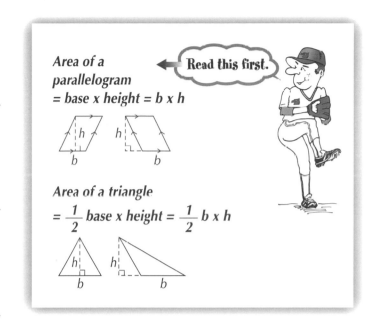

Area of a parallelogram
= base x height = b x h

Read this first.

Area of a triangle
= $\frac{1}{2}$ base x height = $\frac{1}{2}$ b x h

⑪ Olive cut out a parallelogram from the middle of C as shown.

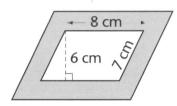

a. What was the area of the cardboard left?

Answer : _____

b. What was the perimeter of the cutout part?

Answer : _____

⑫ Olive cut out a triangle from the middle of D. What was the area of the cardboard left?

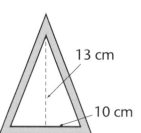

Answer : _____

Solve the problems. Show your work.

Lori had a design project for school. She had to design a house for the future.

⑬ Lori wanted to have a rectangular living room which had 180 m² of space. If its length was 15 m long, what was its width?

Answer : _____

⑭ If all the ceilings were 3 m high, how much wallpaper would be needed to cover all the walls of the living room? (Ignore the windows and doors.)

Answer : _____

⑮ Lori wanted to carpet the living room, leaving a 1-m border of hardwood all the way around the room. How much carpeting would she need?

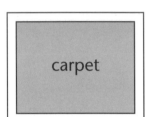

Answer : _____

⑯ Lori's kitchen was in the shape of a triangle as shown. What was the perimeter of her kitchen?

Lori's kitchen

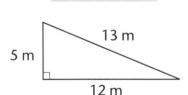

Answer : _____

⑰ How many square metres of tiles would Lori need to cover the kitchen?

Answer : _____

⑱ If 1 can of paint could cover 5 m² and Lori wanted to paint the walls of the kitchen, how many cans of paint would Lori need? (Ignore the windows and doors.)

Answer : _____

⑲ The bedroom was going to be in the shape of a parallelogram, 18 m long and 16 m high. How much carpeting would Lori need to cover the floor area?

Answer : _____

Each small square has an area of 1 cm². Sketch the shapes and solve the problems.

⑳ A square with an area of 36 cm².

㉓ A triangle with an area of 18 cm².

㉑ A rectangle with an area of 24 cm² and a perimeter of 22 cm.

㉔ Lori said, 'I can make different parallelograms, each with an area of 24 cm² and a base of 6 cm.' Draw 3 different parallelograms in the box to show that what Lori said is correct.

㉒ A parallelogram with an area of 36 cm².

㉕ Tim said, 'I can make different triangles, each with an area of 18 cm² and a base of 6 cm.' Draw 3 different triangles in the box to show that what Tim said is correct.

CHALLENGE

① What is the perimeter of the shaded part?

Answer : _____

② What is the area of the shaded part?

Answer : _____

← 8 cm →
10 cm
6 cm
18 cm
30 cm
← 24 cm →

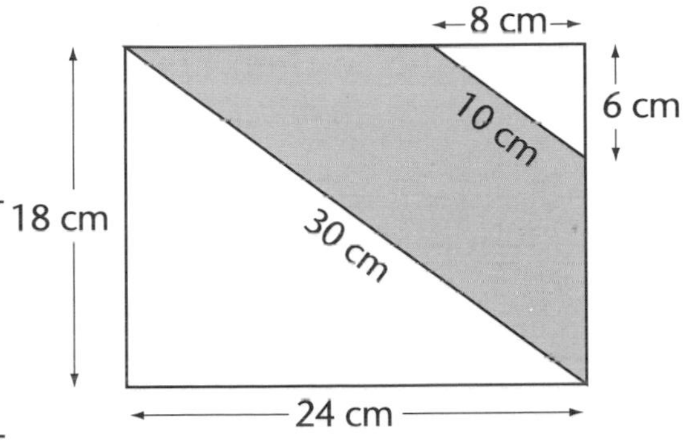

Volume

EXAMPLE

When Dylan put a stone into a rectangular aquarium 50 cm long and 30 cm wide, the water level rose 5 cm. What was the volume of the stone?

Think :   Volume of a rectangular prism
= Surface area of the base × height

          Volume of the stone
= Volume of the water displaced

Volume :   (50 × 30) × 5 = 7500

Answer :   The volume of the stone was 7500 cm³.

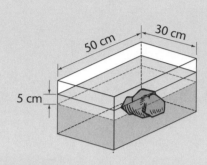

Solve the problems. Show your work.

Gary wants to find the volume of each brick. He puts each of them in a container with 200 mL of water.

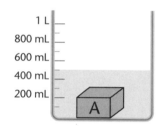 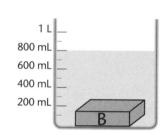 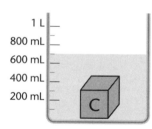 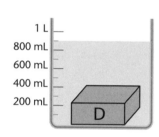

①   What is the volume of brick A?

Answer : The volume is _____ .

②   What is the volume of brick B?

Answer : _____

③   What is the volume of brick C?

Answer : _____

④   What is the volume of brick D?

Answer : _____

⑤   List the bricks in order from the one with the greatest volume to the least.

Answer : _____

⑥   If brick A is 5 cm high, what is the area of its base?

Answer : _____

⑦   If brick A is 6 cm wide, what is its length?

Answer : _____

⑧ If brick B is 6 cm high, what is the area of its base?

Answer : _____

⑨ If brick B is 25 cm long, what is its width?

Answer : _____

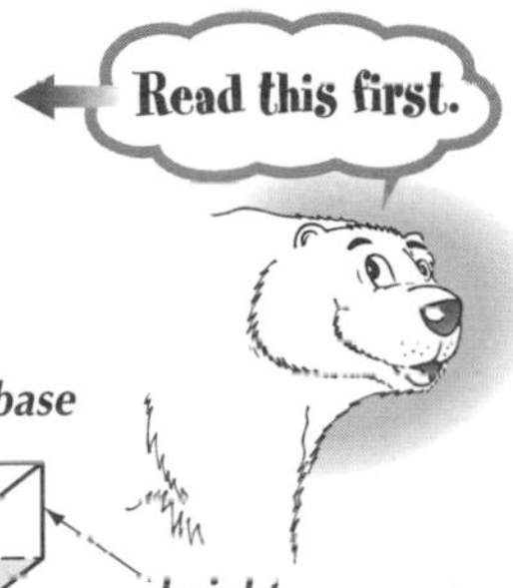

⑩ If the area of the base of brick D is 140 cm², what is its height?

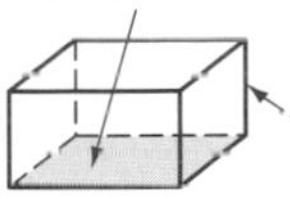

Answer : _____

⑪ Gary wants to pack as many bricks A as he can into the transparent container on the right. Draw the top, front and side view of the container in the space below to show how many A bricks you can see.

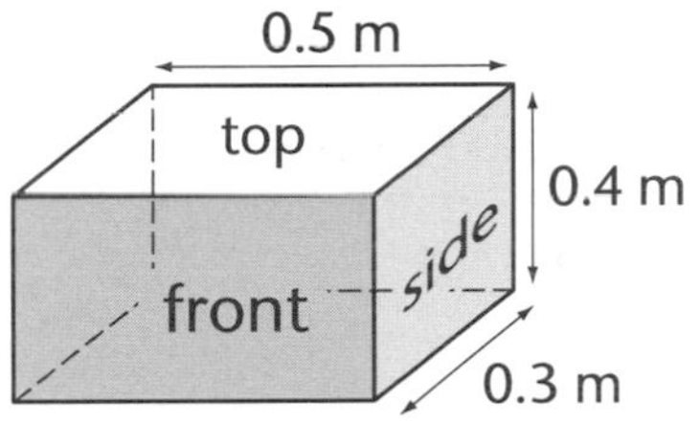

0.5 m
top
0.4 m
front   side
0.3 m

Top view	Side view	Front view

⑫ How many layers of bricks are there in the container ? How many bricks are in each layer?

Answer : _____

⑬ How many bricks can be put in the container?

Answer : _____

⑭ How many litres of water can the container hold?

Answer : _____

Dolores has a plastic box in the shape of a rectangular prism. Its base area is 120 cm^2 and its volume is 1500 cm^3.

⑮ The length of the box is 15 cm. What is its width?

Answer : _____

⑯ What is the height of the box?

Answer : _____

⑰ How many litres of water can the box hold?

Answer : _____

⑱ Dolores is going to use her box to fill two containers with sand. Container A is a rectangular prism 0.5 m long, 0.45 m wide and 0.2 m high. What is its volume?

Answer : _____

⑲ How many boxes of sand does Dolores need to fill up container A?

Answer : _____

⑳ Dolores uses 40 boxes of sand to fill up container B. What is the volume of container B?

Answer : _____

㉑ If the height of container B is 60 cm, what is its base area?

Answer : _____

㉒ If Dolores empties the sand in container A into container B, how high will the sand reach?

Answer : _____

Jillian lives in a condominium where there is a huge swimming pool.

㉓ The swimming pool is 30 m long, 21 m wide and 1.8 m deep. What is the volume of the pool?

Answer : _____

㉔ How many litres of water can the swimming pool hold?

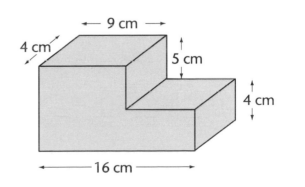

$1\ m^3 = 1\ 000\ 000\ cm^3$

$1000\ cm^3 = 1\ L$

$1\ m^3 = (1\ 000\ 000 \div 1000)\ L$
      $= 1000\ L$

e.g. $15\ 000\ L$
      $= (15\ 000 \div 1000)\ m^3$
      $= 15\ m^3$

Read this first.

Answer : _____

㉕ If the swimming pool is filled to a depth of 1.6 m, how many litres of water will there be?

㉗ If 30 000 L of water is pumped into the swimming pool each hour, how long will it take to fill up the entire swimming pool?

Answer : _____

㉖ How much water should be pumped into the swimming pool to raise the water level from 1.6 m to 1.7 m?

Answer : _____

㉘ If 126 000 L of water is pumped into the swimming pool, how much will the water level rise?

Answer : _____

Answer : _____

CHALLENGE

What is the volume of the solid on the right?

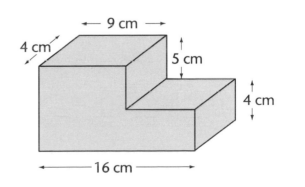

9 cm

4 cm

5 cm

4 cm

16 cm

Answer : _____

Two- and Three-Dimensional Figures

EXAMPLE

Marci says, 'These 2 triangles are congruent.' Is he correct? Explain.

Think :   Method 1 – Trace and cut out one of the figures. Then flip, slide or turn the cutout to see if it matches the other figure. If the 2 figures match, they are congruent.

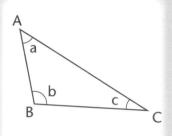

Method 2 – Measure the corresponding sides and angles. If they are equal, the figures are congruent.

AB = PQ = 2cm ; BC = QR = 3 cm ;
AC = PR = 4 cm ;

$a = p = 47° ; b = q = 105° ; c = r = 28°$

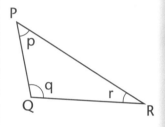

Answer :   Marci is correct because the corresponding sides and angles of the 2 triangles are equal.

Donny has drawn 4 triangles. Measure the triangles to complete the table. Then solve the problems.

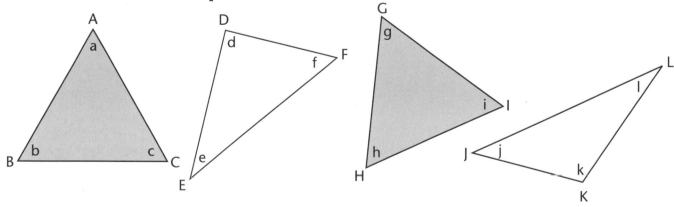

	Triangle	Side			Angle		
①	ABC	AB =	BC =	CA =	a =	b =	c =
②	DEF	DE =	EF =	FD =	d =	e =	f =
③	GHI	GH=	HI =	IG =	g =	h =	i =
④	JKL	JK =	KL =	LJ =	j =	k =	l =

⑤ Which 2 triangles are congruent? Explain.

Answer : _____

⑥ Which triangles are acute triangles?

Answer : _____

⑦ Which triangle is a right triangle?

Answer : _____

⑧ Which triangle is an obtuse triangle?

Answer : _____

⑨ Which triangles are equilateral triangles?

Answer : _____

⑩ Which triangles are scalene triangles?

Answer : _____

⑪ Construct an acute scalene triangle in the box.

Donny has made 4 solids. Name the solids and complete the table. Solve the problems.

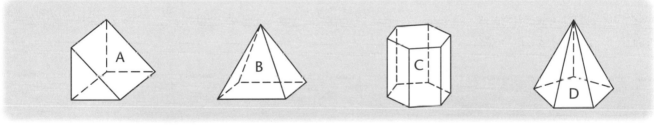

		Name	No. of vertices	No. of faces	No. of edges
⑫	A				
⑬	B				
⑭	C				
⑮	D				

⑯ Draw the top view and side view of solid B.

Top view	Side view

⑰ Draw the top view and side view of solid C.

Top view	Side view

Draw the missing face of each net. Then solve the problems.

⑱ a.

b. What is the solid that can be made from this net?

Answer : _____

c. How many triangular faces does this solid have?

Answer : _____

⑲ a.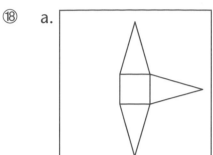

b. What is the solid that can be made from this net?

Answer : _____

c. How many rectangular faces does this solid have?

Answer : _____

⑳ a.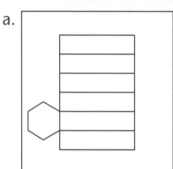

b. What is the solid that can be made from this net?

Answer : _____

c. How many triangular faces does this solid have?

Answer : _____

㉑ a.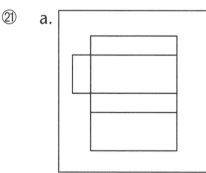

b. What is the solid that can be made from this net?

Answer : _____

c. How many rectangular faces does this solid have?

Answer : _____

㉒ a.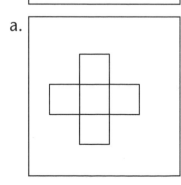

b. What is the solid that can be made from this net?

Answer : _____

c. Draw this solid on the dot paper.

Look at the shapes. Solve the problems. Show your work.

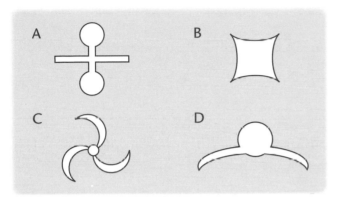

A pattern has rotational symmetry if it can be rotated about a point or a line. e.g.

← Read this first.

This shape fits on itself 4 times in one complete rotation. It has rotational symmetry of order 4.

㉓ How many lines of symmetry does A have? Does it have rotational symmetry? If so, what is its order?

Answer :

㉔ How many lines of symmetry does B have? Does it have rotational symmetry? If so, what is its order?

Answer :

㉕ How many lines of symmetry does C have? Does it have rotational symmetry? If so, what is its order?

Answer :

㉖ How many lines of symmetry does D have? Does it have rotational symmetry? If so, what is its order?

Answer :

CHALLENGE

Sally used 7 interlocking cubes to build a solid and she drew the top view of the solid. Help her draw the front and side view of the solid on the dot paper.

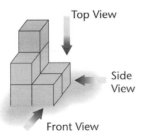

Top View

Side View

Front View

Top view	Front view	Side view

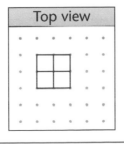

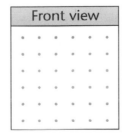

Kelly and Louis went to their favourite flea market which was 56.07 km from their house.

① What was the distance between the flea market and Kelly's house in metres?

Answer : _____

② They left home at 9:47 a.m. and took 42 minutes to reach the flea market. At what time did they arrive there?

Answer : _____

③ What was their average speed in kilometres per hour?

Answer : _____

④ If they wanted to reach the flea market 4 minutes earlier, at what speed would they have to drive then? (correct to the nearest whole number)

Answer : _____

⑤ Kelly was looking for a frame for her picture. Her picture was 48 cm long and 36 cm wide. What were the length and width of her picture in dm?

Answer : _____

⑥ What was the area of her picture in square centimetres?

Answer : _____

⑦ What was the perimeter of her picture?

Answer : _____

⑧ If Kelly wanted to leave a border of 2.5 cm on all sides of her picture, what would the the length and width of the frame be?

Answer : _____

⑨ What would the outside perimeter of the border be?

Answer : _____

⑩ The pattern on Kelly's frame is shown on the right. Does this pattern have lines of symmetry? If so, how many lines of symmetry does it have? Does it have rotational symmetry? If so, what is its order?

Answer : _____

⑪ The cost of the frame was $57.64. If Kelly bought the frame and gave the cashier two $50 bills, how could the cashier give her the change with the fewest bills or coins?

Answer : _____

⑫ Louis was looking for a paperweight. A booth displayed their paperweights as a tower. Draw the top, front, and side view of the tower in the space below to show how it looks.

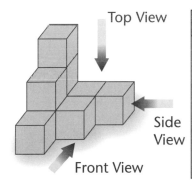

Top View	Front View	Side View
· · · · · ·	· · · · · ·	· · · · · ·
· · · · · ·	· · · · · ·	· · · · · ·
· · · · · ·	· · · · · ·	· · · · · ·
· · · · · ·	· · · · · ·	· · · · · ·
· · · · · ·	· · · · · ·	· · · · · ·
· · · · · ·	· · · · · ·	· · · · · ·

⑬ If each side of a paperweight was 4 cm long, what was its volume?

Answer : _____

⑭ Louis bought 2 paperweights for $4.79 each. The cashier charged him an additional $1.29 for taxes. If the cashier gave him the change with the fewest coins or bills, what was his change from a $20 bill?

Answer : _____

Sally has drawn 2 nets on a piece of cardboard.

A.

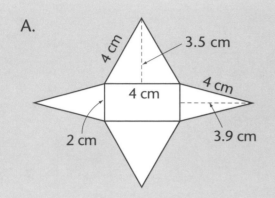

3.5 cm
4 cm
4 cm
4 cm
2 cm
3.9 cm

B.

1 cm
1 cm
3 cm
7 cm

⑮ What is the solid which can be made from net A?

Answer : _____

⑯ What is the solid which can be made from net B?

Answer : _____

⑰ How many square centimetres of cardboard does Sally need to make net A?

Answer : _____

⑱ How many square centimetres of cardboard does Sally need to make net B?

Answer : _____

⑲ If Sally cuts out net A and makes solid A, how many edges does solid A have?

Answer : _____

⑳ If Sally decorates solid A by putting a braid along each edge, how long will the braid be?

Answer : _____

㉑ If the cost of the braid is $0.16 per cm, how much will Sally pay for the braid?

Answer : _____

㉒ Sally cuts out net B and makes solid B. What is the volume of solid B?

Answer : _____

㉓ Draw solid B on the dot paper.

Circle the correct answer in each problem.

24 How many centimetres are there in one kilometre?

A. 1 000 cm
B. 1 000 000 cm
C. 10 000 cm
D. 100 000 cm

25 If Emily buys 160 g of candies every day for a week, how many kilograms of candies will she have at the end of the week?

A. 1.02 kg
B. 11.2 kg
C. 1.12 kg
D. 1120 kg

26 If a car travels at an average speed of 45.8 km/h, how far will it go between 9:45 a. m. and 2:30 p.m.?

A. 194.65 km
B. 217.55 km
C. 240.45 km
D. 222.13 km

27 Peter wants to paint an area in the shape of a parallelogram 1.45 m long and 0.84 m high. What is the area of the parallelogram in square centimetres?

A. 121.8 cm²
B. 12 180 cm²
C. 121 800 cm²
D. 12 280 cm²

28 If Joan changes her $5 bill into quarters, how many quarters will she get?

A. 20
B. 12
C. 200
D. 40

29 Rebecca says, 'I have five thousand six hundred four dollars and three cents'. How much does Rebecca have?

A. $5640.03
B. $5604.30
C. $5604.03
D. $5640.30

30 A rectangular box is 1.4 m long, 0.5 m wide and 0.8 m high. What is its volume?

A. 0.56 m³
B. 5.6 m³
C. 4.6 m³
D. 0.46 m³

31 How many litres of water can the rectangular box hold?

A. 5600 L
B. 5.6 L
C. 56 L
D. 560 L

32 The area of a triangle is 7.15 cm². If the base is 2.2 cm, what is its height?

A. 1.625 cm
B. 3.25 cm
C. 7.865 cm
D. 6.5 cm

UNIT 7 Coordinates

Solve the problems. Show your work.

Fred and Ted were doodling on some graph paper. Help them graph each set of ordered pairs and join them to form polygons. Then identify each polygon.

① (0, 5), (7, 3), (7, 0), (0, 0)

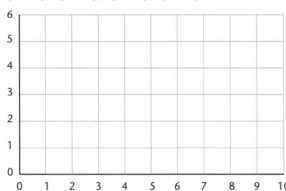

Answer : It is a _____ .

② (3, 0), (1, 3), (3, 6), (6, 6), (8, 3), (6, 0)

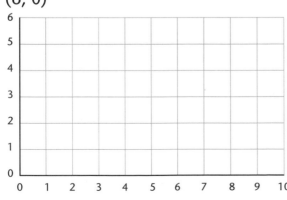

Answer : _____

③ (2, 0), (0, 2), (0, 4), (2, 6), (4, 6), (6, 4), (6, 2), (4, 0)

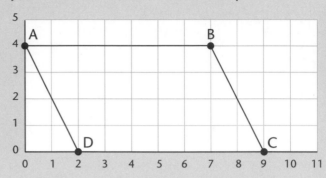

Answer : _____

④ (3, 0), (1, 3), (5, 6), (9, 3), (7, 0)

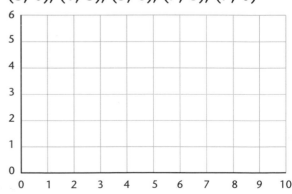

Answer : _____

Mr Lister draws a grid over the map of St. Louis Zoo. Use his grid to find the coordinates of all the places and locate the public washrooms.

⑤ The gate is at (__ , __).

⑥ The Patting Zoo is at (__ , __).

⑦ The Butterfly House is at (__ , __).

⑧ The Insect Dome is at (__ , __).

⑨ The Restaurant is at (__ , __).

⑩ The Gift Shop is at (__ , __).

⑪ The Stage is at (__ , __).

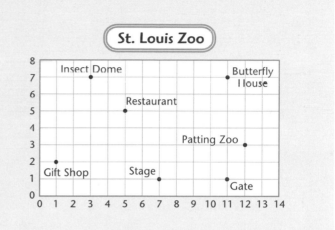

⑫ There are 5 public washrooms. They are at (10, 1), (8, 7), (4, 6), (3, 4) and origin. Label them A, B, C, D and E respectively.

⑬ Mr Lister sets a route for his class. Follow his instructions and join the places in order to show the route.

| Entrance gate | → | Stage | → | Patting Zoo | → | Butterfly House | → | Insect Dome | → | Restaurant | → | Gift Shop |

⑭ Larry wants to enlarge the map with a scale two times larger than the original. Help him label the axes and all the places in the zoo on the grid below. Then join the places to show the route.

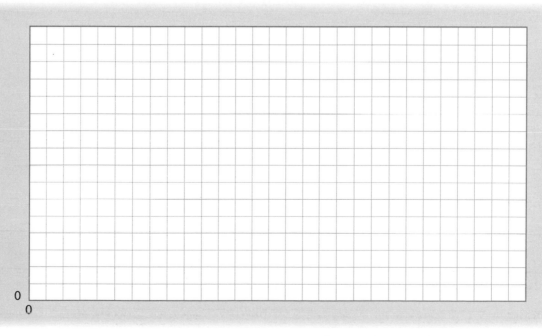

Miss Led decided to set up her classroom on a grid. Write the names of the children in the boxes and solve the problems.

⑮

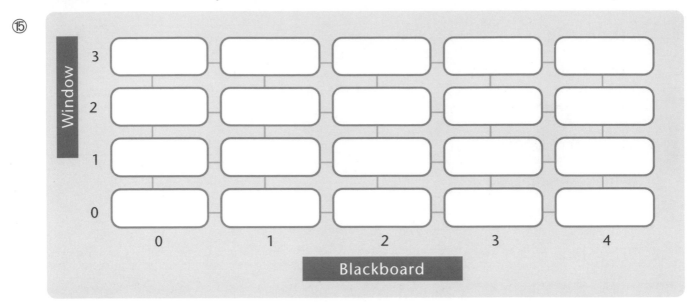

⑯ Uma was assigned (1, 0) and her best friend, Emily, was assigned (4, 3). Would they be happy with the seating? Explain.

Answer : _____

⑰ The three most talkative students, Ted, George and Jiffy, were assigned (4, 2), (3, 2) and (3, 1) respectively. Would this be a good idea if the teacher wanted a quiet class? Explain.

Answer : _____

⑱ Billy always complained about reflection from the sun in his glasses. If you were Miss Led, would you assign Billy to sit at (0, 1) or (3, 3)? Explain.

Answer : _____

⑲ Rebecca had trouble hearing the teacher. If you were Miss Led, would you assign Rebecca to sit at (2, 0) or (1, 3)? Explain.

Answer : _____

⑳ Miss Led said that she didn't want Olive, Gerry or Terry to sit beside each other. If Olive was assigned (1, 2), which seats couldn't the other 2 sit at?

Answer : _____

㉑ Gerry was the tallest student in the class. Miss Led wanted to assign Gerry and Terry to sit at (0, 0) or (0, 3). Where should each sit? Explain.

Answer : _____

㉒ Miss Led wanted to assign Raymond and Louis to sit beside Olive, but she knew that Raymond was George's best friend. Where should Raymond and Louis sit? Explain.

Answer : _____

㉓ Elaine's seat was between Raymond and Terry. Stephanie's seat was between Louis and Rebecca. Write the ordered pairs of Elaine's and Stephanie's seats.

Answer : _____

㉔ Katherine sat in front of Olive and David sat behind Olive. Write the ordered pairs of Katherine's and David's seats.

Answer : _____

㉕ Vera's seat was 2 units right and 1 unit down from Katherine's seat. Write the ordered pairs of Vera's seat.

Answer : _____

㉖ How many empty seats were there in the class? Write the ordered pairs of the empty seats.

Answer : _____

CHALLENGE

Larry went skiing. He used the following points to show his run. Could he easily ski this run?

(0, 7), (2, 6), (4, 5), (5, 4), (7, 4), (8, 3), (11, 5), (12, 1), (13, 0)

Answer : _____

EXAMPLE

Ivy moves a triangle 3 units left and 2 units down and labels the translated image I. She then flips figure I over the line *l* and labels the flipped image II. What will be the ordered pairs of the vertices of figure II?

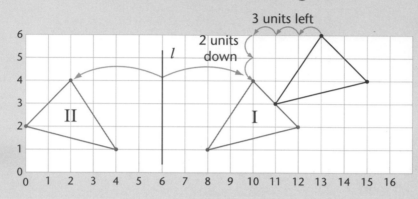

Answer : The vertices of figure II are (2, 4), (0, 2) and (4, 1).

Solve the problems. Show your work.

① Which figures are the translation images of the shaded triangle?

Answer : _____ are the translation images of the shaded triangle.

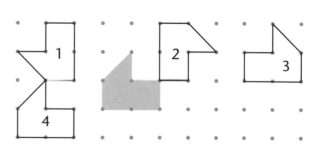

② Which figures are the rotation images of the shaded figure?

Answer : _____

③ Which figures are the reflection images of the shaded figure?

Answer : _____

Draw the figures on the grids and solve the problems.

④ a. Translate the figure 3 units left and 3 units down. Then label it I.

b. Turn figure I 180° about the point (5, 3). Then label it II.

c. What are the ordered pairs of the vertices of figure II?

Answer : The ordered pairs of the vertices are _____ .

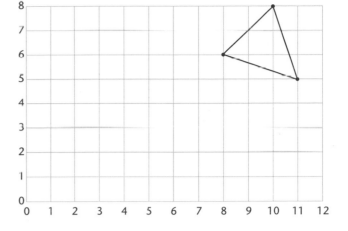

⑤ a. Flip the figure over the line *l*. Then label it I.

b. Translate figure I 5 units right and 3 units up. Then label it II.

c. What are the ordered pairs of the vertices of figure II?

Answer : _____

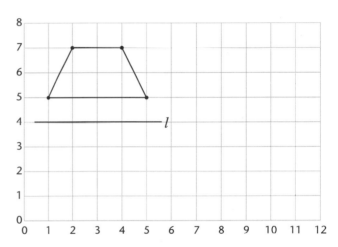

⑥ a. Make $\frac{1}{4}$ turn counterclockwise about the point (7, 5) of the figure. Then label it I.

b. Flip figure I over the line *l*. Then label it II.

c. What are the ordered pairs of the vertices of figure II?

Answer : _____

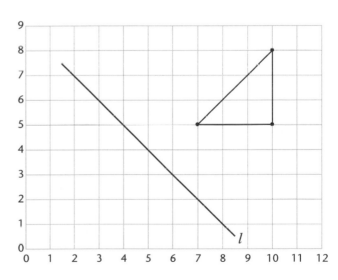

⑦ After translation, rotation or reflection of a figure, is the image congruent with, or similar to, the original figure?

Answer : _____

Complete the tiling patterns and solve the problems.

⑧ a.

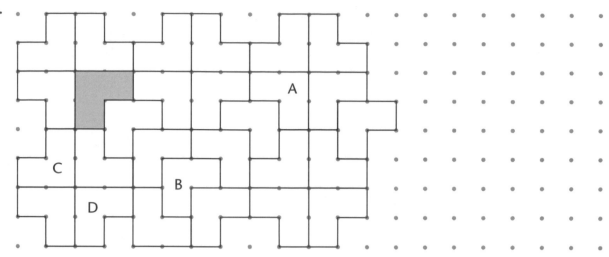

b. A is a _____ image of the shaded tile.

c. B is a _____ image of the shaded tile.

d. C is a _____ image of the shaded tile.

e. Without using translation, what transformation(s) will you use to transfer the shaded tile to D? How?

Answer : _____

⑨ a.

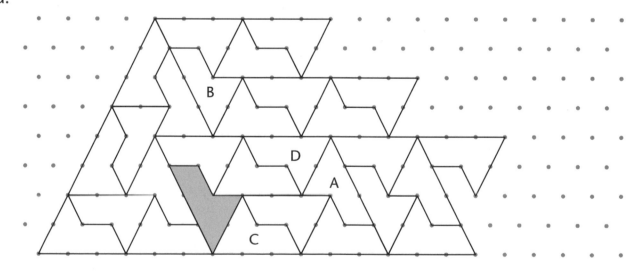

b. A is a _____ image of the shaded tile.

c. B is a _____ image of the shaded tile.

d. C is a _____ image of the shaded tile.

e. What transformation(s) will you use to transfer the shaded tile to D?

Answer : _____

Joan has to find one of the keys below to open the treasure chest. If she picks the wrong one, she will be trapped. Follow the clues to draw lines on the grid to find the reflection image of the figure on the right key.

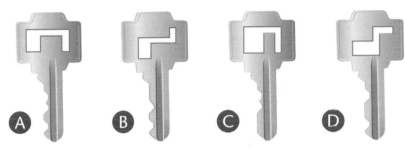

Mark all the points as you go.

- Begin at start and go upward 3 units. Then make:

- $\frac{1}{4}$ turn counterclockwise and go forward 4 units,

- $\frac{1}{4}$ turn clockwise and go forward 3 units,

- $\frac{1}{4}$ turn counterclockwise and go forward 2 units,

- $\frac{1}{4}$ turn counterclockwise and go forward 4 units,

- $\frac{1}{4}$ turn counterclockwise and go forward 5 units,

- $\frac{1}{4}$ turn clockwise and go forward 2 units,

- $\frac{1}{4}$ turn counterclockwise and go forward 1 unit.

⑩

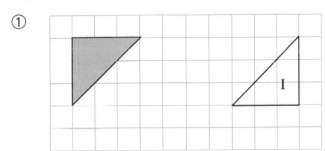

Start

⑪ Which is the key to open the treasure chest?

Answer : _____

CHALLENGE

Jimmy used 2 transformations to transfer each shaded figure to the labelled figure. Describe each translation, rotation and reflection clearly.

① 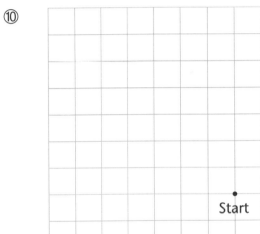   ②

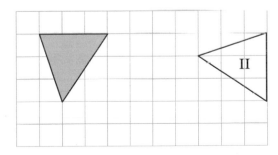

Answer : _____   Answer : _____

Graphs

EXAMPLE

Look at Peter's table which shows his earnings in the past 6 months. Use his table to make a bar graph and a line graph.

Month	Jan	Feb	Mar	Apr	May	Jun
Earnings ($)	200	300	300	500	800	600

a.   Bar graph

b.   Line graph

Solve the problems. Show your work.

Barney kept track of the number of books borrowed each week in his school library.

Week	1st	2nd	3rd	4th	5th	6th
No. of fiction books borrowed	70	75	65	50	40	70
No. of non-fiction books borrowed	55	90	60	50	15	45

① Use his table to complete the bar graph.

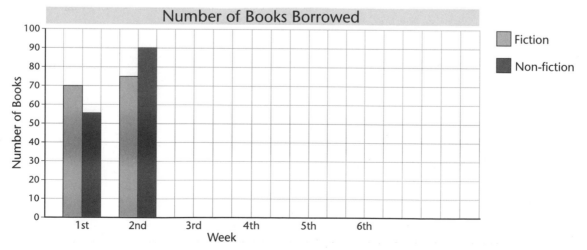

② How many more fiction books were borrowed than non-fiction books in the 1st week?

Answer : _____

③ In which week was the number of fiction books borrowed the same as the number of non-fiction books borrowed?

Answer : _____

④ In which week was the number of non-fiction books borrowed more than the number of fiction books borrowed?

Answer : _____

⑤ How many fiction books were borrowed over the six weeks?

Answer : _____

⑥ How many non-fiction books were borrowed over the six weeks?

Answer : _____

⑦ There were only 3 school days in one of the past 6 weeks. Which week was it? Explain.

Answer : _____

⑧ When Barney checked over the Math books, he found that a quarter of them were textbooks, a quarter activity books and the rest workbooks.

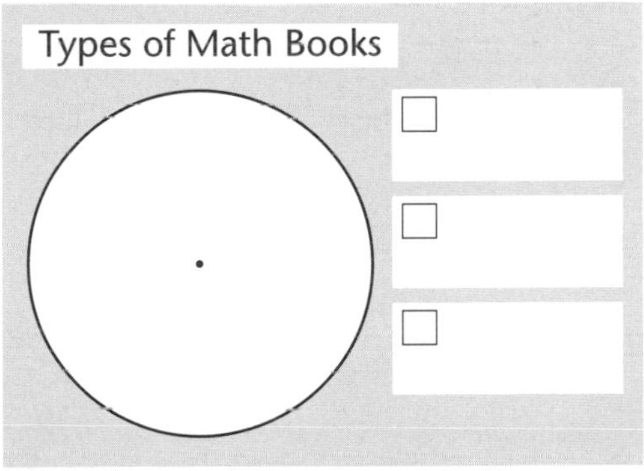

Types of Math Books

a. Draw a circle graph to show the types of Math books.

b. If there were 120 Math books, how many were activity books?

Answer : _____

c. How many were workbooks?

Answer : _____

Brenda and Tammy used a table to record their spending on groceries each month.

	Brenda's spending	Tammy's spending
JAN	$275	$325
FEB	$300	$200
MAR	$250	$75
APR	$350	$200
MAY	$175	$225
JUN	$225	$300

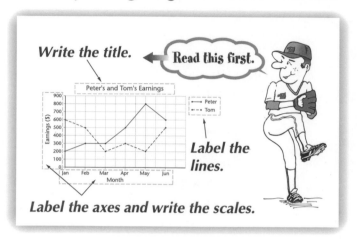

⑨ Use a line graph to show their spending.

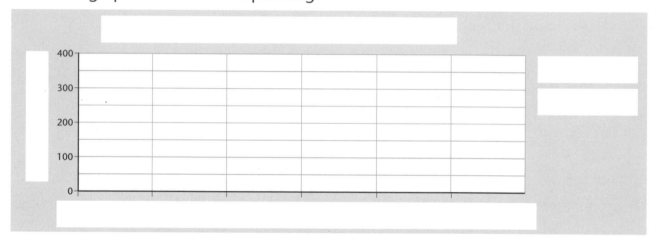

⑩ How much more did Brenda spend than Tammy in April?

Answer : _____

⑪ How much more did Tammy spend than Brenda in June?

Answer : _____

⑫ In which month did Brenda spend the most on groceries? How much more when compared with the month she spent the least?

Answer : _____

⑬ In which month did Tammy spend the least on groceries? How much less when compared with the month she spent the most?

Answer : _____

⑭ In which month was the difference between Brenda's and Tammy's spending the greatest?

Answer : _____

⑮ Who spent more money in the six months? How much more?

Answer : _____

⑯ In February, one-third of Brenda's spending was on meat, one-sixth on vegetables and the rest on fruit. Use a circle graph to show Brenda's spending in February.

Brenda's Spending in February

☐
☐
☐

⑰ How much did Brenda spend on meat in February?

Answer : _____

⑱ How much did Brenda spend on fruit in February?

Answer : _____

⑲ In February, a quarter of Tammy's spending was on meat, one-eighth on vegetables and the rest on fruit. Use a circle graph to show Tammy's spending in February.

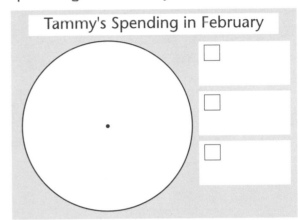

Tammy's Spending in February

☐
☐
☐

⑳ How much did Tammy spend on fruit in February?

Answer : _____

㉑ Did Tammy spend more money on fruit than Brenda in February? Explain.

Answer : _____

𝒞ℋ𝒜𝘓𝘓ℰ𝒩𝒢ℰ

① Measure the angle of each sector to complete the table.

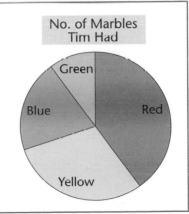

No. of Marbles Tim Had

Marble	Red	Yellow	Blue	Green
Angle				

② If Tim had 120 red marbles, how many green marbles did he have?

Answer : _____

EXAMPLE

Louie kept track of the number of apples he ate each month on a circle graph. Which month did Louie eat the most apples? If Louie ate 5 apples in December, would you assume that Louie liked apples? Explain.

Think : Louie ate the most apples in November since that is the largest area in the circle graph. If Louie ate 5 apples in December, it would mean he ate just a few more than 5 in November and fewer than 5 in January. Louie probably didn't like apples that much.

Answer : Louie ate the most apples in November and he probably didn't like apples.

Use the graphs to solve the problems. Show your work.

Each month, Jody's grandfather brought her a bag of jellybeans. Jody liked jellybeans, especially the red ones. She noticed that the number of red jellybeans varied from month to month and decided to keep track of the number of each colour on a line graph.

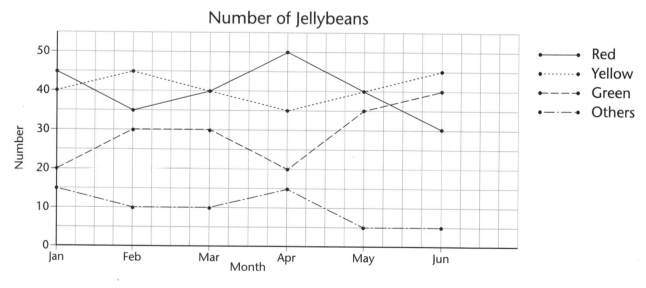

① How many jellybeans were in a bag? Did each bag have the same number of jellybeans?

Answer : _____ jellybeans were in a bag. Each bag _____.

② In which month would Jody be happiest with her jellybeans? Explain.

Answer : _____

③ In which month would Jody be unhappiest with her jellybeans? Explain.

Answer : _____

④ In which month did Jody get the least yellow jellybeans?

Answer : _____

⑤ How many more green jellybeans than red jellybeans did Jody get in June?

Answer : _____

⑥ If the company making the jellybeans discovered that the red jellybeans were the most expensive to make, can you tell when they made this discovery?

Answer : _____

⑦ Describe the change in the number of yellow jellybeans between April and June.

Answer : _____

⑧ If this tendency had continued, how many yellow jellybeans do you think Jody would have got in July?

Answer : _____

⑨ Describe the change in the number of red jellybeans between April and June.

Answer : _____

⑩ If this tendency had continued, how many red jellybeans do you think Jody would have got in July?

Answer : _____

⑪ What was the median number of red jellybeans Jody got for the past 6 months?

Answer : _____

The median in a set of numbers is the middle number when the numbers are arranged in order. If there are 2 middle numbers, take their average as the median.

Read this first.

e.g. 1 3 ⑨ 12 15
9 is the median.

1 3 ⑦ ⑨ 12 15

median : $(7 + 9) \div 2 = 8$

8 is the median.

Every student in Fred's class had to record the number of vehicles passing a certain point. Fred kept track of the vehicles near a construction site for 2 hours.

⑫ Use Fred's graph to complete the table.

Vehicle	Tally	Frequency
Car		
Van		
Jeep		
Truck		
Bus		

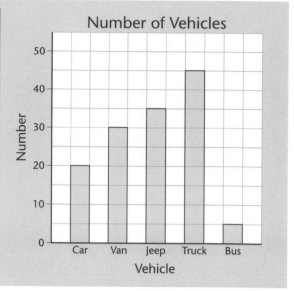

⑬ How many cars did Fred see?

Answer : _____

⑭ How many more Jeeps than vans did Fred see?

Answer : _____

⑮ How many vehicles did Fred see in all?

Answer : _____

⑯ On average, how many vehicles did Fred see per hour?

Answer : _____

⑰ If Fred did the recording near his home, do you think that he would collect similar data?

Answer : _____

⑱ Fred's friend, Peter, did his survey and made a bar graph shown below.

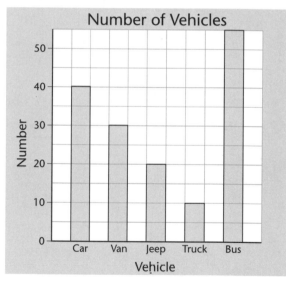

a. Can you tell where Peter collected the data?

Answer : _____

b. In what ways are Fred's graph and Peter's graph the same?

Answer : _____

Peter and Darlene kept track of the postal deliveries to their house each month on a bar graph.

⑲ What type of mail did they receive the most each month?

Postal Deliveries

Answer : _____

⑳ Why do you think they received more magazines in January than November or December?

Answer : _____

㉑ In which month did they receive the most letters?

Answer : _____

㉒ Why do you think they received the most letters in that month?

Answer : _____

㉓ In which month did they receive the most junk mail?

Answer : _____

㉔ Why do you think they received the most junk mail in that month?

Answer : _____

CHALLENGE

Mrs Diaz measures the heights of 5 of her students. Their heights are 165 cm, 137 cm, 140 cm, 151 cm and 144 cm. If Peter joins the 5 students, the median height will be 143 cm.

① How tall is Peter?

② What is the mean height?

Answer : _____   Answer : _____

EXAMPLE

Paula has a bag with 1 red marble, 1 yellow marble and 1 green marble. She picks 1 marble from the bag and flips a coin. How many possible outcomes are there? What is the probability that she will get a green marble and a head?

Think : There are 3 marbles and 1 coin. Use a tree diagram to find all the possibilities.

Write : Tree diagram

Marble	Coin	Result
Red	H	(R, H)
	T	(R, T)
Yellow	H	(Y, H)
	T	(Y, T)
Green	H	(G, H)
	T	(G, T)

Possible outcomes :

(R, H), (R, T), (Y, H),
(Y, T), (G, H), (G, T)

There are 1 out of 6 chances to get a green marble and flip a head.

P(a green marble and a head) = $\frac{1}{6}$

Answer : There are 6 possible outcomes. The probability that Paula will get a green marble and a head is $\frac{1}{6}$.

Solve the problems. Show your work.

Charlie has a bag. It contains 10 marbles, 2 red, 2 yellow, 2 green, 2 blue and 2 white. All the marbles have the same size and weight. Marley is going to draw a marble from Charlie's bag.

① How many possible outcomes are there?

R Red
B Blue
G Green
Y Yellow
W White

Answer : There are _____ .

② What is the probability that the marble will be blue?

Answer : _____

③ What is the probability that the marble will be green or yellow?

④ Is each outcome equally likely? Explain.

Answer : _____

Answer : _____

⑤ Marley has drawn a green marble from the bag. If he is to draw one more from the remaining marbles, will the outcomes be equally likely? Explain.

Answer : _____

⑥ Charlie puts 3 more white marbles and 2 more yellow marbles in his bag and then asks Marley to draw a marble again. How many possible outcomes are there? What are they?

R Red
B Blue
G Green
Y Yellow
W White

Answer : _____

⑦ Are the outcomes equally likely? Explain.

Answer : _____

⑧ What is the most likely outcome if a marble is drawn?

Answer : _____

⑨ What is the probability that the marble will be red?

Answer : _____

⑩ What is the probability that the marble will be white?

Answer : _____

⑪ Charlie says, 'If I draw out a marble from my bag now, the most likely marble is yellow'. Is he correct? Explain.

Answer : _____

⑫ If Charlie wants each outcome to be equally likely, at least how many more marbles does he need to put into the bag? What are they?

Answer : _____

Sally makes 5 cards marked 1, 2, 3, 4 and 5 and turns them face down on a table. She shuffles the cards and lines them up. Gary has a loonie. They try to select 1 card and flip the coin once. After every pick, the card is put back and is shuffled with other cards.

⑬ Complete the tree diagram to show all the possible outcomes.

Card	Loonie	Result
1	H T	(1, H) (1, T)

⑭ How many possible outcomes are there?

Answer : _____

⑮ Are the outcomes equally likely?

Answer : _____

⑯ What is the probability that they will get a 1 and a head?

Answer : _____

⑰ What is the probability that they will get a 5 and a tail?

Answer : _____

⑱ What is the probability that they will get an even number and a head?

Answer : _____

⑲ What is the probability that they will get an odd number and a tail?

Answer : _____

⑳ The player who gets a 1 and a head first win. Sally goes first and gets a 2 and a head. What is the probability that Gary will win?

Answer : _____

㉑ Gary says, 'If both Sally and I lost in our first try, Sally will have a greater chance to win than before'. Is he correct? Explain.

Answer : _____

Sally uses her 5 cards to play another game with Gary. This time, she shuffles the cards and lets Gary draw 2 cards.

㉒ Draw a tree diagram to show all the possible outcomes.

1st draw	2nd draw	Result

Read this first.

After drawing out 1 card, there are 4 cards left.

$\begin{pmatrix} 1st\ draw : 5\ cards \\ 2nd\ draw : 4\ cards \end{pmatrix}$

㉓ How many possible outcomes are there?

Answer : _____

㉔ Is each outcome equally likely?

Answer : _____

㉕ What is the probability that Gary will get 2 even numbers?

Answer : _____

㉖ What is the probability that he will get 2 cards that add up to 6 or more?

Answer : _____

㉗ What is the probability that he will get 2 cards that add up to 1?

Answer : _____

㉘ What is the probability that he will get 2 cards with the same number?

Answer : _____

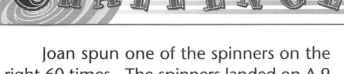

CHALLENGE

Joan spun one of the spinners on the right 60 times. The spinners landed on A 9 times, B 19 times and C 32 times. Which spinner did Joan likely spin? Explain.

Answer : _____

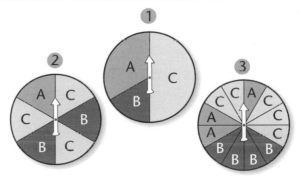

Solve the problems. Show your wrok.

Mr Bush recorded the number of toothbrushes produced by his factory last year.

① How many toothbrushes were produced in the 1st quarter?

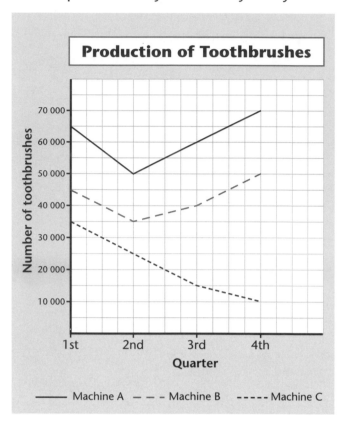

Answer : _____

② How many toothbrushes were produced in the 3rd quarter?

Answer : _____

③ How many more toothbrushes were produced in the 4th quarter than in the 2nd quarter?

Answer : _____

④ If each toothbrush cost $0.53, how much money would Mr Bush have collected last year?

Answer : _____

⑤ Describe the change in the number of toothbrushes produced by machine A.

Answer : _____

⑥ Describe the change in the number of toothbrushes produced by machine C.

Answer : _____

⑦ If Mr Bush had to shut down the least efficient machine, which one would it be? Explain.

Answer : _____

⑧ Use the clues to find the locations of the places. Mark the places on the grid and find the coordinates.

- Wellness Drug Mart is 4 units up from Bond's Convenience Store.
- Family Mart is 2 units left from Wellness Drug Mart.
- Echo Convenience Store is 4 units right and 3 units up from Bond's Convenience Store.
- Mayor Mart is 5 units right from Echo Convenience Store.
- Al's Bargain Place is 2 units left and 9 units up from Mayor Mart.
- Venus Mart is 1 unit right and 9 units up from the origin.

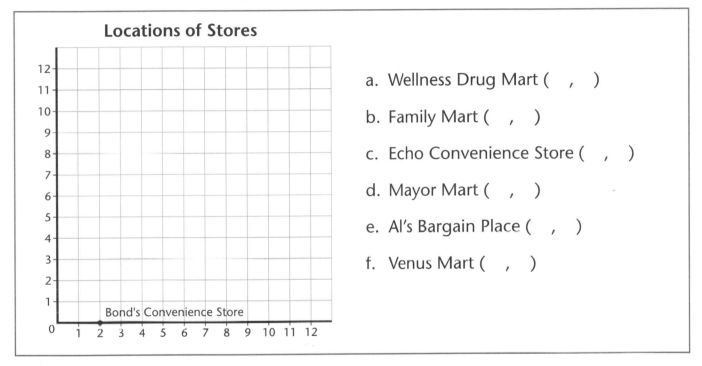

Locations of Stores

a. Wellness Drug Mart (,   )

b. Family Mart (,   )

c. Echo Convenience Store (,   )

d. Mayor Mart (,   )

e. Al's Bargain Place (,   )

f. Venus Mart (,   )

⑨ Mr Bush sets a delivery route. Follow his instructions and join the places in order to show the route on the grid.

Bond's Convenience Store → Echo Convenience Store → Mayor Mart → Al's Bargain Place → Venus Mart → Wellness Drug Mart → Family Mart

⑩ If the delivery man left Bond's Convenience Store at 1:46 p.m. and took 3 hours 35 minutes to complete the deliveries, at what time did he finish the job?

Answer :

⑪ The distance between Mayor Mart and Al's Bargain Place is 18.9 km. If the delivery man drove at an average speed of 60 km/h, how long would he take to drive from Mayor Mart to Al's Bargain Place?

Answer :

Carl lives in downtown near a public car park. He records the number of vehicles entering the parking lot from 9:00 a.m. to noon.

⑫ Use Carl's table to draw a bar graph.

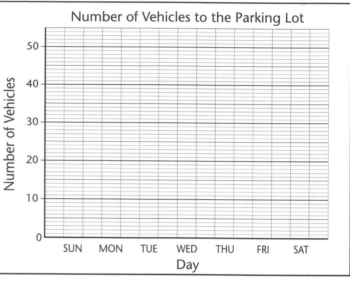

Day	Number of Vehicles
SUN	15
MON	25
TUE	33
WED	38
THU	42
FRI	43
SAT	12

⑬ How would you describe the bars on the graph to compare the volume of traffic throughout the week?

Answer : _____

⑭ Explain the sharp drop on Saturday and Sunday.

Answer : _____

⑮ What was the median number of vehicles entering the car park?

Answer : _____

⑯ Carl found that 14 vans, 21 cars and 7 Jeeps drove into the parking lot on Thursday. Draw a circle graph to show the types of vehicles. What fraction of the vehicles were vans?

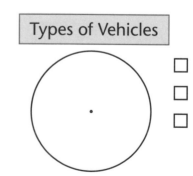

Answer : _____

⑰ If one of the vehicles in question 16 left the parking lot, what would be the probability that it was a van?

Answer : _____

⑱ There were only 1 car, 1 Jeep and 1 van in the parking lot and a driver came to pick up his or her vehicle. Complete the tree diagram to show all the possible outcomes.

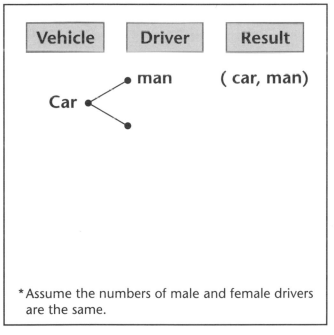

| Vehicle | Driver | Result |

Car ● man (car, man)

*Assume the numbers of male and female drivers are the same.

⑲ What would be the probability that a male driver came to pick up the Jeep?

Answer : _____

⑳ If there were 3 cars, 1 Jeep and 1 van in the parking lot, what would be the probability that a female driver came to pick up her car?

Answer : _____

㉑ The parking lot is rectangular in shape with an area of 612 m². The length of the parking lot is 25.5 m long. What is its width?

Answer : _____

㉒ The total area of the lanes is one-third of the whole parking lot. If the parking space for a vehicle is 3.4 m long and 2 m wide, how many parking spaces will there be?

Answer : _____

㉓ What is the perimeter of the parking lot?

Answer : _____

㉔ Look at the signs below.

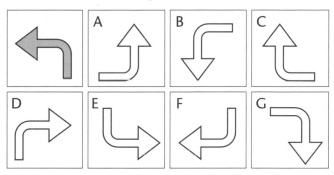

a. Which signs are the rotation images of the shaded sign?

Answer : _____

b. Which signs are the reflection images of the shaded sign?

Answer : _____

㉕ The parking fee for the 1st hour is $3.25 and $2.15 for every extra half hour. A whole day ticket is $18.00. If Mr Winter parked his car in the car park for 3 hours 48 minutes, would it be wise to buy a whole day ticket?

Answer : _____

Circle the correct answer in each problem.

㉖ How many millimetres are there in a metre?

    A. 10 mm   B. 100 mm   C. 1000 mm   D. 10 000 mm

㉗ If Jimmy spends $7.75 on magazines and $2.50 on newspapers, how much change will he get from a $20 bill?

    A. $10.25   B. $9.75   C. $9.65   D. $9.25

㉘ Which has the greatest area : a rectangle 5 cm by 8 cm, a triangle with base 18 cm and height 6 cm, a parallelogram with base 12 cm and height 3 cm, or a square with sides 7 cm?

    A. the rectangle   B. the triangle   C. the parallelogram   D. the square

㉙ If water cost $12.50 a cubic metre, how much would it cost to fill a rectangular tank 3 m by 2.5 m by 2 m?

    A. $187.50   B. $177.50   C. 188.50   D. 178.50

㉚ How many faces does a triangular pyramid have?

    A. 3   B. 6   C. 5   D. 4

㉛ What is the order of rotational symmetry of the figure on the right?

    A. 4   B. 5

    C. 6   D. 7

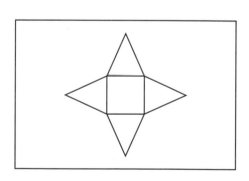

㉜ The figure in question 31 is a net of a geometric solid. If the net is folded, what geometric solid can you get?

    A. Triangular Prism   B. Rectangular Prism

    C. Square Pyramid   D. Triangular Pyramid

1. Place Value

↦ Through practice, children get an in-depth understanding of the place value of each digit of decimals to thousandths and of large numbers to millions.

↦ Parents should remind children to start with the digit with the highest place value when comparing numbers.

2. Divisibility

↦ Children should recognize the divisibility rules for the numbers 2, 3, 4, 5, 6, 9 and 10. The divisibility rules help them in calculating equivalent fractions, G.C.F. and L.C.M..

↦ Parents may give children more practice in divisibility using larger numbers to hundreds and thousands.

3. Multiples, Factors, G.C.F. and L.C.M.

↦ Children review how to write a number as a product of prime factors using factorization, and determine the G.C.F. and L.C.M. of two numbers.

↦ Parents should not ask children to write the product of prime factors using index notation at this stage.

↦ In solving word problems, children usually find it difficult to determine whether a problem is solved by finding the G.C.F. or L.C.M.. Parents could help by explaining the questions to them.

4. Fractions

↦ To add or subtract fractions with unlike denominators, children should write equivalent fractions with a common denominator first and then add or subtract the numerators.

↦ To multiply two fractions, multiply their numerators and denominators respectively. Encourage children to simplify the fractions (by dividing the numerators and denominators by their common factors) before multiplying in order to minimize the chance of making mistakes.

Example

$$\frac{7}{8} \times \frac{5}{21} = \frac{7 \times 5}{8 \times 21}$$ ⟵ multiply the numerators and denominators respectively

$$= \frac{35}{168}$$

$$= \frac{35 \div 7}{168 \div 7}$$ ⟵ reduce to lowest terms

$$= \frac{5}{24}$$

$$\frac{7}{8} \times \frac{5}{21} = \frac{\overset{1}{7}}{8} \times \frac{5}{21_3}$$ ⟵ simplify the fractions by dividing the numerator and denominator by their common factor

$$= \frac{1 \times 5}{8 \times 3}$$

$$= \frac{5}{24}$$

↦ When dividing, remind children to invert the fraction immediately after the "÷" sign and change the "÷" sign to "x".

5. Decimals

↠ Make sure that children know how to place the decimal point correctly in a product or a quotient. Also, children should know how to make the divisor a whole number, and move the decimal point in the dividend correspondingly.

Example $\qquad$ $2.73 \div 0.3 = 27.3 \div 3 = 9.1$

The decimal point in the dividend is also moved one place to the right.

Move the decimal point one place to the right to make the divisor a whole number.

↠ Remind children to pay special attention to cases where "0"s have to be added, either in the dividend or in the quotient.

↠ Make sure that children have a good grasp of the skills of conversion between fractions and decimals, and are able to use the skills in solving problems. Children should not use calculators at this stage.

6. Percents, Decimals and Fractions

↠ Children learn the application of percents in everyday situations such as calculating discounts and sales tax.

↠ Encourage children to practise the conversion of percents to fractions or decimals without using calculators.

7. Perimeters and Areas

↠ Children practise the use of formulas to find the area of a rectangle, a parallelogram and a triangle. Remind them that the height of a parallelogram or a triangle is the perpendicular distance from a vertex to its opposite side. Children often mistake the slanted side for the height in calculating areas.

↠ At this stage, children should not be asked to find the base or the height of a 2-D shape from the given area.

8. Circles

↠ Children recognize the relationship between the radius/diameter and the circumference or area of a circle, and practise calculating circumference and area of a circle using formulas.

↠ Do not ask children to explore and approximate the value of π (=3.14) at this stage.

9. Angles

↠ Children learn the names and definitions of different types of angles, and the symbol ($\angle$) representing an angle. Remind them that the size of an angle does not relate to the length of the two arms of the angle. Extending the arms of the angle, therefore, does not affect the measurement.

10. Two- and Three-Dimensional Figures

- Children learn to classify triangles according to angle and side properties. Parents may explain to children the conditions that make two shapes similar or congruent.

- Parents should make sure that children are able to recognize and sketch the front, side and back views of 3-D figures.

- Help children identify and draw nets for a variety of 3-D figures through exploration of different 3-D figures.

- Remind children that the order of rotational symmetry of a figure is determined by the number of times it fits on itself in one complete rotation.

  Example

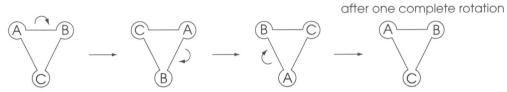

after one complete rotation

  The figure fits on itself 3 times in one complete rotation; it therefore has rotational symmetry of order 3.

11. Squares and Roots

- The meaning of perfect squares is introduced through the relationship between the area and side lengths of a square. Encourage children to find the square roots by using factorization instead of calculators. Parents should not ask children to find the square root of a non-perfect square number at this stage.

- Remind children to remove the square root sign after finding the square root of a number.

  Example $\sqrt{81} = 9$ ✔ ⟵ 9 is the square root of 81 $\sqrt{81} - \sqrt{9}$ ✗

12. Number Patterns and Patterns

- Children's interest in learning math can be fostered and their thinking and reasoning abilities reinforced through the appreciation of the structure and pattern of triangular and square numbers.

- Children practise how to recognize patterns, make predictions using patterns, and solve patterning problems.

13. Ratios and Rates

- Stress to children that ratios carry no units. The quantities to be compared should be converted to the same unit first. Then the unit is deleted before calculating the numerical value of the ratio. Parents can use examples with simple numbers to help children practise the skills of finding the ratio of two quantities in lowest terms.

  Example   The width of a red ribbon is 8 mm. The width of a yellow ribbon is 1.2 cm. The ratio of the width of the red ribbon to the yellow ribbon is:

  $8 : 12 = 2 : 3$ (1.2 cm = 12 mm)

↝ A rate has a unit, e.g. the rate of a car travelling on a road is 50 km per hour (50 km/h). Tell children that "/" means per. Remind them that the second term in a rate is usually reduced to 1, so that the speed of the car is 50 km/h, not 100 km/2 h.

14. Simple Equations

↝ Children learn to solve simple equations requiring at the most two steps in the solutions. Make sure that children grasp the following skills:

a. Understand what the unknown in an equation represents;

b. Know how to write an equation for solving a problem;

c. Are able to apply the balance principle in solving equations;

d. Check the answer by substituting the answer for the unknown in an equation.

15. Coordinates and Transformations

↝ Children review the concept of similar and congruent figures, and coordinate systems.

↝ Explain to children that a tiling pattern can be constructed by using tiles which are obtained by reflecting, translating or rotating a certain 2-D shape, so that there is no gap or overlap.

16. Graphs

↝ Remind children that the size of the circle graph has nothing to do with the total number surveyed, but the size of a sector representing a particular category is directly proportional to that category's percentage of the total.

↝ At this stage, children are asked to construct circle graphs divided into simple fractions only.

17. Analysis of Data

↝ Parents should help children recognize the difference between mean and median.

↝ Remind children to arrange the data in order for ease of identifying the mode or median.

18. Probability

↝ Children learn to use the concept of probability in solving simple problems.

↝ Remind children that the probability is zero if the event never occurs, and the sum of the probability of all possible outcomes must be equal to 1.

1 Introducing Percent

1. 63%   2. 42%   3. 18%   4. 45%
5. 82%   6. 35%   7. 25%   8. 20%
9. 33%   10. 50%   11. 60%   12. 50%
13. 25%   14. 75%
15. 16. 17. 18.

19. 20. 21. 22.

23. 0% 10% 20%   70% 75%   90% 100%

24. 0%   33%   66%   100%

25a. 10%   b. 25%   c. 50%   d. 75%
26a. 20%   b. 60%   c. 80%   d. 90%
27. 0%   20%   100%

28. 0% 10%   100%

29. 0%   25%   100%

30. 0%   50%   100%

31. 7%   32. 65%   33. 99%   34. 100%
35. 36%   36. 20%   37. 200%   38. 8%
39. 72%   40. 45%   41. $\frac{9}{100}$ 42. $\frac{16}{100}$
43. $\frac{20}{100}$ 44. $\frac{108}{100}$ 45. $\frac{300}{100}$ 46. $\frac{62}{100}$
47. $\frac{82}{100}$ 48. $\frac{33}{100}$ 49. $\frac{51}{100}$ 50. 60 ; 60%
51. 20 ; 20%   52. 12 ; 12%   53. 8 ; 8%
54. 28%   55. 60%
56a. 47%   b. 53%   57a. 38%   b. 62%
58. 60%   59. 45%   60. 20%
61. It means Dave gets 90 out of 100 on his test.

2 Rate and Unit Price

1. $2.75   2. $3.30
3. $1.40   4. $0.60
5. $1.25   6. $0.25
7. $0.33   8. $0.84
9. $2.60/kg 10. $0.90/bar
11. $0.58/notebook 12. $12.40/CD
13. $6.20/pizza   14. $0.83/chicken wing
15. $2.37   16. $4.35   17. $19.96   18. $15.60
19. $15.92   20. $30.00   21. $0.65 ✓ ; $0.66
22. $2.13 ; $2.12✓   23. 0.83 x 6 = 4.98 ; 4.98
24. 12.50 x 5 = 62.50 ; Peggy can save $62.50 in 5 weeks.
25. 0.75 x 4 = 3.00 ; 4 litres cost $3.00.
26. 1.42 ÷ 2 = 0.71 ; The price per litre is $0.71.
27. 24.4 ÷ 8 = 3.05 ; Two adjacent posts are 3.05 m apart.

28. 39.95 x 2 = 79.90 ; He pays $79.90
29. 87.00 ÷ 6 = 14.50 ; Each child spends $14.50.
30. 2.5 ÷ 8 = 0.31 ; Each drinks 0.31 litre.
31. 0.3 x 2 x 7 = 4.2 ; Kate drinks 4.2 L of milk per week.
32. 22.50 ÷ 5 = 4.50 , 12.75 ÷ 3 = 4.25 ; Susan is better paid.
33a. 14.70 ÷ 3 = 4.90 ; The price for each T-shirt is $4.90.
   b. 5 x 4.90 = 24.50 ; 5 T-shirts cost $24.50.
34. 0.15 x 6 = 0.9 , 0.9 + 3.2 = 4.1 ; She weighs 4.1 kg at 6 weeks.

3 Ratio and Rate

2. 4 : 3   3. 3 : 7   4. 4 : 7   5. 5 : 6
6. 6 : 5   7. 6 : 11   8. 5 : 11   9. 2 : 3
10. 3 : 2   11. 2 : 5   12. 3 : 5
13. - 20. (Order may vary.)
13. 2 to 3 ; $\frac{2}{3}$ 14. 5 : 9 ; $\frac{5}{9}$ 15. 15 : 4 ; $\frac{15}{4}$ 16. 7 to 11 ; $\frac{7}{11}$
17. 6 : 13 ; $\frac{6}{13}$ 18. 7 to 12 ; $\frac{7}{12}$
19. 3 to 8 ; 3 : 8   20. 6 to 17 ; 6 : 17
21. – 28. (Suggested answers)
21. 6 : 8 ; 9 : 12   22. 2 : 1 ; 8 : 4
23. 1 : 3 ; 4 : 12   24. 4 : 5 ; 12 : 15
25. 2 : 3 ; 8 : 12   26. 14 : 8 ; 21 : 12
27. 4 : 2 ; 6 : 3   28. 2 : 5 ; 8 : 20
29. 2 : 3   30. 22 : 25   31. 3 : 4   32. 4 : 5
33. 2 : 5   34. 49 : 2   35. 19 : 2   36. 13 : 9
37. 3 : 25   38. 2 : 3   39. 3 : 1   40. 1 : 12
42. Daisy : Rose   43. Daisy : Flowers
44. Tulip : Daisy   45. Rose : Flowers
46. Flowers : Tulip   47. 6 ; 8 ; 10 ; 12 ; 14 ; 16
48. 2 : 1   49. 24   50. 10   51. 1 : 3
52. 10 km/hour   53. 5 books/week
54. 20 words/ minute   55. 2 pages/minute
56. $\frac{9}{12} = \frac{3}{4} = \frac{6}{8}$ books/day ; $\frac{5}{8}$ books /day ; Shelia
57a. 150 ÷ 12 = 12.5 ; Her reading rate is 12.5 words/minute.
   b. 12.5 x 20 = 250 ; She reads 250 words in 20 minutes.
58. 90 ÷ 2 = 45, 126 ÷ 3 = 42 ; Mr Wong drives faster.
59. 7.50 ÷ 5 = 1.50 ; The cost per pair is $1.50.
60a. 4 : 6 = 2 : 3 ; The ratio is 2 : 3.
   b. 6 : 10 = 3 : 5 ; The ratio is 3 : 5.
61a. 96 ÷ 2 = 48 ; Fred's speed is 48 km per hour.
   b. 120 ÷ 3 = 40 ; Ivan's speed is 40 km per hour.
   c. 48 : 40 = 6 : 5 ; The ratio is 6 : 5.

4 Relating Fractions to Decimals, Percents, Rates and Ratios

2. $\frac{40}{100}$; 40   3. $\frac{75}{100}$; 75   4. $\frac{50}{100}$; 50   5. $\frac{5}{100}$; 5
6. $\frac{80}{100}$; 80   7. $\frac{76}{100}$; 76   8. $\frac{9.5}{100}$; 9.5   9. $\frac{1}{2}$
10. $\frac{35}{100}$; $\frac{7}{20}$ 11. $\frac{8}{100}$; $\frac{2}{25}$ 12. $\frac{18}{100}$; $\frac{9}{50}$ 13. $\frac{15}{100}$; $\frac{3}{20}$
14. $\frac{60}{100}$; $\frac{3}{5}$ 15. 0.2   16. 0.25   17. 0.19

18. 0.7   19. 0.12   20. 0.135   21. $\frac{65}{100}$; $\frac{13}{20}$

22. $\frac{22}{100}$; $\frac{11}{50}$ 23. $\frac{25}{100}$; $\frac{1}{4}$ 24. $\frac{90}{100}$; $\frac{9}{10}$ 25. $\frac{15}{100}$; $\frac{3}{20}$

26. $\frac{84}{100}$; $\frac{21}{25}$ 27. 0.4 ; 40%   28. 7 : 20 ; $\frac{7}{20}$; 35%

29. 27 : 100 ; $\frac{27}{100}$; 0.27   30. 3 : 4 ; 0.75 ; 75%

31. 0.55   32. 0.86   33. 0.8   34. 0.25

35. 0.08   36. 0.96   37. $\frac{1}{10}$ 38. $\frac{19}{20}$

39. $\frac{8}{10}$ 40. $\frac{1}{5}$ 41. $\frac{17}{25}$ 42. $\frac{9}{10}$

43. <   44. =   45. <   46. >

47. >   48. <   49. 0.1 , 20% , $\frac{1}{4}$

50. 70% , 0.73 , $\frac{3}{4}$ 51. 10% , $\frac{3}{25}$, 0.15

52a. 2 : 6 = 1 : 3 = $\frac{1}{3}$; $\frac{1}{3}$ of the letters are vowels.

  b. $\frac{1}{3} \approx \frac{33}{100}$; 33% of the letters are vowels.

  c. 4 : 6 = $\frac{4}{6} \approx \frac{67}{100}$; 67 % of the letters are consonants.

53a. 24 : 12 = 2 : 1 ; The ratio is 2 : 1

  b. 24 : 36 = 2 : 3 = $\frac{2}{3}$; $\frac{2}{3}$ of the total is collected by Annie.

54a. 18 : 30 = 3 : 5 = $\frac{3}{5}$; $\frac{3}{5}$ of the students have brown eyes.

  b. $\frac{3}{5} = \frac{60}{100}$ = 60% ; 60% of the students have brown eyes.

  c. 18 : 12 = 3 : 2 ; The ratio is 3 : 2.

Just for Fun

5 Adding and Subtracting Decimals

1. 5.912   2. 11.784   3. 7.854   4. 9.069
5. 16.3   6. 8.3   7. 1.581   8. 4
9. 3.3   10. 10   11. 35.948   12. 210
13. 10   14. 9.109   15. 15.951   16. 88.145
17. 1.191   18. 6.045   19. 4.002   20. 11.119
21. 1.757   22. 15.083   23. 3.769   24. 8.263
25. 24.497   26. 6.06   27. 16.071   28. 6.01
29. 1.293   30. 15.051   31. 8.139   32. 105.491
33. 325.082   34. 3297.32   35. 110.097   36. 0.056
37. 0.68   38. 90   39. 70   40. 4
41. 8
42. = 5.706 + 1.429 =7.135   43. = 227.129 – 63.258= 163.871
44. =10.1 – 0.874 = 9.226   45. = 12.537 – 8.799 = 3.738
46. = 90.71 – 0.984 = 89.726   47. = 24.82 – 7.345 = 17.475
50, 51, 53, 54 and 56. Answers are not between 10 and 20.
48. 12.14   49. 19.732   52. 18.28   55. 10.551
57a. A = 5.984 + 2.198 = 8.182   b. B = 9.10 + 7.293 = 16.397
  c. A + B = 8.182 + 16.397 = 24.579
  d. B – A = 16.397 – 8.182 = 8.215

Just for Fun
1. 123 + 4 – 5 – 67 = 55   2. 12 – 3 + 45 – 6 + 7 = 55

6 Multiplying and Dividing Decimals

1. 6.482   2. 0.03984   3. 0.0523   4. 0.12
5. 12.5   6. 1.2   7. 6   8. 7593.7
9. 5.291   10. 3.98   11. 1.231   12. 3.412
13. 14.655   14. 27.468   15. 5.948   16. 29.268
17. 24.792   18. 11.289   19. 2.639   20. 1.412
21. 2.967   22. 2.071   23. 24.915   24. 6.655

25. 23.121   26. 8.231   27. 0.528   28. 2.9
29. 2.4   30. 10.2   31. 6   32. 10
33. 2   34. 10   35. 0.32   36. 0.035
37. 10.15   38. 0.212   39. 0.833   40. 1.275
41. 9.13   42. 0.136
44, 46, 50 and 51. Answers are not between 5 and 10.
43. 5.943   45. 5.382   47. 5.784   48. 6.309
49. 6.608   52. 5.382 , 5.784 , 5.943 , 6.309 , 6.608
53. 0.825 x 6 = 4.95 ; 4.95
54. 33.68 ÷ 8 = 4.21 ; Each book is 4.21 cm thick.
55. 2.937 x 7 = 20.559 ; Each share costs $20.56.
56. 3.283 x 5 = 16.415 ; There are 16.415 feet in 5 metres.
57a. A = 5.923 x 2 = 11.846 ; B = 33.981 ÷ 3 = 11.327 ;
    C = 6.094 x 3 = 18.282
  b. 11.846 + 11.327 – 18.282 = 23.173 – 18.282 = 4.891
  c. 11.846 – 11.327 + 18.282 = 0.519 + 18.282 = 18.801

Just for Fun
0.3 + 0.15 + 0.075 ; 4.725

7 Estimating Answers to Operations with Decimals

1. 60 , 17 ; 43 2. 73 , 90 ; 163 3. 4 , 2 ; 8   4. 4 , 2 ; 2
5. 16 , 4 ; 4 6. 36 , 6 ; 6 7. 12 , 5 ; 2.4 8. 100 , 25 ; 4
9. 144 , 12 ; 12   10. 200 , 79 ; 121
11. 6 , 10 ; 16   12. 20 , 3 ; 60
13. 10.11 ; 20 – 10 = 10   14. 21.29 ; 101 – 79 = 22
15. 10.74 ; 30 – 19 = 11   16. 28.58 ; 212 – 184 = 28
17. 1.63 ; 201 – 199 = 2   18. 399.59 ; 201 + 199 = 400
19. 20.8 ; 6 + 3 + 12 = 21   20. 11.19 ; 10 + 9 – 8 ; 11
21. ✓ 10 kg for $13.45   22. ✓ 12 crayons for $0.99
23. ✓ 2L for $0.99   24. ✓ 100 m for $9.95
25. ✓ 5 kg for $5.29   26. ✓ 10 packs for $7.90
27. $7.00   28. $24.00   29. $8.00   30. $18.00
31. $17.00   32. $3, $14, $4, $4, $5, $30
33. $8, $9, $2, $19
34. 50 x 6.75 ≈ 50 x 7 = 350 ; $350
35. 3 x 2.25 ≈ 6 ; 4 x 2.49 ≈ 8 ; 20 – 6 – 8 = 6 ; $6
36. 7 + 5 + 11 + 2 = 25 ; $25

Just for Fun
1.8

8 Calculating Percents

1. 75   2. 48   3. 24   4. 80
5. 15   6. 34   7. 50   8. 200
9. 18   10. 18   11. 15   12. 20
13. 75   14. 55   15. 25   16. 4
17. $\frac{10 \div 2}{100 \div 2} = \frac{5}{50}$; $5   18. $\frac{25 \times 3}{100 \times 3} = \frac{75}{300}$; $75
19. $\frac{75 \times 4}{100 \times 4} = \frac{300}{400}$; $300   20. $\frac{24 \div 4}{100 \div 4} = \frac{6}{25}$; $6
21. $\frac{4 \times 2}{50 \times 2} = \frac{8}{100}$; 8%   22. $\frac{9 \times 5}{20 \times 5} = \frac{45}{100}$; 45%
23. $\frac{7 \times 4}{25 \times 4} = \frac{28}{100}$; 28%   24. $\frac{29 \times 2}{50 \times 2} = \frac{58}{100}$; 58%
25. $\frac{19}{25} = \frac{76}{100}$; His test percentage is 76%.
26. $\frac{80}{100} = \frac{16}{20}$; Her mark is 16.
27. $\frac{18}{25} = \frac{72}{100}$; $\frac{16}{20} = \frac{80}{100}$; May has the better grade.
28. $\frac{6}{25} = \frac{6 \times 4}{25 \times 4} = \frac{24}{100}$ = 24% ; 24

29. $\frac{60}{100} = \frac{60 \div 20}{100 \div 20} = \frac{3}{5}$;

He has completed 3 pages of his homework.

30. $\frac{4}{5} = \frac{4 \times 20}{5 \times 20} = \frac{80}{100} = 80\%$;

80% of the people in Britain are English.

31. $\frac{9}{20} = \frac{9 \times 5}{20 \times 5} = \frac{45}{100} = 45\%$; 45% of the people use floss.

32. $\frac{65}{100} = \frac{65 \div 10}{100 \div 10} = \frac{6.5}{10}$; 6.5 million people voted.

33a. $\frac{77}{140} = \frac{11}{20}$; $\frac{11}{20}$ of the students are girls.

b. $\frac{11}{20} = \frac{11 \times 5}{20 \times 5} = \frac{55}{100} = 55\%$; 55 % of the students are girls.

c. $\frac{140 - 77}{140} = \frac{63}{140} = \frac{9}{20} = \frac{9 \times 5}{20 \times 5} = \frac{45}{100}$;
45% of the students are boys.

34a. $\frac{22}{50} = \frac{44}{100}$; 44% are boys. b. $\frac{28}{50} = \frac{56}{100}$; 56% girls.

35a. $3 was reduced.

b. $\frac{7}{10} = \frac{70}{100}$; Tom paid 70% of the original price.

c. $\frac{3}{10} = \frac{30}{100}$; 30% was off the original price.

36a. Sally paid 60% of the original price.

b. $\frac{60}{100} = \frac{3}{5}$; Sally paid $\frac{3}{5}$ of the original price.

c. $\frac{60}{100} = \frac{120}{200}$; Sally paid $120.

Just for Fun
(Suggested answers)
1. 1 ; 2   2. 2 ; 4

Midway Review

1. B   2. B   3. A   4. C
5. D   6. A   7. C   8. C
9. A   10. B   11. D   12. C
13. B   14. $\frac{3}{25}$, 0.15 , 35% , $\frac{2}{5}$
15. 0.73 , $\frac{3}{4}$, 82% , $\frac{17}{20}$ 16. $\frac{12}{25}$, 51% , $\frac{27}{50}$, 0.55
17. 8   18. 5   19. 10   20. 9
21. 9   22. 120   23. 6.471   24. 0.503
25. 12.22   26. 11.803   27. 88.524   28. 3.852
29. 1.452   30. 1.265   31. 2.973   32. 20.615
33. 1.492   34. 0.47   35. 259.3   36. 0.189
37. 127.85   38. 0.8942   39. 2.4   40. 27
41. 10   42. 320   43. 8.3   44. 2
45. 10   46. 100   47. 0.7   48. F
49. T   50. F   51. T   52. T
53. F
54. $75 \% = \frac{75}{100} = \frac{75 \times 4}{100 \times 4} = \frac{300}{400}$;
There are 400 pages in his book.
55. $\frac{6}{25} = \frac{6 \times 4}{25 \times 4} = \frac{24}{100}$; 24% of the class are boys.
56. 20 : 30 = 2 : 3 ; The ratio is 2 : 3.
57. $\frac{27}{50} = \frac{27 \times 2}{50 \times 2} = \frac{54}{100}$; $\frac{11}{20} = \frac{11 \times 5}{20 \times 5} = \frac{55}{100}$;
Carol gets the lower grade.
58. $\frac{200}{10} = \frac{20}{1}$; $\frac{450}{25} = \frac{18}{1}$; Mary types faster.
59. 8 km/h = 4 km/$\frac{1}{2}$h ; 10 km/h = 5 km/ $\frac{1}{2}$h ; 5 – 4 = 1 ;
They are 1 km apart after $\frac{1}{2}$ hour.

9 More Operations with Decimals

1. = 0.3 + 2.4 = 2.7   2. = 9.5 − 3.3 = 6.2

3. = 0.4 + 5.1 = 5.5   4. = 12.4 − 2 = 10.4
5. = 5 ÷ 2.5 = 2   6. = 5.1 + 7.1 = 12.2
7. = 3.1 x 2 = 6.2   8. = 27 ÷ 3 = 9
9. = 6.3 + 10.4 = 16.7   10. = 8.4 − 3.3 = 5.1
11. = 2.5 − 1.6 = 0.9   12. = 6.0 + 2.1 = 8.1
13. = 9.72 − 1.23 = 8.49   14. = 5.78 − 4.92 = 0.86
15. = 11.82 ÷ 3 = 3.94   16. = 3.1 − 1.9 = 1.2
17. = 12 − 11.82 = 0.18   18. = 0.93 + 0.66 =1.59
19. = 1.12 + 12.13 = 13.25   20. = 2.11 − 1.11 = 1
21. = 11 x 0.2 = 2.2   22. = 4 ÷ 2 = 2
23. = 6.3 ÷ 3 = 2.1   24. = 18.9 ÷ 3 x 2 = 6.3 x 2 = 12.6
25. = 3.05 + 2.46 = 5.51   26. = 5.1 0.3 = 4.8
27. = 8.018 + 3.054 = 11.072   28. = 4.3 x 10 x 0.1 = 4.3
29. = 2.4 x 100 = 240   30. = 50.1 − 10.8 = 39.3
31. 10 − 5 x 1.25 = 10 − 6.25 = 3.75 ; $ 3.75
32. (100 − 9.7) ÷ 2 = 90.3 ÷ 2 = 45.15 ; Each pair costs $45.15.
33. 5 x 0.39 + 3 x 0.69 + 10 x 0.29 = 1.95 + 2.07 + 2.9 = 6.92 ;
She pays $6.92 in all.
34. 20 − 3 x 2.25 − 2 x 5.99 = 20 − 6.75 − 11.98 = 1.27 ;
He gets $1.27 change.
35. (Answer may vary.)
Bob buys 5 loaves of bread at $1.19 each. How much
change does he get from $10.00?
36. 100 x 0.449 − 25 = 44.90 − 25 = 19.90 ; 19.90
37a. 100 x 5.173 − 200 = 517.3 − 200 = 317.3 ; He has HK$317.3 left.
b. HK$5 ≈ C$1 ; So HK$300 ≈ C$60 ; Approximately C$60 is left.
38a. 100 x 0.664 − 50 − 9.80 = 66.4 − 50 − 9.8 = 6.60 ;
He has US$6.60 left.
b. US$0.66 ≈ C$1 ; So US$6.60 ≈ C$10 ;
Approximately C$10 is left.

Just for Fun
(Suggested answers)
1. (4 + 4 + 4) ÷ 4 = 3   2. (4 + 4) ÷ 4 + 4 = 6
3. 4 + 4 − 4 ÷ 4 = 7   4. 4 + 4 + 4 ÷ 4 = 9

10 Equivalent Fractions, Simplifying and Comparing Fractions

1. $\frac{9}{10}$ 2. $\frac{5}{11}$ 3. $\frac{7}{8}$ 4. $\frac{19}{20}$
5. $\frac{99}{100}$ 6. $\frac{7}{11}$ 7. $\frac{7}{9}$ 8. $\frac{5}{6}$
9. $\frac{11}{14}$ 10. $\frac{3}{5}$ 11. $\frac{6}{11}$ 12. $\frac{1}{3}$
13. $\frac{1}{15}$ 14. $\frac{11}{30}$

15. – 18. (Suggested answers)

15. $\frac{10}{18}, \frac{15}{27}, \frac{50}{90}$ 16. $\frac{14}{16}, \frac{21}{24}, \frac{35}{40}$
17. $\frac{18}{20}, \frac{27}{30}, \frac{90}{100}$ 18. $\frac{3}{20}, \frac{6}{40}, \frac{9}{60}$
19. $\frac{10}{18}, \frac{12}{18}, \frac{17}{18}, \frac{14}{18}$; $\frac{5}{9} < \frac{2}{3} < \frac{7}{9} < \frac{17}{18}$
20. $\frac{16}{20}, \frac{18}{20}, \frac{14}{20}, \frac{15}{20}$; $\frac{14}{20} < \frac{3}{4} < \frac{4}{5} < \frac{9}{10}$
21. $\frac{9}{12}, \frac{16}{12}, \frac{20}{12}, \frac{10}{12}, \frac{18}{12}$; $\frac{3}{4} < \frac{5}{6} < \frac{4}{3} < \frac{3}{2} < \frac{5}{3}$
22. $\frac{32}{30}, \frac{48}{30}, \frac{40}{30}, \frac{27}{30}, \frac{20}{30}$; $\frac{10}{15} < \frac{9}{10} < \frac{16}{15} < \frac{4}{3} < \frac{8}{5}$
23.

24. $2\frac{7}{8} > 2\frac{3}{4} > 2\frac{5}{8} > 2\frac{1}{2} > 1\frac{7}{8} > 1\frac{3}{4}$
25. $3\frac{9}{10} > 3\frac{4}{5} > 3\frac{1}{2} > 3\frac{1}{4} > 3\frac{1}{8} > 3$

26. $1\frac{2}{3}$ 27. $1\frac{1}{4}$ 28. $1\frac{1}{18}$ 29. $3\frac{1}{7}$

30. $1\frac{4}{5}$ 31. $1\frac{1}{3}$ 32. $3\frac{1}{12}$ 33. $10\frac{5}{9}$

34. $4\frac{2}{7}$

35A. $\frac{1}{8}$ B. $\frac{1}{2}$ C. $\frac{9}{10}$ D. $\frac{4}{3}$

E. $\frac{3}{2}$ F. $\frac{8}{4}$ G. $\frac{9}{4}$ H. $\frac{17}{6}$

36. > 37. = 38. > 39. =

40. < 41. > 42. > 43. =

44. >

45.

46. $\frac{2}{3};\frac{14}{21}$ 47. $\frac{21}{24};\frac{28}{32}$ 48. $\frac{5}{10};\frac{1}{2}$ 49. $\frac{10}{9};\frac{30}{27}$

50. $\frac{27}{30};\frac{9}{10}$ 51. $\frac{30}{36};\frac{15}{18}$

52. $\frac{1}{4}$ lb for \$1.00 is 1 lb for \$4.00 ; $\frac{1}{3}$ lb for \$1.30 is 1 lb for \$3.90 ;

$\frac{1}{3}$ lb for \$1.30 is the better buy.

53. $\frac{9}{10}=\frac{72}{80}$; $\frac{7}{8}=\frac{70}{80}$;

Pat has completed the larger part of his homework.

54. $\frac{5}{4}=1\frac{1}{4}$, $\frac{7}{6}=1\frac{1}{6}$, $\frac{9}{8}=1\frac{1}{8}$, $\frac{17}{16}=1\frac{1}{16}$; Since $\frac{1}{4}>\frac{1}{6}>\frac{1}{8}>\frac{1}{16}$,

$\frac{5}{4}>\frac{7}{6}>\frac{9}{8}>\frac{17}{16}$

Just for Fun

1st column ÷ 2nd column + 1 = 3rd column ;
(Suggested answer) 35 ; 5 ; 8

11 Adding and Subtracting Fractions with Like Denominators

1. $\frac{2}{7}$ 2. $\frac{6}{7}$ 3. $\frac{7}{13}$ 4. $\frac{8}{9}$

5. 0 6. $\frac{17}{18}$ 7. $\frac{9}{10}$ 8. $\frac{23}{27}$

9. $\frac{1}{11}$ 10. $\frac{38}{45}$ 11. $\frac{10}{11}$ 12. $\frac{24}{35}$

13. $\frac{27}{28}$ 14. $\frac{143}{144}$ 15. $\frac{3}{100}$ 16. $\frac{5}{9}$

17. $\frac{14}{15}$ 18. $\frac{7}{8}$ 19. $\frac{5}{12}$ 20. $\frac{10}{20};\frac{1}{2}$

21. $\frac{16}{16};1$ 22. $\frac{20}{30};\frac{2}{3}$ 23. $\frac{20}{5};4$ 24. $\frac{22}{11};2$

25. $\frac{10}{18};\frac{5}{9}$ 26. $\frac{7}{14};\frac{1}{2}$ 27. $\frac{14}{21};\frac{2}{3}$ 28. $\frac{24}{28};\frac{6}{7}$

29. $\frac{40}{100};\frac{2}{5}$ 30. $\frac{9}{54};\frac{1}{6}$ 31. $\frac{7}{56};\frac{1}{8}$ 32. $\frac{16}{56};\frac{2}{7}$

33. $\frac{20}{40};\frac{1}{2}$ 34. $\frac{75}{50};1\frac{1}{2}$ 35. $\frac{20}{25};\frac{4}{5}$ 36. $\frac{46}{74};\frac{23}{37}$

37. $\frac{40}{80};\frac{1}{2}$ 38. $\frac{30}{35};\frac{6}{7}$ 39. $\frac{14}{42};\frac{1}{3}$

40, 41, 43, 44 and 48. Answers are not between 1 and 2.

42. $1\frac{1}{8}$ 45. $1\frac{7}{10}$ 46. $1\frac{7}{16}$ 47. $1\frac{2}{3}$

49. $1\frac{1}{8}<1\frac{7}{16}<1\frac{2}{3}<1\frac{7}{10}$ 50. $1\frac{1}{2}$ 51. $2\frac{1}{4}$

52. 3 53. 5 54. 4 55. $1\frac{1}{4}$

56. 3 57. $1\frac{2}{3}$ 58. $1\frac{3}{5}$ 59. $1\frac{1}{2}$

---

60. 5 61. $1\frac{2}{3}$ 62. $\frac{1}{3}$ 63. $\frac{3}{8}$

64. $\frac{7}{9}$ 65. $\frac{1}{4}$ 66. $\frac{1}{2}$ 67. $\frac{1}{4}$

68. $\frac{1}{6}$ 69. $\frac{1}{6}$ 70. $\frac{5}{8}$ 71. $\frac{3}{10}$

72. 1 73. $1\frac{2}{7}$ 74. > 75. =

76. < 77. > 78. = 79. <

80a. $\frac{1}{4}$ b. $\frac{1}{2}$ 81a. $\frac{2}{3}$ b. 4

82a. $\frac{17}{30}$ b. $\frac{4}{15}$ c. $\frac{11}{15}$ d. $\frac{5}{6}$

e. $\frac{13}{30}$ f. 1

Just for Fun

8

12 Adding Fractions with Unlike Denominators

1. 4 2. 6 3. 6 4. 10

5. 15 6. 14 7. 21 8. 8

9. 16 10. 24 11. 9 12. 18

13. 30 14. 40 15. 30 16. 51

17. 39 18. 18 19. 24

20. $\frac{1}{2}$ 21. $\frac{2}{3}$ 22. $\frac{9}{10}$ 23. $\frac{7}{15}$

24. $\frac{1}{8}$ 25. $\frac{14}{15}$ 26. $\frac{2}{3}$ 27. $\frac{5}{8}$

28. $\frac{13}{14}$ 29. $\frac{13}{51}$ 30. $\frac{5}{9}$ 31. $\frac{10}{39}$

32. $\frac{7}{18}$ 33. $\frac{17}{40}$ 34. $\frac{17}{24}$ 35. $\frac{15}{16}$

36. $\frac{12}{30}+\frac{5}{30};\frac{17}{30}$ 37. $\frac{5}{10}+\frac{2}{10};\frac{7}{10}$

38. $\frac{9}{63}+\frac{14}{63};\frac{23}{63}$ 39. $\frac{33}{88}+\frac{16}{88};\frac{49}{88}$

40. $\frac{20}{45}+\frac{9}{45};\frac{29}{45}$ 41. $\frac{8}{12}+\frac{3}{12};\frac{11}{12}$

42. $\frac{3}{18}+\frac{8}{18};\frac{11}{18}$ 43. $\frac{4}{60}+\frac{9}{60};\frac{13}{60}$

44. $\frac{15}{60}+\frac{20}{60}+\frac{12}{60};\frac{47}{60}$ 45. $\frac{6}{18}+\frac{3}{18}+\frac{4}{18};\frac{13}{18}$

46. $1\frac{24}{30}+\frac{25}{30};2\frac{19}{30}$

47. $2\frac{28}{36}+\frac{24}{36};3\frac{4}{9}$

48. $\frac{15}{18}+1\frac{5}{18};2\frac{1}{9}$

49. $4\frac{4}{24}+1\frac{21}{24};6\frac{1}{24}$

50. $1\frac{7}{8}+2\frac{2}{8};4\frac{1}{8}$ 51. $2\frac{9}{15}+3\frac{10}{15};6\frac{4}{15}$

52. $\frac{1}{2}+\frac{3}{4}=1\frac{1}{4}$ 53. $\frac{3}{8}+\frac{1}{4}=\frac{5}{8}$

54.

55.

56a. $\frac{1}{4}$ b. $\frac{1}{12}$ c. $\frac{1}{4}+\frac{1}{12}=\frac{3}{12}+\frac{1}{12};\frac{1}{3}$

57a. $\frac{3}{10}$ b. $\frac{7}{10}$ c. $\frac{3}{10}+\frac{7}{10};1$

Just for Fun
1

13 Subtracting Fractions with Unlike Denominators

1. $\frac{2}{12} - \frac{1}{12}$; $\frac{1}{12}$
2. $\frac{14}{40} - \frac{1}{40}$; $\frac{13}{40}$
3. $\frac{27}{30} - \frac{11}{30}$; $\frac{8}{15}$
4. $\frac{6}{16} - \frac{1}{16}$; $\frac{5}{16}$
5. $\frac{15}{30} - \frac{11}{30}$; $\frac{2}{15}$
6. $\frac{6}{14} - \frac{5}{14}$; $\frac{1}{14}$
7. $\frac{13}{24}$
8. $\frac{11}{35}$
9. $\frac{11}{20}$
10. $\frac{5}{18}$
11. $1\frac{7}{12}$
12. $1\frac{21}{40}$
13. $\frac{8}{15}$
14. $2\frac{11}{24}$
15. $2\frac{1}{50}$
16. $\frac{19}{36}$
17. $\frac{1}{6}$
18. $\frac{5}{6}$
19. $1\frac{1}{3}$
20. $\frac{5}{6}$
21. $1\frac{3}{14}$
22. $\frac{1}{3}$
23. $\frac{2}{3} - \frac{1}{2} = \frac{4}{6} - \frac{3}{6}$; $\frac{1}{6}$
24. $\frac{1}{3} - \frac{1}{4} = \frac{4}{12} - \frac{3}{12}$; $\frac{1}{12}$
25. $\frac{3}{7} - \frac{1}{5} = \frac{15}{35} - \frac{7}{35}$; $\frac{8}{35}$
26. $\frac{7}{8} - \frac{3}{4} = \frac{7}{8} - \frac{6}{8}$; $\frac{1}{8}$
27. 4
28. 12
29. 3
30. 3
31. 2
32. 4
33. $\frac{18}{6} - \frac{11}{6} = \frac{2}{6}$; $\frac{5}{6}$
34. $\frac{70}{14} - \frac{45}{14} = \frac{22}{14}$; $\frac{3}{14}$
35. $\frac{40}{10} - \frac{4}{10} = \frac{13}{10}$; $2\frac{3}{10}$
36. $\frac{24}{8} - \frac{6}{8} = \frac{11}{8}$; $\frac{7}{8}$
37. $\frac{3}{4} - \frac{3}{8} = \frac{3}{8}$

38. $\frac{5}{6} - \frac{2}{3} = \frac{1}{6}$

39. $\frac{3}{4} - \frac{2}{3} = \frac{9}{12} - \frac{8}{12} = \frac{1}{12}$; $\frac{1}{12}$
40. $\frac{2}{3} - \frac{1}{2} = \frac{4}{6} - \frac{3}{6} = \frac{1}{6}$; She still has to wait $\frac{1}{6}$ hour.
41. $2\frac{1}{12} - 1\frac{1}{3} = \frac{25}{12} - \frac{16}{12} = \frac{9}{12} = \frac{3}{4}$;
    He spent $\frac{3}{4}$ hour longer on Monday.
42a. $\frac{1}{3} - \frac{1}{12} = \frac{4}{12} - \frac{1}{12} = \frac{3}{12} = \frac{1}{4}$;
    She read $\frac{1}{4}$ less on Saturday than Sunday.
  b. $1 - \frac{1}{3} - \frac{1}{12} = \frac{12}{12} - \frac{4}{12} - \frac{1}{12} = \frac{7}{12}$;
    $\frac{7}{12}$ of the book has not been read.
43. $1 - \frac{1}{4} - \frac{1}{6} = \frac{12}{12} - \frac{3}{12} - \frac{2}{12} = \frac{7}{12}$; $\frac{7}{12}$ of the pie was left for Tom.

Just for Fun
    12 ; 10 ; 2

14 Multiplying Fractions by Whole Numbers

1. 1
2. 1
3. 3
4. 5
5. 1
6. 3
7. 2
8. 3
9. 7
10. $\frac{3}{4}$
11. $\frac{1}{2}$
12. $\frac{2}{3}$
13. $\frac{1}{2}$
14. $\frac{4}{5}$
15. $\frac{1}{4}$
16. $\frac{3}{4}$
17. $\frac{1}{4}$
18. $\frac{1}{2}$
19. $\frac{2}{3}$
20. $\frac{1}{3}$
21. $\frac{1}{6}$
22. $\frac{5}{7}$
23. $\frac{2}{3}$
24. $\frac{3}{4}$

25. 15
26. 14
27. 10
28. 6
29. 10
30. 21
31. 70
32. 32
33. 6
34. 35
35. 49
36. 28
37. 84
38. $\frac{3}{8}$
39. 20
40. $\frac{5}{2} \times 2$; 5
41. $\frac{10}{3} \times 3$; 10
42. $\frac{11}{8} \times 8$; 11
43. $\frac{12}{5} \times 5$; 12
44. $\frac{21}{2} \times 2$; 21
45. $\frac{17}{3} \times 3$; 17
46. $5\frac{1}{3}$
47. $3\frac{1}{3}$
48. $10\frac{1}{2}$
49. $2\frac{2}{5}$
50. $2\frac{1}{2}$
51. $3\frac{1}{2}$
52. $5\frac{1}{2}$
53. $8\frac{1}{3}$
54. $4\frac{3}{8}$
55. $2\frac{2}{5}, 2\frac{1}{2}, 3\frac{1}{3}, 3\frac{1}{2}, 4\frac{3}{8}, 5\frac{1}{3}, 5\frac{1}{2}, 8\frac{1}{3}, 10\frac{1}{2}$
56. 5
57. 17
58. 1
59. 2
60. 3
61. 2
62. 20
63. 7
64. 3
65, 70, 71, 72 and 73. Answers are not between 1 and 2.
66. $1\frac{1}{2}$
67. $1\frac{2}{7}$
68. $1\frac{1}{5}$
69. $1\frac{3}{11}$
74. 9
75. 8
76. 4
77. 12
78. 3
79. $\frac{2}{3} \times 2 = \frac{4}{3} = 1\frac{1}{3}$; $1\frac{1}{3}$
80. $3 \times 1\frac{1}{2} = 3 \times \frac{3}{2} = \frac{9}{2} = 4\frac{1}{2}$; He buys $4\frac{1}{2}$ lbs of flour.
81. $12 \times \frac{1}{3} = 4$; 4 L of juice is needed.
82. $1\frac{3}{4} \times 3 = \frac{7}{4} \times 3 = \frac{21}{4} = 5\frac{1}{4}$; They watch TV for $5\frac{1}{4}$ hours.
83. $6 \times \frac{1}{2} + 3 \times \frac{1}{3} = 3 + 1 = 4$; 4 litres of soup is consumed.

Just for Fun
    15

15 Dividing Whole Numbers by Fractions

1. $\frac{6}{7}$
2. $\frac{5}{4}$
3. $\frac{10}{9}$
4. $\frac{8}{7}$
5. $\frac{7}{5}$
6. $\frac{11}{4}$
7. 2
8. $\frac{6}{5}$
9. 4
10. 8
11. $\frac{13}{6}$
12. $\frac{3}{2}$
13. $\frac{9}{2}$
14. 15
15. 6
16. 12
17. 6
18. 10
19. 30
20. 10
21. 6
22. 30
23. 35
24. 14
25. 20
26. 108
27. 200
28. 75
29. 64
30. 9
31. 42
32. 9
33. 18
34. 15
35. 13
36. 34
37. 102
38. 7
39. 16
40. 22
41. 35
42. $6 \times \frac{2}{3}$; 4
43. $10 \times \frac{4}{5}$; 8
44. $5 \times \frac{3}{5}$; 3
45. $4\frac{1}{2}$
46. $17\frac{1}{2}$
47. $7\frac{1}{2}$
48. $3 \div \frac{1}{4} = 12$
49. 8
50. $2 \div \frac{1}{5} = 10$

1	4	5	8
2	3	6	7

51. 6
52. $2 \div \frac{1}{6} = 12$

1	3	5
2	4	6

53. 8
54. $3 \div \frac{1}{3} = 9$

1	2	3	4
5	6	7	8

55. 4

56. 15

57. $\frac{1}{2}$ 58. 4   59. $\frac{1}{4}$ 60. 2

61. $\frac{3}{2}$ 62. 10   63. $6 \div \frac{3}{8} = 6 \times \frac{8}{3} = 16$; 16

64. $3 \div \frac{1}{4} = 3 \times 4 = 12$; Bob has 12 quarters.

65. $3 \div \frac{1}{8} = 3 \times 8 = 24$; There are 24 guests at Carol's party.

66. $6 \div 1\frac{1}{2} = 6 \cdot \times \frac{2}{3} = 4$; Barbara can make 4 skirts.

Just for Fun
1881

16 More Operations with Fractions

1. 1   2. 3   3. 2   4. 2
5. 3   6. 2   7. 12   8. 20
9. 2   10. 2   11. 4   12. 4
13. 3   14. 7   15. $\frac{2}{5}$ 16. $\frac{1}{6}$
17. $1\frac{3}{5}$ 18. 6   19. 1   20. $\frac{1}{18}$
21. $\frac{6}{7}$ 22. $\frac{2}{3}$ 23. $\frac{2}{7}$ 24. $\frac{15}{22}$
25. $1\frac{2}{5}$ 26. 2   27. 5   28. 10
29. 2   30. $\frac{1}{3}$ 31. 2   32. 1
33. 1   34. $\frac{1}{2}$ 35. $3\frac{3}{4}$ 36. 15
37. $2\frac{1}{25}$ 38. 9   39. $\frac{1}{2}$ 40. $2\frac{1}{3}$
41. 1   42. $\frac{1}{4}$ 43. $\frac{2}{9}$ 44. $\frac{1}{5}$
45. $4\frac{3}{7}$ 46. 1

47. $1\frac{2}{3} \div \frac{1}{3} = \frac{5}{3} \times 3 = 5$

48. $1\frac{1}{2} \div \frac{1}{2} = \frac{3}{2} \times 2 = 3$

49. $1\frac{5}{6} \div \frac{1}{6} = \frac{11}{6} \times 6 = 11$

50. $1\frac{1}{4} \times \frac{1}{2} = \frac{5}{4} \times \frac{1}{2} = \frac{5}{8}$; $\frac{5}{8}$

51. $9\frac{1}{2} \times \frac{1}{2} = \frac{19}{2} \times \frac{1}{2} = \frac{19}{4} = 4\frac{3}{4}$; The willow tree is $4\frac{3}{4}$ m tall.

52a. $2\frac{1}{2} \times 2 + 1\frac{1}{2} \times 2 = 5 + 3 = 8$; The perimeter is 8 metres.

b. $2\frac{1}{2} \times 1\frac{1}{2} = \frac{5}{2} \times \frac{3}{2} = \frac{15}{4} = 3\frac{3}{4}$; The area is $3\frac{3}{4}$ square metres.

53. $12 \times \frac{1}{8} + 5 \times \frac{1}{2} = \frac{3}{2} + \frac{5}{2} = \frac{8}{2} = 4$; 3 pizzas are left.

Just for Fun
1.   2.

Final Review

1. C   2. D   3. B   4. C
5. D   6. A   7. B   8. C
9. A   10. C   11. D   12. A
13. B   14. C   15. A   16. D
17. B   18. D   19. A   20. B
21. C   22. A   23. D   24. B
25. $\frac{19}{20}$ 26. $3\frac{11}{14}$ 27. $1\frac{7}{8}$ 28. $5\frac{3}{10}$
29. $\frac{1}{12}$ 30. $\frac{11}{20}$ 31. $8\frac{1}{3}$ 32. $19\frac{1}{5}$
33. 15   34. $\frac{3}{23}$ 35. $1\frac{2}{3}$ 36. $1\frac{1}{4}$
37. $1\frac{1}{12}$ 38. $\frac{1}{9}$ 39. $10\frac{1}{2}$ 40. $1\frac{1}{2}$
41. $\frac{1}{18}$ 42. $8\frac{1}{10}$ 43. $2\frac{7}{8}$ 44. $1\frac{2}{3}$
45. $5\frac{2}{3}$ 46. $4\frac{7}{12}$ 47. $\frac{8}{9}$ 48. $2\frac{9}{10}$
49. $\frac{1}{3}$ 50. 2   51. $\frac{1}{3}$ 52. $\frac{1}{8}$
53. $\frac{16}{3}$ 54. $\frac{3}{16}$ 55. $1\frac{1}{2}$ 56. $\frac{3}{4}$
57. $2\frac{3}{5}$ 58. T   59. T   60. F
61. F   62. T   63. F   64. T
65. F   66. T   67. F

68a. $\frac{3}{16} + \frac{1}{8} = \frac{3}{16} + \frac{2}{16} = \frac{5}{16}$;

He read $\frac{5}{16}$ of the book over the first two days.

b. $1 - \frac{5}{16} = \frac{16}{16} - \frac{5}{16} = \frac{11}{16}$; $\frac{11}{16}$ of the book remains to be read.

c. $320 \times \frac{11}{16} = 220$; 220 pages of the book remains to be read.

69a. $100 \times \frac{1}{4} = 25$; 25 marbles are either white or red.

b. $25 - 15 = 10$; 10 marbles are white.

c. $100 \times \frac{1}{2} = 50$; 50 marbles are blue.

d. $1 - \frac{1}{4} - \frac{1}{2} = \frac{4}{4} - \frac{1}{4} - \frac{2}{4} = \frac{1}{4}$;

$\frac{1}{4}$ of the marbles are neither white, red nor blue.

70. $10 - 1.79 \times 5 = 10 - 8.95 = 1.05$; He gets $ 1.05 change.

Review

1. 1.05
2. 9800
3. 32.58
4. 413 ; 1180 ; 1593
5.
```
        820
    9 ) 7380
        72
        18
        18
```
6.
```
         6.4 8
    5 ) 3 2.4
         30
         2 4
         2 0
          4 0
          4 0
```
7. 103
8. 5900
9. 1200
10. 10.2
11. 1
12. 8.01
13. ✔ ; 591 x 5 = 2955
14. 564 x 7 = 3948
15. ✔ ;398 x 6 + 2 = 2390
16. ✔; 50 x 80 = 4000
17. ✔ ; 4000 ÷ 10 = 400
18. 50 x 40 = 2000
19. a. 0.29   b. 1.35   c. $\frac{5}{10}$ d. $\frac{8}{100}$ e. $1\frac{13}{100}$
20. a. $2\frac{1}{3}$ b. $4\frac{3}{7}$ c. $\frac{5}{4}$ d. $\frac{22}{5}$ e. $\frac{31}{8}$
21. 16 ; 22 ; 29
22. 64 ; 128 ; 256
23. 10 ; 12 ; 13
24. 65 ; 55 ; 50
25. 10 ; 14
26. 9 ; 12
27. 10.8 ; 15.6
28. 200
29. 50
30. 100
31. 10
32. 105
33. 55
34. $\frac{1}{4}$
35. 324
36. (Suggested answers) 12 , 27 ; 6 , 54 ; 4 , 81 ; 3 , 108
37. 150
38.
39. ✔
40. ✔
41.
42. ✔
43. ✔
44. A (3 , 2)   B (3 , 4)   C (5 , 2)   D(4 , 0)   E (0 , 5)   F (6 , 4)
45. triangle
46. A ; B ; C ; E
47.
48.
49.
50. Rotation
51. Reflection
52. Translation
53. Reflection
54. 150
55. 250

1 Operations with Whole Numbers

1. 11 157
2. 8119
3. 9035
4. 56 119
5. 43 652
6.
```
      523
    x  14
     2092
     5230
     7322
```
7.
```
      278
    x  36
     1668
     8340
    10008
```
8.
```
      901
    x  49
     8109
    36040
    44149
```
9.
```
      645
    x  28
     5160
    12900
    18060
```
10.
```
        46
    13 ) 598
        52
        78
        78
```
11.
```
         182
    27 ) 4914
         27
         221
         216
          54
          54
```
12.
```
         39R4
    36 )1408
         108
         328
         324
           4
```
13.
```
         454R6
    13 )5908
         52
         70
         65
          58
          52
           6
```

14. 2000 ; 1000 ; 3000 ; 6000 ; 6487
15. 6000 ; 2000 ; 1000 ; 9000 ; 9188
16. 12 000 ; 1000 ; 11 000 ; 11 217
17. 17 000 ; 5000 ; 12 000 ; 12 129
18. 9481 ; 20 ; 500 ; 10 000
19. 4368 ; 200 ; 20 ; 4000
20. 16 128 ; 400 ; 40 ; 16 000
21. 115 ; 6000 ; 50 ; 120
22. 157 R 5; 3000 ; 20 ; 150
23. 108 R 22 ; 4000 ; 40 ; 100
24. C ; F ; F ; G ; H
25. 24 ; 119
26. 17 ; 46
27. 300 + 34 ; 334
28. 512 – 4 ; 508
29. 7 + 360 ; 367
30. Ming has: 12 x 25 + 15 x 10 + 13 x 5 = 515 ; 515
31. Susanna has: 108 x 25 = 2700 ; 2700
32. No. of dimes: 56 x 25 ÷10 = 140 ; 140
33. Difference in amount: 458 x 25 – 192 x 10 = 9530 ; 9530
34. No. of chocolate eggs : 365 x 12 = 4380
    He eats 4380 chocolate eggs.
35. No. of small boxes : 4380 ÷ 50 = 87R30
    Keith will eat about 87 small boxes of chocolate.
36. No. of chocolate eggs : 58 x 3 + 96 x 2 = 366
    He has 366 chocolate eggs in all.
37. Dave's guess is the closest, only 8 more than the actual amount.
38. No. of chocolate eggs : 2858 ÷ 30 = 95R8
    Each bag contains about 95 chocolate eggs.

Mind Boggler

148

2 Decimals

1. 200 + 50 + 7 + 0.1 + 0.02 + 0.008 ; Two hundred fifty-seven and one hundred twenty eight thousandths
2. 300 + 50 + 1 + 0.08 + 0.002 ; Three hundred fifty-one and eighty-two thousandths
3. 5406.903
4. 620.58
5. 59.01 < 59.05 < 59.1 < 59.15
6. 15.224 < 15.238 < 15.304 < 15.322
7.
8. 0.004
9. 0.008
10. 0.012
11. 0.021
12. 0.026
13. 0.045
14. 50.05
15. 6.16
16. 11.87
17. 11.13
18. 1.406
19. 4.172
20. 0.306
21. 14.505
22. 2936
23. 5873
24. 1390.5
25. 91 640
26. 25 110
27. 402.3
28. 2 ; 1080
29. 9 ; 765
30. 2.35 x 100 x 8 ; 1880
31. 12.4 x 10 x 6 ; 744
32. 569.43
33. 27.18
34. 1623.78
35. 650.36
36. 2500.46
37. 2292.227
38. 365.048
39. 265.92
40. 5.823
41. 2.513
42. 2.465
43. 4.25
44. 28.59
45. 23.94
46.
```
         3.87
    6 ) 2 3.2 2
        18
        5 2
        4 8
         4 2
         4 2
```
47.
```
         4 7.5
    9 ) 4 2 7.5
        3 6
        6 7
        6 3
         4 5
         4 5
```

48.
```
   30.18
7)211.26
  21
   12
    7
     56
     56
```

49.
```
   12.08
8)96.64
  8
  16
  16
     64
     64
```

50. 1.154 51. 7.482 52. 7.523
53. 6.88 54. 4.087 55. 19.253
56. ✗ 57. ✔ 58. ✗
59. ✗ 60. ✔ 61. ✔
62. 0.65 63. 1.485 64. 26.04
65. 9.96 66. 1.07
67. 2.49 – 0.25 x 9 = 0.24 ; She needs to pay $0.24 more.
68. 4.34 x 3 + 3.24 x 2 = 19.50 ; She needs to pay $19.50.
69. 0.495 ÷ 3 = 0.165 ; There is 0.165 kg of shredded wheat in each portion.

Mind Boggler

1.127

3 Integers and Number Theory

1. A –3 ; B –2 ; C 0 ; D 5
2. 3 3. –3 4. 2 5. 0
6. 1 7. –2 8. 0 9. 4
10. –3°C ; –2°C ; 4°C ; 3°C ; 0°C ; 2°C ; –1°C
11. Sunday 12. Tuesday
13. 3 14. Thursday

15.-17.

1	2	3	(4)	5	~~6~~	7	(8)	9	10
11	~~(12)~~	13	14	15	(16)	17	~~18~~	19	(20)
21	22	23	~~(24)~~	25	26	27	(28)	29	~~30~~
31	(32)	33	34	35	~~(36)~~	37	38	39	(40)
41	~~42~~	43	(44)	45	46	47	~~(48)~~	49	50

18. 5 ; 20 and 40 19. 6 ; 12, 24, 36 and 48
20. 20 21. 12
22. 3, 6, 9, 12, 15, 18, 21, 24, 27, 30
23. 5, 10, 15, 20, 25, 30, 35, 40, 45, 50
24. 8, 16, 24, 32, 40, 48, 56, 64, 72, 80
25. 10, 20, 30, 40, 50, 60, 70, 80, 90, 100
26. 15, 30, 45 ; 24, 48, 72 ; 40, 80, 120 ; 10, 20, 30
27. 15 ; 24 ; 40 ; 10 28. 12 ; 6 ; 4 ; 1, 2, 3, 4, 6, 12
29. 20 ; 10 ; 5 ; 1, 2, 4, 5, 10, 20
30. 1, 2, 4 ; 4
31. 1, 2, 4, 8, 16 ; 1, 2, 3, 6, 9, 18 ; 1, 2 ; 2
32. 1, 3, 5, 15 ; 1, 2, 3, 5, 6, 10, 15, 30 ; 1, 3, 5, 15 ; 15
33. 1, 2, 5, 10 ; 1, 2, 3, 4, 6, 8, 12, 24 ; 1, 2 ; 2

34.

(2)	(3)	63	(29)	16	25	(97)
(19)	87	(73)	77	51	(23)	46
32	(31)	(11)	24	(67)	(13)	81

35.
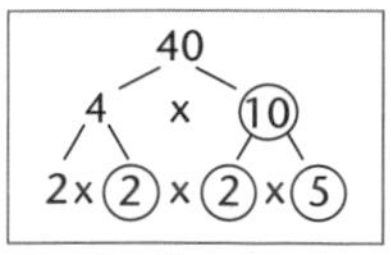

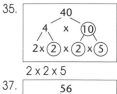

2 x 2 x 5

36.
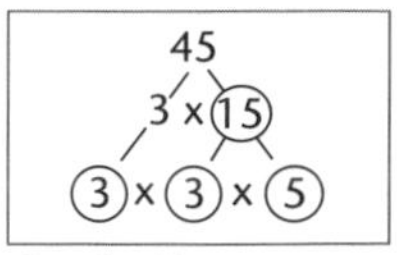

3 x 3 x 5

37.
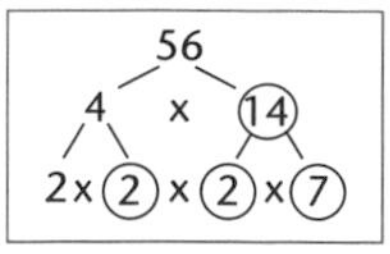

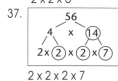

2 x 2 x 2 x 7

38. 2 x 2 x 2 x 3 x 3 39. 2 x 2 x 2 x 2 x 2
40. 2 x 2 x 3 x 5 41. 2 x 5 x 5
42. 2 x 3 x 3 x 3 43. 2 x 2 x 2 x 2 x 5
44. 3 x 7 ; 2 x 2 x 7 ; 7 ; 84
45. 2 x 2 x 2 x 2 ; 2 x 2 x 2 x 3 ; 8 ; 48
46. 3 ; 4 ; 21 ; 28 ; 49 47. 7 ; 2 ; 84 ; 24 ; 60
48. 20 ; 7 ; 180 ; 63 ; 243 49. 50 ; 1 ; 400 ; 8 ; 392
50. 2 ; 100 ; 2 ; 500 ; 10 ; 490

Mind Boggler

1. 34 ; even 2. 22 ; even 3. 25 ; odd

4 Percent

1. 69% 2. 100% 3. 8%
4. 26% 5. 42% 6. 7%
7. 83% 8. 98% 9. 32%
10. 8% 11. 55% 12. 78%

13.
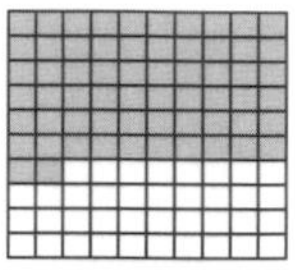
14.
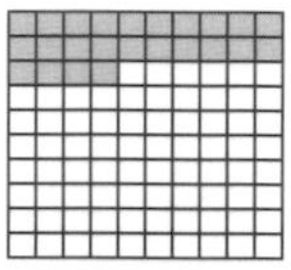
15.
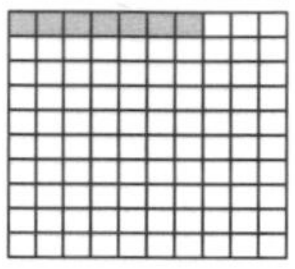
16.
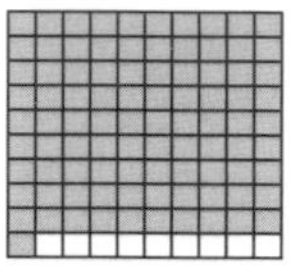

17. 15 ; 15 ; 15 18. 25 ; 25 ; 25
19. 60 ; 60 ; 60 20. 30 ; 60 ; 80
21. 25 ; 50 ; 75 22. 86 ; 86
23. 85 ; 85 24. 90 ; 90
25. 65 ; 65 26. 92 ; 92
27. 85 ; 85 28. $\frac{1}{5}$
29. $\frac{1}{4}$ 30. $\frac{1}{2}$ 31. $\frac{3}{4}$
32. $\frac{41}{50}$ 33. $\frac{2}{25}$ 34. $\frac{4}{25}$
35. $\frac{33}{100}$ 36. 2 37. 0.26
38. 0.37 39. 0.95 40. 0.66
41. 0.09 42. 0.74 43. $\frac{1}{8}$
44. $\frac{19}{25}$ 45. $\frac{7}{10}$ 46. $\frac{9}{20}$
47. 0.7 ; $\frac{7}{100}$; $\frac{7}{10}$ 48. 60% ; $\frac{60}{100}$; $\frac{3}{5}$
49. 45% ; 0.45 ; $\frac{9}{20}$ 50. 5% ; 0.05 ; $\frac{5}{100}$
51. 26% 52. 78%
53. 86% 54. 52%
55. 11% 56. 7%
57. 0.27 ; $\frac{19}{50}$; 59% 58. 64% ; $\frac{18}{25}$; 0.93
59. 71% ; 0.73 ; $\frac{3}{4}$ 60. 75 ; 75
61. 35 ; 35 62. 186 ; 186
63. 11 ; 11
64. a. 43% b. 27% c. 30% d. 38% e. 62%
65. a. 20% b. 80% c. 50% d. 40%
66. Tim eats: $\frac{18}{30} = \frac{6}{10} = \frac{60}{100} = 60\%$

Ray eats : $\frac{16}{25} = \frac{64}{100} = 64\%$

Tim eats 60% and Ray eats 64%. Ray's percent is higher.

Mind Boggler

If there are same numbers of marble in each colour, there should be 25 marbles in each colour. Then each colour should make up 25% instead of 26% of the marbles.

5 Fractions

1. $1\frac{1}{2}$ 2. $1\frac{4}{5}$ 3. $2\frac{5}{6}$
4. $2\frac{1}{6}$ 5. $1\frac{1}{4}$ 6. $6\frac{1}{2}$
7. $1\frac{11}{18}$ 8. $2\frac{1}{5}$ 9. $2\frac{1}{3}$
10. $1\frac{1}{6}$ 11. $1\frac{7}{18}$ 12. $1\frac{5}{18}$

13. PRACTICE MAKES PERFECT

14. $\frac{4}{8} < \frac{5}{8} < \frac{7}{8}$ 15. $\frac{9}{10} < \frac{9}{7} < \frac{9}{4}$

16. $2\frac{3}{5} < 2\frac{4}{5} < 3\frac{1}{5}$ 17. $1\frac{1}{6} < 1\frac{5}{6} < 2\frac{5}{6}$

18. $\frac{5}{2}$ 19. $\frac{8}{5}$ 20. $\frac{13}{12}$

21. $\frac{13}{4}$ 22. $\frac{15}{6}$ 23. $\frac{12}{5}$

24. $\frac{16}{6}$ 25. $\frac{17}{4}$ 26. $\frac{16}{7}$

27. $\frac{2}{6} ; \frac{3}{6} ; \frac{5}{6}$ 28. $\frac{4}{9} ; \frac{2}{9} ; \frac{6}{9} ; \frac{2}{3}$

29. $\frac{5}{8} ; \frac{4}{8} ; \frac{1}{8}$ 30. $\frac{5}{6} ; \frac{2}{6} ; \frac{3}{6} ; \frac{1}{2}$

31. $\frac{6}{18} ; \frac{1}{3}$ 32. $\frac{14}{20} ; \frac{7}{10}$ 33. $\frac{30}{30} ; 1$

34. $\frac{6}{15} ; \frac{2}{5}$ 35. $\frac{20}{25} ; \frac{4}{5}$ 36. $\frac{12}{42} ; \frac{2}{7}$

37. $\frac{2}{12} ; \frac{1}{6}$ 38. $\frac{1}{6} ; \frac{1}{2} ; \frac{1}{6} ; \frac{3}{6} ; \frac{4}{6} ; \frac{2}{3}$

39. $\frac{6}{8} ; \frac{1}{2} ; \frac{6}{8} ; \frac{4}{8} ; \frac{2}{8} ; \frac{1}{4}$

40. $2 ; 3 ; \frac{1}{2}$ 41. $5 ; 4 ; \frac{2}{5}$

42. $7 ; 14 ; 9 ; 1\frac{1}{8}$ 43. $5 ; 20 ; 27 ; 2\frac{1}{4}$

44. $\frac{3}{6} + \frac{2}{6} = \frac{5}{6}$ 45. $\frac{9}{15} - \frac{5}{15} = \frac{4}{15}$

46. $\frac{7}{3} - \frac{7}{15} = \frac{35}{15} - \frac{7}{15} = 1\frac{13}{15}$

47. $\frac{23}{6} - \frac{5}{4} = \frac{46}{12} - \frac{15}{12} = 2\frac{7}{12}$

48. $\frac{7}{5} + \frac{21}{10} = \frac{14}{10} + \frac{21}{10} = 3\frac{1}{2}$

49. $\frac{15}{8} + \frac{11}{4} = \frac{15}{8} + \frac{22}{8} = 4\frac{5}{8}$

50. $\frac{7}{4} - \frac{5}{8} = \frac{14}{8} - \frac{5}{8} = 1\frac{1}{8}$

51. $\frac{10}{3} - \frac{9}{4} = \frac{40}{12} - \frac{27}{12} = 1\frac{1}{12}$

52. $2\frac{1}{4}$ 53. 4 54. $\frac{1}{2}$

55. $2\frac{3}{10}$ 56. $1\frac{11}{12}$ 57. $2\frac{1}{12}$

58. $5\frac{1}{4}$ 59. $3\frac{3}{8}$ 60. $1\frac{7}{8}$

61. $\frac{2}{3}$

Mind Boggler

1

6 Rate and Ratio

1. 2.5 2. 20 3. 60
4. 6 5. 3 6. 4
7. 2.5 8. 14 9. 0.40
10. 1.20 11. 4.27
12. 6.60 ; 6.45 ; 6.85 ; B   13. 1.19 ; 1.25 ; 1.42 ; A
14. 0.79 ; 0.68 ; 0.89 ; B
15.-18. (Suggested answers)
15. 10 : 14; 15 : 21   16. 8 : 18 ; 12 : 27
17. 2 : 3 ; 20 : 30   18. 3 : 5 ; 6 : 10
19. 3 : 1   20. 1 : 4   21. 17 : 3
22. 7 : 18   23. 2 : 3   24. 6 : 5
25. 5 : 4   26. 2 : 3   27. 1 : 3
28. 2 : 5   29. $\frac{9}{25}$; 0.36 ; 36%
30. 2 : 5 ; 0.4 ; 40%   31. 41 : 50 ; $\frac{41}{50}$; 82%
32. 13 : 20 ; $\frac{13}{20}$; 0.65   33. 3 : 20 ; $\frac{3}{20}$; 15%
34. 2 : 1   35. 2 : 3   36. 5 : 9
37. 1 : 3   38. 2 : 3   39. 2 : 5
40. 3 : 5   41. 1 : 3   42. 2 : 3
43. $1.62   44. $6.48   45. 48¢
46. 15 stickers   47. 23 : 22   48. 15 stickers/day
49. a. 2 : 1   b. 1 : 3   c. 0.5 balloon/min
50. a. 5 : 2   b. 35 cards/year   c. 175 cards
    d. 49 cards/year   e. 490 cards

Mind Boggler

1. $2400/month   2. $900
3. $600   4. 1 : 2

7 Time, Distance and Speed

1. 16:35   2. 06:12   3. 11:25:46
4. 22:42:11   5. 16:27:53
6.   7.

5:35:10 p.m.   5:32:02 a.m.

8.    9.

12:05:33 p.m.   9:16:45 p.m.

10. 22:11:20   11. 07:31:05   12. 13:37:50
13. 2 h 10 min 35 s 14. 8 h 44 min 43 s 15. 120
16. 5   17. 800   18. 9
19. 4000   20. 2.5   21. 840
22. 0.66   23. 2.5   24. 7.5
25. 37.2   26. 4.52   27. 28 m
28. 30 cm   29. 9 mm   30. 560 km
31. 3000   32. 2   33. 0.6
34. 1.5   35. 4.4   36. 4
37. The shortest distance is to pass through the community centre and the museum. The distance is 5.4 km.
38. 25 km/h   39. 64 km/h   40. 2.5 m/s
41. 92 km   42. 70 km   43. 2 s
44. 25 s   45. 80 km/h   46. 10 h

47. 11.5 km/h 48. 51.75 km 49. 7 h
50. Paul's speed : 7 km in $\frac{1}{2}$ h → 14 km in 1 h ;

Pat's speed : 24 km in 2 h → 12 km in 1 h ; Paul

51. a. 10:20:50 ; 10:20:55 ; 10:21:00 ; 10:21:04 ; 10:21:05
b. 12:11:45 ; 12:12:15 ; 12:12:30 ; 12:12:40 ; 12:12:55
52. 15 s 53. 1 h 45 min 10 s
54. 36 s 55. 540 s or 9 min
56. 100 m 57. 2 m/s 58. 120 m

Mind Boggler

2000

Progress Test

1. C 2. D 3. A
4. A 5. B 6. B
7. C 8. D 9. B
10. B 11. D 12.

$$\begin{array}{r} 123 \\ \times\ 47 \\ \hline 4920 \\ 861 \\ \hline 5781 \end{array}$$

13. 2400.65
14.
$$\begin{array}{r} 54 \\ 29\overline{)1566} \\ 145 \\ \hline 116 \\ 116 \\ \hline \end{array}$$
15.
$$\begin{array}{r} 8.64 \\ 3\overline{)25.92} \\ 24 \\ \hline 19 \\ 18 \\ \hline 12 \\ 12 \\ \hline \end{array}$$

16. 4 x 25 x 5.2 = 520 17. 52 + 45 = 97
18. 15 x (50 + 3) = 750 + 45 = 795
19. 600 + 13 = 613
20. $\frac{21}{4} - \frac{5}{2} = \frac{21}{4} - \frac{10}{4} = \frac{11}{4} = 2\frac{3}{4}$
21. $\frac{14}{30} - \frac{5}{30} = \frac{9}{30} = \frac{3}{10}$
22. $\frac{13}{4} + \frac{15}{8} = \frac{26}{8} + \frac{15}{8} = \frac{41}{8} = 5\frac{1}{8}$
23. 0.123
24. $\frac{3}{4} = \frac{3 \times 25}{4 \times 25} = \frac{75}{100} = 75\%$
25. $1\frac{3}{4} = 1\frac{9}{12}$; $1\frac{2}{3} = 1\frac{8}{12}$; $1\frac{3}{4}$ is bigger.
26. 21 = 3 x 7 ; 35 = 5 x 7 ; G.C.F. of 21 and 35 = 7
27. 25 = 5 x 5 ; 40 = 2 x 2 x 2 x 5 ;
L.C.M. of 25 and 40 = 2 x 2 x 2 x 5 x 5 = 200
28. A = 07:00 B = 22:00 C = 08:30 D = 23:30
29. 15 hours 30. 15 hours 31. 6.2 m/s
32. 133 s 33. 240 s
34. She should go to Lucy's convenience store because Ben's convenience store will be closed as she needs 133 s to go there.
35. Amount : 15 x 20 + 12 x 5 = 360 ; She has $360 in all.
36. Amount in $20 : 15 x 20 = 300
Fraction : $\frac{300}{360} = \frac{5}{6}$

$\frac{5}{6}$ of Mrs. Saura's money is in $20 bill.
37. $\frac{1}{3}$ 38. $\frac{2}{15}$ 39. 33.33%
40. 20% 41. 1 : 5 42. 69 popiscles
43. $29.95 44. $0.45 45. 3 packs
46. $33.92 47. $15 48. 200 slices

8 Perimeter and Area

1. 8 ; 12 ; 11 ; 20 ; 20 ; 32
2. 4 ; 8 ; 7 ; 25 ; 21 ; 64
3. P : (7 + 6) x 2 ; 26   A : 7 x 5 ; 35
4. P : (12 + 10) x 2 ; 44   A :12 x 9 ; 108
5. P : (60 + 25) x 2 ; 170   A : 60 x 20 ; 1200
6. P : (18 + 3.5) x 2 ; 43   A : 18 x 3 ; 54
7. P : 8 + 11 + 12 ; 31   A : 12 x 7 ÷ 2 ; 42
8. P : 13 + 5 + 12 ; 30   A : 12 x 5 ÷ 2 ; 30
9. P : 16 + 10 + 10 ; 36   A : 16 x 6 ÷ 2 ; 48
10. P : 6.4 + 4.5 + 3 ; 13.9   A : 3 x 4 ÷ 2 ; 6
11.-15. (Suggested answers)
11.

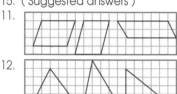

12.

13.

b. 26
14. a.

b. 20
15. a.

b. the same c. different d. the same
16. a. Fencing needed : 8.5 x 2 + 6 x 2 = 17 + 12 = 29 ;
29 m of fencing are needed to enclose the field.
b. Turf needed : 8.5 x 6 = 51 ;
51 m² of turf must be laid to cover the whole field.
17. No. of times : (27 x 21) ÷ (9 x 7) = 9 ;
The poster is 9 times bigger than the card.
18. a. Area of the door : 2 x 1.2 = 2.4 ;
Area of the door is 2.4 m².
b. Total area of the wall and the door: 5 x 2.4 = 12 ;
Area of the wall : 12 – 2.4 = 9.6 ;
Area of the wall is 9.6 m².
19. Area enclosed : 13 x 20 ÷ 2 = 130 ;
Area enclosed is 130 km².

Mind Boggler

21 m²

9 Volume and Mass

1. 750 cm³ 2. 78 m³ 3. 9.6 m³
4. 1 km³ 5. 24 cm³ 6. 60 cm³
7. 4913 cm³ 8. 28 km³ 9. 384 cm²
10. 1536 cm³ 11. 30 720 cm³
12. Yes. Thickness of each book is 4 cm, so the total thickness of 20 books is 80 cm or 0.8 m.
13. B 14. 84 blocks
15. 24 blocks 16. 19 ; 6 ; 25 ; 2850 cm³
17. 12 ; 12 ; 12 ; 1728 cm³ 18. 12 ; 6 ; 6 ; 432 cm³
19. 5 ; 6 ; 21 ; 630 cm³
20. 22 ; 5 ; 3 ; 330 cm³ 21. 15 ; 4 ; 23 ; 1380 cm³

22. E; C; D; F; B; A   23. 1000
24. 37.5   25. 7   26. 20
27. 111 cm³   28. 96 cm³   29. 81 cm³
30. Amount of water : 60 x 30 x 15 ÷ 1000 = 27 ;
     It contains 27 litres of water.
31. Increase in depth : 16 – 15 = 1 cm ;
     Increase in volume of water : 60 x 30 x 1 = 1800 cm³
     = 1800 mL ; 1.8 L of water must be added.
32. Volume of water : 18 L = 18 000 mL ;
     Base area of the pool : 60 x 30 = 1800 cm² ;
     Depth of the water : 10 cm ;
     Depth of water in the pool is 10 cm.
33. Capacity : 60 x 30 x 25 = 45 000 mL ;
     Capacity of the pool is 45 L.
34. 290 g   35. 350 g
36. 110 g   37. 81 g
38. 11.6 kg   39. 4.05 kg
40. 3 tablets   41. 1 g

Mind Boggler

1. 0.25 g   2. 7.75 g

10 Symmetry, 2-D and 3-D Figures

1.  ②
2. ④
3. ③

4. ②
5. ⑥
6. ⑤

7. ④
8. ?

9.
10.
11.

12.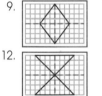
13.
14.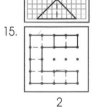

15.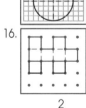
16.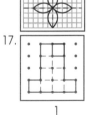
17.
     2   2   1

18. 3   19. 6   20. 2
21. 2   22. 2   23. 4
24. - 30. (Suggested answers)

24.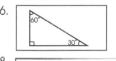
25.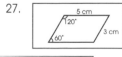

26.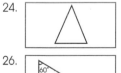
27.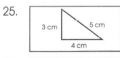

28.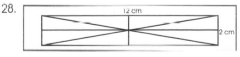

29.
30.

31. ; 4
32. ; 5

33. ; 5
34. ; 8

35. 36. 37.

38. A : square ; B : rhombus ; C : trapezoid ;
     D : parallelogram ; E : kite ; F : rectangle
39. Rectangle ; Rhombus ; Parallelogram ; Square
40. Rhombus ; Square   41. Rectangle; Parallelogram
42. Rectangle ; Square   43. Rhombus ; Parallelogram
44. Cube   45. Tetrahedron
46. Rectangular pyramid , Triangular prism, or Square pyramid
47. Square

Mind Boggler

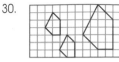

11 Transformations and Coordinates

1.-4. (Suggested answers)

1.
2.

3. 4.

5. 6.

7. 8. D ; I ; J

9.-11. 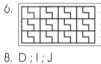 ; Yes
12-14. 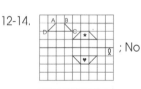 ; No

15.-17. ; No
18.-19.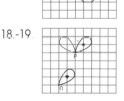

20. (Suggested answer)

    Rotate ♥ $\frac{1}{4}$ turn counter clockwise about 0. Then translate it 4 units up and 2 units right.

21. A (2 , 6) ; B (6 , 1) ; C (12 , 0) ; D (0 , 3) ; E (5 , 6) ;
     F (5 , 12) ; G (8 , 12) ; H (3 , 0) ; I (1 , 12) ; J (0 , 10)
22. Parallelogram   23. E and F
24. I, F and G   25. H and C

26. D and J
27. 9 square units
28. 7 square units
29. (7 , 9)
30. 6 units down and 3 units left
31. 9 units right

32.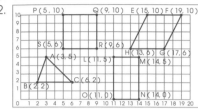

33. Its ordered pair will be (4 , 6), ABC is an isosceles triangle.
34. Its ordered pair will be (15 , 6), EFGH is a trapezoid.

Mind Boggler

(3 , 4)

12 Patterns and Simple Equations

1. 80 ; 70 ; 58 ;
   The numbers decrease by 2 more each time.
2. 120 ; 720 ; 5040 ;
   The numbers multiply by 1 more each time.
3. 52 ; 50 ; 53 ; The numbers decrease by 2 and then increase by 1 alternatively.
4. 65 ; 129 ; 257 ;
   The numbers double the previous number and minus 1.
5. 25 ; 36 ; 49 ; The numbers are 1x1, 2x2, 3x3, ...
6.-8. (Suggested answers for the number pairs)
6. 6 ; 4 ; 9 ; 1st + 2nd – 1 = 3rd
7. 24 ; 6 ; 5 ; 1st ÷ 2nd + 1 = 3rd
8. 6 ; 8 ; 22 ; 1st + 2nd x 2 = 3rd
9. a. 2000 ; 2005 ; 125 ; 149   b. 2 010
10. a. 1999 ; 2000 ; 9.00 ; 9.50   b. $10.50
11. a. 4 ; 5 ; 6 ; 4.6 ; 5.2 ; 5.9   b. 8 months
12. a.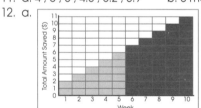

    b. $13   c. Week 19
    d. His savings increase by $1 more each week.
13. a.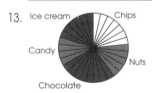

    b. 82.5¢ per litre   c. November
14. a.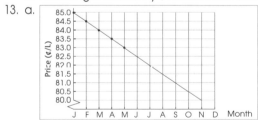

    b. Each triangle is 1 block wider and 1 block taller than the previous one.
    c. Each square is 1 block longer than the previous one.
    d. The diameter of each circle is 1 block longer than the previous one.

15. a.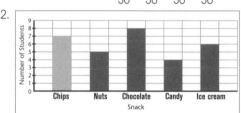

    b. Each triangle is 1 block narrower and 1 block taller than the previous one.
    c. Each rectangle is 1 block shorter and 1 block taller than the previous one.
    d. The number of circle decreases by 1 each time.
16. 28   17. 100   18. 28
19. 15   20. 22   21. 88
22. 115   23. 147   24. 4
25. 9   26. 5   27. 96
28. 15   29. 20   30. 6
31. 7   32. 26   33. 7

Mind Boggler

13 ; 16 ; 19 ; 22 ; 25 ; 31

13 Data and Graphs

1. L   2. B   3. C   4. B
5. L   6. C   7. B   8. L
9. B   10. B
11. a. 5 ; 8 ; 4 ; 6 ;   b. $\frac{5}{30}$; $\frac{8}{30}$; $\frac{4}{30}$; $\frac{6}{30}$

12.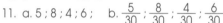

13.

14. a. 80.1¢/L   b. 79.2 ¢/L   c. 76.9 ¢/L
15. a. 3   b. 2.5   c. 2   16. a. 18   b. 15   c. 15
17. a. 50% , 50% , 50% , 60% , 60% , 80% , 80% , 80% , 80% , 80%
    b. 67%   c. 70%   d.   80%
18. $\frac{1}{4}$ 19. $\frac{4}{9}$ 20. $\frac{3}{4}$

21. a.
No. of Minutes	Tally	No. of Students
1 - 20	|||	3
21 - 40	++++	5
41 - 60	|||	3
61 - 80	|||	3
81 -100	|	1

b.

c. 4 students

22. a.
No. of Hours	Tally	No. of Students
1 - 2	|||	3
3 - 4	|	1
5 - 6	||||	4
7 - 8	|||	3
9 - 10	||||	4

b.

c. 7 students

Mind Boggler

(Suggested answer) 4, 8 and 18

14 Probability

1. a. $\frac{5}{20}$ or $\frac{1}{4}$ b. $\frac{6}{20}$ or $\frac{3}{10}$ c. $\frac{4}{20}$ or $\frac{1}{5}$
   d. $\frac{2}{20}$ or $\frac{1}{10}$ e. $\frac{3}{20}$ f. $\frac{9}{20}$

2.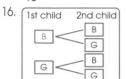

3. (Suggested answer)
   Put more red marbles into the box.

4. Cloudy   5. Rainy   6. $\frac{7}{10}$

7. $\frac{1}{6}$, $\frac{1}{5}$, $\frac{3}{10}$, $\frac{1}{3}$

8. Misty, Sunny, Rainy, Cloudy

9.

X	1	2	3	4
1	1	2	3	4
2	2	4	6	8
3	3	6	9	12
4	4	8	12	16

10. 16

11. 4   12. $\frac{3}{16}$ 13. 3

14. $\frac{3}{16}$ 15. $\frac{4}{16}$ or $\frac{1}{4}$

16.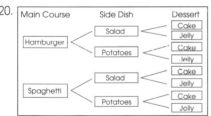

17. 4 ; BB, BG, GB and GG

18. $\frac{1}{4}$ 19. $\frac{2}{4}$ or $\frac{1}{2}$

20.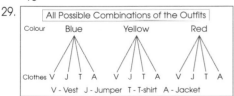

21. 8   22. 4   23. 4

24. 2   25. $\frac{1}{8}$ 26. $\frac{1}{8}$

27. 10 combinations. They are S & Co, S & T, H & Co, H & T, D & Co, D & T, M & Co, M & T, C & Co and C & T.

28. $\frac{1}{10}$

29.

All Possible Combinations of the Outfits

Colour   Blue   Yellow   Red

Clothes V J T A   V J T A   V J T A

V - Vest   J - Jumper   T - T-shirt   A - Jacket

30. $\frac{1}{12}$ 31. $\frac{4}{12}$ or $\frac{1}{3}$ 32. $\frac{3}{12}$ or $\frac{1}{4}$

33. a. 9   b. Jacket   c. $\frac{1}{12}$
    d. $\frac{2}{12}$ or $\frac{1}{6}$ e. $\frac{2}{12}$ or $\frac{1}{6}$

Mind Boggler

$\frac{2}{6}$ or $\frac{1}{3}$

Final Test

1. A   2. D   3. A
4. C   5. A   6. C
7. B   8. C   9. C
10. D   11. A   12. B
13. C   14. C   15. B
16. C   17. A   18. C
19. C   20. B   21. D
22. C   23. B   24. B
25. C   26. B   27. 3.249
28. 9.84   29. 17.946   30. 108.3
31. 108   32. 164   33. 20
34. 211   35. 5 ; 75   36. 4 ; 49
37. 18 ; 25   38. 16 ; 2 ; 32
39. a. 2 x 3 x 3 ; 2 x 2 x 2 x 3   b. 6 ; 72
40. a. 2 x 2 x 3 x 3 ; 2 x 2 x 11   b. 4 ; 396
41. $1\frac{5}{12}$ 42. $\frac{1}{8}$ 43. $\frac{7}{20}$
44. $\frac{13}{24}$ 45. $\frac{3}{8}$ 46. $\frac{1}{12}$
47. $\frac{1}{2}$ 48. $\frac{3}{10}$ 49. $\frac{7}{8}$
50. $\frac{9}{20}$ 51. $1\frac{2}{9}$ 52. $2\frac{19}{30}$
53. 3300 cm³   54. 5.4 m³   55. 4875 cm³
56. B
57. 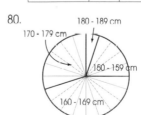 ; 4   58. ; 4   59. 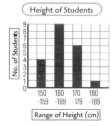 ; 1

60. 129 , 257 , 513; Time 2, minus 1.
61. 50, 35, 27.5; Divide by 2, plus 10.   62. 2
63. 27   64. 12.5   65. 5.3
66. 262.5   67. 56   68. Steve
69. Fred   70. $2\frac{11}{12}$ 71. $1\frac{1}{12}$
72. $1.08   73. 11.25 kg   74. 40
75. 80   76. 18   77. 12
78. 14

79.

Range of Height (cm)	Tally	No. of Students	Fraction of the Whole
150 - 159	IIII	4	$\frac{4}{20}$
160 - 169	HHH IIII	9	$\frac{9}{20}$
170 - 179	HHH I	6	$\frac{6}{20}$
180 - 189	I	1	$\frac{1}{20}$

80.

81.

82. $\frac{4}{20}$ or $\frac{1}{5}$ 83. 160 – 169 cm

84. $\frac{5}{6}$ 85. 166.3 cm

ANSWERS – SECTION III

Unit 1

1. Total no. of books : 2492 + 4716 = 7208   7208
2. Difference : 4716 – 2492 = 2224
   There are 2224 more paperback books than hardcover ones.
3. No. of shelves needed : 2492 ÷ 16 = 155...12
   The library will need 156 shelves to hold all the hardcover books.
4. No. of wire racks needed : 378 ÷ 48 = 7...42
   The library will need 8 wire racks to hold all the magazines.
5. No. of magazines : 378 + 17 x 8 = 514
   The library will have 514 magazines after 8 months.
6. No. of non-fictional paperback books : 4716 – 1296 = 3420
   There are 3420 non-fictional paperback books.
7. Amount spent on Rock and Roll CDs : 14 x 142 = 1988
   Kelly spent $1988 on Rock and Roll CDs.
8. Amount spent on Rhythm and Blue CDs : 11 x 57 = 627
   Kelly spent $627 on Rhythm and Blue CDs.
9. Cost of 1 Country CD : 1892 ÷ 86 = 22
   Each Country CD was worth $22.
10. Time taken : 53 x (142 + 57 + 86) = 15105
    It would take Kelly 15 105 min to listen to all of her CDs.
11. No. of songs : 12 x (142 + 57 + 86) = 3420
    There are 3420 songs in Kelly's collection.
12. Total weight : 89 x (142 + 57 + 86) = 25365
    The total weight of Kelly's CDs is 25 365 g.
13. Difference : 1000 – (142 + 57 + 86) = 715
    Kelly must buy 715 more CDs.
14. No. of CD holders needed : (142 + 57 + 86) ÷ 16 = 17...13
    Kelly needs 18 CD holders.
15. No. of candies sold : 128 x 18 = 2304
    2304 candies were sold yesterday.
16. Total no. of candies sold : (128 x 18) + (72 x 32) + (48 x 56) = 7296
    7296 candies were sold in all.
17. Money collected : 42 x 18 = 756
    Loni collected $756 from the sales of the big bags.
18. Average weight : 1584 ÷ 72 = 22
    The average weight of 1 candy was 22 g.
19. Weight : 22 x 128 = 2816   They were 2816 g.
20. No. of candies in big bags : 128 x 60 = 7680
    No. of candies in regular bags : 72 x 102 = 7344
    60 big bags contained more candies.
21. Regular bags needed : 9504 ÷ 72 = 132
    Loni needed 132 regular bags.
22. No. of regular bags : (4872 – (48 x25)) ÷ 72 = 51
    Loni needed 51 regular bags.
23. No. of small bags sold : (3600 – (128 x 18)) ÷ 48 = 27
    Loni sold 27 small bags.
24. No. of pencils in packages of 36 : 10320 – 6144 = 4176
    There will be 4176 pencils in packages of 36.
25. No. of packages : 6144 ÷ 64 = 96
    96 packages of 64 pencils are produced each day.
26. No. of packages : 4176 ÷ 36 = 116
    116 packages of 36 pencils are produced each day.
27. Average no. of rollerball pens : 44000 ÷ 25 = 1760
    On average, 1760 rollerball pens are produced in one day.
28. No. of cartons : 2816 + 3844 = 6660
    6660 cartons of pens are being delivered.
29. Cost of delivery : 2816 ÷ 32 x 148 = 13024
    The cost of delivering the pens to Vancouver will be $13 024.00.

Challenge

No. of paper clips and push pins each student got : 4448 ÷ 32 = 139 ;   No. of push pins each student got : 139 – 64 = 75
Each student got 75 push pins.

Unit 2

1. – 4.

1	2	3	4	5	6	7	8	9	10
11	12	13	14	15	16	17	18	19	20
21	22	23	24	25	26	27	28	29	30
31	32	33	34	35	36	37	38	39	40
41	42	43	44	45	46	47	48	49	50
51	52	53	54	55	56	57	58	59	60
61	62	63	64	65	66	67	68	69	70
71	72	73	74	75	76	77	78	79	80
81	82	83	84	85	86	87	88	89	90
91	92	93	94	95	96	97	98	99	100

5. 2, 4, 6, 8, 10.
6. The first 5 multiples of 4 are 4, 8, 12, 16 and 20.
7. The first 5 multiples of 5 are 5, 10, 15, 20 and 25.
8. The first 5 multiples of 10 are 10, 20, 30, 40 and 50.
9. The ones digits of the multiples of 2 are 2, 4, 6, 8 or 0.
10. The ones digits of the multiples of 5 are 5 or 0.
11. Yes.   12. Yes.   13. Suggested answer: 20, 40, 60.
14. Suggested answer: 10, 20, 30.
15. James would have to say 6, 12, 18 and 24.
16. Ken would have to say 8, 16, 24, 32 and 40.
17. James would have to say 3, 6, 9 and 12.
18. Ken would have to say 4 and 8.
19. Ken said '5'.
20. Ken said '11' and James said '5'.
21. The missing numbers were 27 and 36.
    James said '9' and Ken said '6'.
22. 849, 243 and 552 are the multiples of 3.
23. 392 and 684 are the multiples of 4.
24. The students could be divided into 1 group of 24 students, 2 groups of 12 students, 3 groups of 8 students or 4 groups of 6 students.
25. The factors of 24 are 1, 2, 3, 4, 6, 8, 12, 24.
26. The ribbon could be cut into 1 strip of 18 m, 2 strips of 9 m or 3 strips of 6 m.
27. The factors of 18 are 1, 2, 3, 6, 9, 18.
28. The beads could be put in 1 row with 20 beads, 2 rows with 10 beads each and 4 rows with 5 beads each.
29. The factors of 20 are 1, 2, 4, 5, 10, 20.
30. The common factors of 18, 20 and 24 are 1and 2.
31. 85, 280, 310 and 540 are the multiples of 5.
32. A number is divisible by 5 if its ones digit is 0 or 5.
33. 280, 310 and 540 are the multiples of 10.
34. A number is divisible by 10 if its ones digit is 0.
35. 8, 24, 28, 64, 72, 116, 280 and 540 are the multiples of 4.
36. No.
37. 24, 27, 51, 72, 147, 540 and 573 are the multiples of 3.
38. 24, 72 and 540 are the multiples of 3 and 4.
39. The first 4 common multiples of 3 and 4 are 12, 24, 36 and 48.
40. Number : 280 ÷ 2 = 140   It is 140.
41. Number : 51 ÷ 3 = 17   It is 17.
42. Number : 28 ÷ 2 = 14 (2 x 7 = 14)   It is 7.
43. Factors of 12 : 1 2 3 4 6, 12   Factors of 16 : 1 2 4 8, 16
    The lollipops could be packed in 3 different ways.
44. The ways of packaging the lollipops could be a pack with 1 lollipop, a pack with 2 lollipops or a pack with 4 lollipops.
45. Total no. of lollipops : 12 + 16 = 28 Factors of 28 : 1, 2, 4, 7, 14, 28
    The lollipops could be divided in 6 different ways.
46. They could be divided into 28 groups of 1 lollipop, 14 groups of 2 lollipops, 7 groups of 4 lollipops, 4 groups of 7 lollipops, 2 groups of 14 lollipops and 1 group of 28 lollipops.
47. Chris is not correct, e.g. 25 is greater than 24. 25 has 3 factors (1, 5, 25) but 24 has 8 factors (1, 2, 3, 4, 6, 8, 12, 24).
48.

Number	14	15	16	17	18	19
No. of factors	4	4	5	2	6	2

Judy will buy 18 chocolate bars.
49. He is correct because 9 is a factor of 216 (216 is a multiple of 9).
50. 1, 7 ;   1, 2, 4, 8 ;   1, 3, 9 ;   1, 2, 5, 10
51. 2, 3, 5, 7

52.

1,2,4,8,16	Composite	1,29	Prime
1,5,25	Composite	1,3,17,51	Composite
1,11	Prime	1,2,3,4,6,9,12,18,36	Composite
1,3,13,39	Composite	1,47	Prime

53. 2, 3, 5, 7, 11, 13, 17, 19, 23, 29, 31, 37, 41, 43, 47.

54. Sum : 20 + 21 + 22 + 24 + 25 + 26 + 27 + 28 + 30 = 223
The sum is 223.

55. Sum : 53 + 59 = 112   The sum is 112.

Challenge

1. False   2. True   3. False   4. True

Unit 3

1. Amount : $2\frac{1}{2} - 1\frac{1}{4} = 1\frac{1}{4}$ $1\frac{1}{4}$ m

2. Amount : $2\frac{3}{4} + \frac{1}{8} = 2\frac{7}{8}$ She buys $2\frac{7}{8}$ m of velvet.

3. Amount : $2\frac{1}{5} + \frac{3}{5} + \frac{7}{10} = 3\frac{1}{2}$
She needs to buy $3\frac{1}{2}$ m of cloth.

4. Length : $3\frac{7}{10} - 1\frac{3}{5} = 2\frac{1}{10}$ The other one is $2\frac{1}{10}$ m long.

5. Total : $\frac{2}{5} + \frac{3}{4} = 1\frac{3}{20}$ They carried $1\frac{3}{20}$ pails of water.

6. Difference : $1\frac{1}{2} - 1\frac{3}{20} = \frac{7}{20}$
They would have to carry $\frac{7}{20}$ pail more.

7. Amount : $2\frac{2}{3} - 1\frac{1}{2} = 1\frac{1}{6}$ Wayne carried $1\frac{1}{6}$ pails of water.

8. Difference : $1\frac{1}{2} - 1\frac{1}{6} = \frac{1}{3}$
Perry carried $\frac{1}{3}$ pail more than Wayne.

9. Amount : $\frac{9}{10} - \frac{1}{5} = \frac{7}{10}$
He carried $\frac{7}{10}$ pail of water to the aquarium.

10. Amount : $\frac{3}{4} + \frac{3}{4} + \frac{3}{4} = 2\frac{1}{4}$
He carried $2\frac{1}{4}$ pails of water to the aquarium.

11. Width : $1\frac{1}{5} - \frac{1}{2} = \frac{7}{10}$ The width was $\frac{7}{10}$ m.

12. Height : $\frac{2}{5} - \frac{3}{10} = \frac{1}{10}$ The water level rose by $\frac{1}{10}$ m.

13.

No. of bags	1	2	3	4	5	6
Rise of water level (m)	$\frac{1}{10}$	$\frac{2}{10}$	$\frac{3}{10}$	$\frac{4}{10}$	$\frac{5}{10}$	$\frac{6}{10}$ $\left(\frac{3}{5}\right)$

He put 6 bags of pebbles into the aquarium.

14. No. of boxes : $1\frac{7}{10} + \frac{1}{5} = 1\frac{9}{10}$
Glenda brought $1\frac{9}{10}$ boxes of muffins.

15. No. of boxes left : $1\frac{9}{10} - 1\frac{1}{2} = \frac{2}{5}$
$\frac{2}{5}$ box of muffins were left over.

16. Amount : $2\frac{4}{5} + 1\frac{1}{2} = 4\frac{3}{10}$
Linda brought $4\frac{3}{10}$ kg of cookies to school.

17. Cookies left : $4\frac{3}{10} - 3\frac{1}{10} = 1\frac{1}{5}$ $1\frac{1}{5}$ kg of cookies were left.

18. Boxes of crackers bought : $1\frac{1}{4} + \frac{3}{8} = 1\frac{5}{8}$
Jessica bought $1\frac{5}{8}$ boxes of crackers in all.

19. Total weight : $1\frac{5}{12} + \frac{1}{6} = 1\frac{7}{12}$
Raymond brought $1\frac{7}{12}$ kg of jellybeans to school.

20. Difference : $1\frac{5}{12} - \frac{1}{6} = 1\frac{1}{4}$
Bag A was $1\frac{1}{4}$ kg heavier than Bag B.

21. Pies sold : $\frac{5}{12} + \frac{3}{4} = 1\frac{1}{6}$ $1\frac{1}{6}$ pies were sold.

22. Pies left : $2 - 1\frac{1}{6} = \frac{5}{6}$ $\frac{5}{6}$ of the pies were left over.

23. Length : $35\frac{1}{10} + 4\frac{1}{5} = 39\frac{3}{10}$
The length of the cardboard was $39\frac{3}{10}$ cm.

24. Ribbon left : $4\frac{1}{2} - 1\frac{1}{8} = 3\frac{3}{8}$ $3\frac{3}{8}$ m of ribbon were left.

25. Ribbon left : $3\frac{3}{8} - 1\frac{1}{4} = 2\frac{1}{8}$ $2\frac{1}{8}$ m of ribbon were left.

26. Boxes of beans left : $3\frac{3}{4} - 1\frac{1}{2} = 2\frac{1}{4}$
$2\frac{1}{4}$ boxes of beans were left.

27. Boxes of beans left : $2\frac{1}{4} - 1\frac{1}{5} = 1\frac{1}{20}$
Shirley still had $1\frac{1}{20}$ boxes of beans.

28. Paint at the beginning : $5\frac{1}{3} + 3\frac{1}{6} = 8\frac{1}{2}$
Ryan had got $8\frac{1}{2}$ mL of green paint at the beginning.

Challenge

1.

3	4	5	6
$1\frac{1}{5}$ m	$1\frac{3}{5}$ m	2 m	$2\frac{2}{5}$ m

She got 6 strips.

2. Ribbon left : $2\frac{3}{5} - 2\frac{2}{5} = \frac{1}{5}$ $\frac{1}{5}$ m of ribbon was left.

Unit 4

1. Total weight : 1.465 + 1.389 = 2.854   2.854 kg

2. Total cost : 1.45 + 1.38 = 2.83
The total cost of the apples was $2.83.

3. Difference : 2.15 − 1.309 = 0.841
The weight of the other bag would be 0.841 kg.

4. Total cost : 3.27 + 4.69 = 7.96   Mindy spent $7.96 on onions.

5. Change : 20 − 18.27 = 1.73   Mindy would receive $1.73 change.

6. Original amount : 23.19 + 4.58 = 27.77
Frank had got $27.77 at the start.

7. Difference : 3.068 − 2.544 = 0.524
Mindy is 0.524 km farther from the grocery store than Frank.

8. Distance travelled : 3.068 + 3.068 + 2.544 = 8.68
He would travel 8.68 km.

9. Distance : 3.068 + 3.068 = 6.136
Frank would have to walk 6.136 km in all.

10. Change : 5 − 2.29 = 2.71   Frank got $2.71 change.

11. Change : 2.71 − 0.79 = 1.92
Mindy's mother would get $1.92 change.

12. Change : 0.79 − 0.56 = 0.23
Mindy's mother would get $0.23 more change.

13. Time saved : (15.5 − 11.27) x 2 = 8.46   Frank could save 8.46 min.

Challenge

1. Score : 4.7 + 0.25 + 0.36 = 5.31
Mario's score would have been 5.31 points.

2. Score : 6 − 0.36 = 5.64
The highest score Mario could get would be 5.64 points.

Unit 5

1. Mean : (321.75 + 297.54 + 306.72) ÷ 3 = 308.67   308.67 km

2. Average speed : 321.75 ÷ 3 = 107.25
The average speed was 107.25 km/h.

3. Average speed : 297.54 ÷ 3 = 99.18
The average speed was 99.18 km/h.

4. Time : 306.72 ÷ 90 = 3.408
They drove 3.408 hours.

5. Amount of gasoline used : $297.54 ÷ 12 = 24.795$
They used 24.795 L of gasoline on the second day.

6. Amount of gasoline: $210.72 ÷ 12 = 17.56$
They would need 17.56 L more gasoline to reach there.

7. Speed : $210.72 ÷ 4 = 52.68$
The average speed would be 52.68 km/h.

8. Cost of gasoline : $57 × 94.68 = 5396.76$
They paid 5396.76¢ ($53.97) for the gasoline.

9. Total weight : $1.19 × 3 = 3.57$
The total weight of the candies was 3.57 kg.

10. Cost : $9 × 1.45 = 13.05$ Theresa would pay $13.05 for the jellybeans.

11. Cost (1 pack) : $7.74 ÷ 9 = 0.86$ 1 pack of chewing gum cost $0.86.

12. Cost of 1 box (6 boxes) : $25.53 ÷ 6 = 4.255$
Cost of 1 box (8 boxes) : $32.12 ÷ 8 = 4.015$ $(4.015 < 4.255)$
8 boxes of chocolates were a better buy.

13. Cost : $7.9 × 2.4 = 18.96$ David would pay $18.96.

14. Cost : $23.71 × 0.5 = 11.855$ Theresa would pay $11.855.

15. Cost of 1 tent : $375.06 ÷ 2 = 187.53$ 1 tent cost $187.53.

16. Distance : $28.25 × 5 = 141.25$ They could go 141.25 km.

17. Average speed : $16.1 ÷ 1.4 = 11.5$
Kirby's average speed was 11.5 km/h.

18. Cost of food : $32.78 × 5 = 163.9$
They spent $163.90 on food for 5 days.

19. Cost per person per day : $32.78 ÷ 5 = 6.556$
The food cost per person per day was $6.556.

20. Amount of water : $8.25 × 5 = 41.25$
They would need 41.25 L of water for 5 days.

21. No. of bottles : $13.5 ÷ 1.5 = 9$ They would need 9 bottles.

22. Weight : $12.45 × 1.4 = 17.43$ Kirby's backpack was 17.43 kg.

23. Weight : $17.43 ÷ 0.7 = 24.9$ His father's backpack was 24.9 kg.

24. Volume : $12.8 × 8.4 × 6 = 645.12$ Its volume was 645.12 cm^3.

25. Area : $28 × 15.56 = 435.68$ The area of the court is 435.68 cm^2.

26. Practice time : $1.35 × 8 = 10.8$
Mr Holly's team would have 10.8 hours of practice.

27. Average : $26 ÷ 8 = 3.25$ They ran 3.25 km per day.

28. Average score per game : $277 ÷ 4 = 69.25$
69.25 points per game were scored by Miss Prem's team on average.

29. Total points : $68.25 × 4 = 273$ Mr Holly's team got 273 points in all.

Challenge
Cost (belt) : $35.01 ÷ 1.8 = 19.45$
Cost (tie) : $19.45 × 1.6 = 31.12$
No. of times : $35.01 ÷ 31.12 = 1.125$ A belt costs $19.45. A tie costs $31.12. The scarf costs 1.125 times more than the tie.

Midway Review

1. No. of seats : $(1252 − 28) ÷ (35 − 1) = 36$
There are 36 seats in each row.

2. No. of boys : $33 × 35 − 632 = 523$ There are 523 boys in all.

3. No. of seats left : $1252 − 33 × 35 = 97$
97 seats will be left for the teachers.

4. No. of piles : $1252 ÷ 12 = 104...4$
There will be 104 piles. 4 chairs will be left.

5. Factors of 32 : 1, 2, 4, 8, 16, 32   They can form rows in 3 ways: 1 row of 32 students, 2 rows of 16 and 4 rows of 8.

6. Factors of 36 : 1, 2, 3, 4, 6, 9, 12, 18, 36
They can form rows in 5 ways : 1 row of 36 students, 2 rows of 18, 3 rows of 12, 4 rows of 9 and 6 rows of 6.

7. Factors of 68 : 1, 2, 4, 17, 34, 68   They can form rows in 3 ways: 1 row of 68 students, 2 rows of 34 and 4 rows of 17.

8. Volume : $10 × 5 × 15.5 = 775$
The volume of each box was 775 cm^3.

9. No. of boxes : $(150 × 15) ÷ (10 × 5) = 45$
She could put 45 boxes of popcorn on the shelf.

10. No. of boxes : $45 × 3 = 135$
She could put 135 boxes of popcorn on the shelf.

11. Weight : $0.128 × 135 = 17.28$
The total weight of the popcorn on the shelf was 17.28 kg.

12. Cost : $2.25 × 135 = 303.75$
All the popcorn on the shelf would be worth $303.75.

13. No. of boxes : $20 ÷ 2.25 = 8...2$
She could buy 8 boxes of popcorn. Her change was $2.00.

14. Change : $20 − (2.25 × 9 − 1.95 × 3) = 5.6$
She would receive $5.60 change.

15. Discount : $1.95 × 8 = 15.6$ He would get $15.60 discount.

16. Change : $50 − (2.25 × 26 − 15.6) = 7.1$
He would receive $7.10 change.

17. No. of boxes : $65 × 128 + 16 = 8336$
Jackie sold 8336 boxes of popcorn in all.

18. Area : $21.2 × 27.9 = 591.48$
The area of each piece of cardboard paper is 591.48 cm^2.

19. Area : $591.48 ÷ 8 = 73.935$ The area of each card is 73.935 cm^2.

20. No. of pieces needed : $1280 ÷ 8 = 160$
They need 160 pieces of cardboard paper.

21. Number : $1280 ÷ 160 = 8$ It is 8.

22. No. of cards : $106 × 12 = 1272$ There will be 1272 cards.

23. No. of times : $1272 × 2 ÷ 6 = 424$ He needs to punch 424 times.

24. Ribbon left : $1\frac{4}{5} − 1\frac{1}{2} = \frac{3}{10}$ $\frac{3}{10}$ m of ribbon will be left.

25. No. of rolls : $(27.75 ÷ 9.25) × 2 = 6$ She bought 6 rolls of ribbon.

26. Cost : $5.29 × 12 = 63.48$ 12 packs cost $63.48.

27. No. of packs : $1\frac{1}{5} + 2\frac{2}{3} = 3\frac{13}{15}$
There are $3\frac{13}{15}$ packs of coloured paper.

28. C   29. B   30. A   31. C
32. A   33. D   34. B   35. D

Unit 6

1. Width : $38.88 ÷ 7.2 = 5.4$ 5.4 m

2. Length : $(5.5 + 8.14) × 2 = 27.28$
The length of the border is 27.28 m.

3. Area : $5.5 × 8.14 = 44.77$ The area of the dining room is 44.77 m^2.

4. No. of tiles : $2.4 ÷ 0.3 = 8$
There are 8 tiles in the length of the hallway.

5. No. of tiles : $(2.4 × 1.8) ÷ (0.3 × 0.3) = 48$
There are 48 tiles in the entire hallway.

6. Distance : $259.79 + 302.57 + (225.67 × 2) = 1013.7$
The drove 1013.7 km for the whole trip.

7. Time : $1013.7 ÷ 75 = 13.516$ They drove 13.516 h for the trip.

8. Average : $(46.37 + 49.45 + 42.69) ÷ 3 = 46.17$
They bought 46.17 L of gasoline on average each time.

9. Cost : $27.76 × 3 = 83.28$ The total fill-up cost would be $83.28.

10. Cost : $58.27 + 63.39 + 123.84 = 245.5$
They spent $245.50 on food in all.

11. Cost of food per day : $245.5 ÷ 4 = 61.375$
They spent $61.375 on food per day.

12. Budget : $245.5 − 25.5 = 220$ Their budget for food was $220.00.

13. Difference : $(2.29 × 3 + 3.4 × 4.6) − (0.6 × 2.4 + 1.4 × 3.8) = 15.75$
She spent $15.75 more on meat than on vegetables.

14. Total cost : $26.69 × 4 × 3 = 320.28$
Their total lodging bill would be $320.28.

15. Area : $0.45 × 0.9 = 0.405$
Fred would need 0.405 m^2 of wood for the top of the cabinet.

16. Cost : $57.9 × 0.405 = 23.45$
The cost of the wood for the top was $23.45.

17. Cost : 42.99 x (0.8 x 0.45 x 2) = 30.95
    The cost of the wood for the sides was $30.95.
18. Cost : 60.84 ÷ (0.9 x 0.8 x 2) = 42.25
    The cost of the wood per square metre was $42.25.
19. Cost : 153.27 – 23.45 – 30.95 – 60.84 = 38.03
    The cost of the wood for the bottom was $38.03.
20. Cost : 8.27 ÷ 2 = 4.14   1 hinge cost $4.14.
21. Change : 20 – (8.27 x 2) = 3.46   His change was $3.46.
22. Amount saved : 3.09 x 2 – 5.73 = 0.45   Fred would save $0.45.
23. No. of cans : ((0.8 x 0.45 x 2) + (0.45 x 0.9) + (0.9 x 0.8)) ÷ 0.5 = 3.69   Fred would need 4 cans of paint.
24. Amount collected : 4.29 x 24 = 102.96
    The club will collect $102.96 from its members this year.
25. Money spent : (196.5 + 102.96) ÷ 10 = 29.946
    They can spend $29.95 each month in this school year.
26. Money spent : ((196.5 + 102.96) ÷ 4) ÷ 2 = 37.43
    There will be $37.43 for each issue.
27. Money left : (196.5 + 102.96) – 37.43 x 2 = 224.6
    $224.60 will be left for other activities.
28. Money needed : 9.95 x 24 = 238.8 (238.8 > 224.6)
    No, the club cannot afford to give each member an album.

Challenge
No. of doughnuts : 6 + 48 = 54
No. of paid doughuts : 54 ÷ 6 x 4 = 36
Cost : 0.89 x 36 = 32.04   Harry needs to pay $32.04.

Unit 7

1. $\frac{1}{2} = \frac{1 \times 50}{2 \times 50} = \frac{50}{100} = 50\%$ 50%
2. $20\% = \frac{20}{100} = \frac{1}{5}$ $\frac{1}{5}$ of the price of a suit was reduced.
3. $\frac{4}{5} = \frac{4 \times 20}{5 \times 20} = \frac{80}{100} = 80\%$
   Molly paid 80% of the price of the dress.
4. $\frac{45}{50} = \frac{45 \times 2}{50 \times 2} = \frac{90}{100} = 90\%$ 90% of the items were on sale.
5. $\frac{50}{200} = \frac{50 \div 2}{200 \div 2} = \frac{25}{100} = 25\%$ 25% of the shoes were sold.
6. $\frac{3}{5} = \frac{3 \times 20}{5 \times 20} = \frac{60}{100} = 60\%$
   60% of the weights were over 10 kg.
7. $\frac{3}{10} = \frac{3 \times 10}{10 \times 10} = \frac{30}{100} = 30\%$
   30% of the weights were wrapped in vinyl.
8. 7 out of 10 weights were not wrapped in vinyl. $\frac{7}{10} = \frac{7 \times 10}{10 \times 10}$
   $= \frac{70}{100} = 70\%$ 70% of the weights were not wrapped in vinyl.
9. $0.6 = \frac{6}{10} = \frac{3}{5}$ She did $\frac{3}{5}$ hour aerobics.
10. $85\% = \frac{85}{100} = \frac{85 \div 5}{100 \div 5} = \frac{17}{20}$
    $\frac{17}{20}$ of the people in the class were girls.
11. $\frac{7}{10} = \frac{7 \times 10}{10 \times 10} = \frac{70}{100} = 70\%$ Ron ran 70% of the track.
12. Ron walked $\frac{3}{10}$ of the track. $\frac{3}{10} = \frac{3 \times 10}{10 \times 10} = \frac{30}{100} = 30\%$
    Ron walked 30% of the track.
13. 1 out of 10 means 10 out of 100. Increase in no. of times: 10
    No. of times : 100 + 10 = 110
    She would have to skip 110 times the second day.
14. No. of stickers : 100   No. of ♥ : 25
    25% of Emily's stickers are ♥ .
15. No. of stickers : 100   No. of ◯ : 10
    10% of her stickers are ◯ .
16. No. of stickers : 100   No. of ☀ : 20
    20% of her stickers are ☀ .

17. No. of stickers : 100   No. of ☆ : 45
    45% of her stickers are ☆ .
18. No. of stickers left : 100 – 20 = 80
    Fraction of stickers left : $\frac{80}{100} = \frac{80 \div 20}{100 \div 20} = \frac{4}{5}$
    $\frac{4}{5}$ of her stickers would be left.
19. No. of stickers left : 100 –16 = 84   No. of stickers in all : 100
    84 % of her stickers would be left.
20. $1 – 0.35 = 0.65$, $0.65 = \frac{65}{100} = 65\%$
    65% of her stickers would be left.
21. $1 – \frac{3}{4} = \frac{1}{4}$, $\frac{1}{4} = \frac{1 \times 25}{4 \times 25} = \frac{25}{100} = 25\%$
    25% of her stickers would be left.
22. No. of ♥ : 25   No. of ♥ left : 25 – 10 = 15
    Percent of ♥ left : $\frac{15}{25} = \frac{15 \times 4}{25 \times 4} = \frac{60}{100} = 60\%$
    60% of her ♥ stickers would be left.
23. Fraction of ☀ left : $1 – \frac{12}{20} = \frac{8}{20}$
    Percent of ☀ left : $\frac{8}{20} = \frac{8 \times 5}{20 \times 5} = \frac{40}{100} = 40\%$
    She used 40% of her ☀ stickers.
24. 60% of 100 stickers were 60 stickers.
    No. of stickers left : 100 – 60 = 40   40 stickers would be left.
25. $\frac{5}{8} = 5 \div 8 = 0.625$
    0.625 of the doughnuts in the box are chocolate flavour.
26. $0.625 = \frac{625}{1000} = \frac{62.5}{100} = 62.5\%$
    62.5 % of the doughnuts in the box are chocolate flavour.
27. $\frac{11}{80} = 11 \div 80 = 0.1375$ 0.138 of the students who like Math.
28. $0.138 = \frac{138}{1000} = \frac{13.8}{100} = 13.8\%$
    13.8% of the students in Amy's school like Math.
29. $42.5\% = \frac{42.5}{100} = \frac{425}{1000} = 0.425$
    0.425 of the drinks are grape flavour.
30. $0.425 = \frac{425}{1000} = \frac{425 \div 25}{1000 \div 25} = \frac{17}{40}$
    $\frac{17}{40}$ of the drinks are grape flavour.
31. Fraction of the drinks that are not grape flavour :
    $1 – \frac{17}{40} = \frac{23}{40}$; $\frac{23}{40} = \frac{23 \times 25}{40 \times 25} = \frac{575}{1000} = 57.5$
    57.5% of the drinks are not grape flavour.

Challenge
Candies Jenny ate : 30% of 100 = 30
Candies Jeffrey ate : 50% of 50 = 25   Difference : 30 – 25 = 5
Jenny ate more candies. She ate 5 g more.

Unit 8

1. History books:Geography books = 25:35 = 5:7   5:7
2. Geography books:total no. of books = 35:200 = 7:40
   The ratio is 7:40.
3. History books:total no. of books = 25:200 = 1.8   The ratio is 1:8.
4. Fictions:total no. of books = 100:200 = 1:2   The ratio is 1:2.
5. History books:fictions = 25:100 = 1:4   The ratio is 1:4.
6. New books:old books = 50:200 = 1:4   The ratio is 1:4.
7. History books:total no. of books = 75:250 = 3:10
   The ratio would be 3:10.
8. Procelain faces:faces of other materials = 5:15 = 1:3 The ratio is 1:3.
9. Lace dresses:other types of dresses = 4:16 = 1:4   The ratio is 1:4.
10. Dolls that are taller than 20 cm:total no. of dolls = 12:20 = 3:5
    The ratio is 3:5.
11. More valuable dolls:less valuable dolls = 2.18 = 1:9 The ratio is 1:9.
12. Dolls with leather boots:dolls without leather boots = 6:10 = 3:5
    The ratio is 3:5.

The ratio is 3:5.

13. Daisy's dolls:Molly's dolls = 16:20 = 4:5   The ratio is 4:5.
14. Daisy's dolls:Molly's dolls = 12:24 = 1:2   The ratio is 1:2.
15. Daisy's dolls:Molly's dolls = 20:16 = 5:4   The ratio is 5:4.
16. Cost : 6.45 ÷ 5 = 1.29   1 kg of apples cost $1.29.
17. Cost : 1.29 x 3 = 3.87   Wanda would need to pay $3.87.
18. Cost : 6.76 ÷ 4 = 1.69   1 kg of peaches cost $1.69.
19. Cost : 1.69 x 3 = 5.07   Louis would need to pay $5.07.
20. Cost : 1.96 ÷ 4 = 0.49   1 kg of bananas cost $0.49.
21. Cost : 0.49 x 7 = 3.43   Catherine would need to pay $3.43.
22. Cost of 1 kg (3-kg basket) : 14.97 ÷ 3 = 4.99
    Cost of 1 kg (5-kg basket) : 25.8 ÷ 5 = 5.16   (4.99 < 5.16)
    A 3-kg basket of cherries was a better buy.
23. Cost of 1 kg (2-kg basket) : 5.58 ÷ 2 = 2.79
    Cost of 1 kg (3-kg basket) : 8.07 ÷ 3 = 2.69   (2.69 < 2.79)
    A 3-kg basket of plums was a better buy.
24. Cost : 8.07 x 2 = 16.14   Wanda would need to pay $16.14.
25. No. of baskets : 32.28 ÷ 8.07 = 4
    Wanda bought 4 baskets of plums.

26.

	No. of bags	Total Cost
Bags of 5	350 ÷ 5 = 70	1.35 x 70 = 94.5
Bags of 7	350 ÷ 7 = 50	1.75 x 50 = 87.5

Difference : 94.5 – 87.5 = 7   The shopkeeper should pack his apples in bags of 5. He could earn $7 more.

27. Rate : 3 ÷ 20 x 60 = 9   Edwin's rate of speed is 9 km/h.
28. Rate : 27 ÷ 1.5 = 18   William's reading rate is 18 pages per hour.
29. Amount earned : 77 ÷ 8 = 9.63   Donny earned $9.63 each hour.
30. Shirley's reading rate : 108 ÷ 10 = 10.8
    Henry's reading rate : 147 ÷ 15 = 9.8   Shirley reads faster because she reads 10.8 words in 1 min but Henry reads 9.8 words in 1 min.
31. Cost of 1 Bright Lite bulb : 1.49 ÷ 4 = 0.37
    Cost of 1 Supergood bulb : 4.96 ÷ 12 = 0.41
    A pack of 4 Bright Lite bulbs is a better buy.
32. Supergood offers a better value because a Supergood bulb lasts twice as long as a Bright Lite bulb but does not cost twice as much.

Challenge

	A	B	C
Free muffins:Paid muffins	1:3	2:10 = 1:5	3:12 = 1:4
Cost of 1 muffin ($)	2.45 ÷ 4 = 0.61	8.95 ÷ 12 = 0.75	8.99 ÷ 15 = 0.60

The ratio in A is 1:3, B is 1:5 and C is 1:4. C is the best buy.

Unit 9

1. 10, 15, 20, 25, 30, 35, 40, 45, 50   50
2.

No. of peanuts	3	6	9	12	15	18	21	24	27
No. of hazelnuts	2	4	6	8	10	12	14	16	18

He will have 18 hazelnuts.

3.

No. of almonds	3	6	9	12	15	18	21	24	27
No. of Brazil nuts	2	5	9	14	20	27	35	44	54

+3 +4 +5 +6 +7 +8 +9 +10

He will add 54 Brazil nuts.

4. Length : 20 – 10 = 10   It grew 10 cm.
5. It grew 10 cm each month.
6.

Month	Apr	May	Jun	Jul
Height (cm)	80	90	100	110

It would be 110 cm long in July.

7.

Month	Jul	Aug	Sep
Height (cm)	110	120	130

It would be 130 cm long in the coming September.

8.

Month	Apr	May	Jun	Jul	Aug
Height (cm)	80	87.5	95	102.5	110

It would be 110 cm long in the coming August.

9.

Month	Sep	Oct	Nov	Dec	Jan	Feb	Mar	Apr
No. of new leaves	0	8	16	24	32	40	48	56

56 new leaves grew between September and April.

10.

No. of months	1	2	3
Balance ($)	4250	3500	2750

The balance would be $2750.00.

11.

No. of months	1	2	3	4	5	6
Balance ($)	4250	3500	2750	2000	1250	500

He could pay his rent from his account for 6 months.

12. His balance decreased by $750 each month.

13.

No. of months	2	3	4	5	6
Interest ($)	8.8	7.7	6.6	5.5	4.4

He would receive $4.40 interest.

14. His interest decreased by $1.10 each month.
15. Total interest : 8.8 + 7.7 + 6.6 + 5.5 + 4.4 = 33
    He would receive $33.00 interest.

16.

No. of months	1	2	3	4	5
Balance ($)	4250	3508.8	2766.5	2023.1	1278.6

His balance would be $1278.60.

17. $12 \xrightarrow{+2} 14 \xrightarrow{+2} 16$
    The amount increased by $2.00 each month.

18.

No. of months	1st	2nd	3rd	4th	5th	6th
Money received ($)	12	14	16	18	20	22

She would receive $22.00 in the sixth month.

19. $8 \xrightarrow{+2.5} 10.5 \xrightarrow{+2.5} 13$
    The amount increased by $2.50 each month.

20.

No. of months	1st	2nd	3rd	4th	5th	6th
Money spent ($)	8	10.5	13	15.5	18	20.5

She would spend $20.50 in the sixth month.

21.

No. of months	1st	2nd	3rd	4th	5th	6th
Money saved ($)	4	3.5	3	2.5	2	1.5

Total : 4 + 3.5 + 3 + 2.5 + 2 + 1.5 = 16.5   She would save $16.50.

22.

Month	6th	7th	8th	9th
Money received ($)	22	24	26	28
Money spent ($)	20.5	23	25.5	28

The amount that Erin received would be the same as the amount she spent in the 9th month.

Challenge

b. The next 5 terms are 21, 34, 55, 89, 144.

Unit 10

1. $? \times 3 = 9.75 \times 2$; $? \times 3 = 19.5$; $? = 6.5$ $6.50
2. $(4.86 + 6.98) \div ? = 2.96$; $11.84 \div ? = 2.96$; $? = 4$
   There were 4 children in all.
3. $? - (6.5 + 2.96) = 12.69$; $? = 22.15$
   Tim had got $22.15 at the beginning.
4. $(0.25 \times 4 + 0.1 \times 2) - ? = 0.04$; $1.2 - ? = 0.04$; $? = 1.16$
   The drink cost $1.16.
5. $? \times 3 = 156 \div 4$, $? \times 3 = 39$; $? = 13$
   There were 13 jellybeans in each bag.
6. $20 + 35 + ? = 100$; $? = 45$
   45 of the children there were between 2 and 6 years old.
7. $2.25 \times 2 - ? = 0.75$; $4.5 - ? = 0.75$; $? = 3.75$
   A package of 12 token cost $3.75.
8. $? - 3.75 = 1.25$; $? = 5$ Elaine gave $5.00 to the cashier.
9. $2.25 \times ? = 18.75 - 3.75 \times 2$; $2.25 \times ? = 11.25$; $? = 5$
   Tim bought 5 packages of 6 tokens.
10. $? + 59 = 136 + 216$; $? + 59 = 352$; $? = 293$
    Elaine got 293 points in the third game.
11. $? \div 16 = 3 + 4$; $? \div 16 = 7$; $? = 112$ Tim got 112 coupons in all.
12. $? - 15 = 12$; $? = 27$ The handbag cost $27.
13. $? - 35 = 7$; $? = 42$ Skirt B cost $42.
14. $145 - ? = 25$; $? = 120$ The sweater cost $120.
15. $12 \times 3 + ? = 54$; $36 + ? = 54$; $? = 18$ The shorts cost $18.
16. $20 \times 2 - (? - 8) = 5$; $? - 8 = 35$; $? = 43$
    The jeans cost $43 before discount.
17. $? - (12 - 5) = 3$; $? - 7 = 3$; $? = 10$ Anna gave $10 to the cashier.
18. $? - (56 - 8) = 12$; $? - 48 = 12$; $? = 60$ Harry gave $60 to the cashier.
19. $n \div 2 = 5$; $n = 10$ It is 10.
20. $5 + n = 7$; $n = 2$ It is 2.
21. $3 + n = 12$; $n = 9$ It is 9.
22. $n - 4 = 15$; $n = 19$ It is 19.
23. $n \times 3 = 21$; $n = 7$ It is 7.
24. $4 \times n = 36$; $n = 9$ It is 9.
25. $n + 11 = 26$; $n = 15$ It is 15.
26. $n \div 2 - 12$; $n - 24$ It is 24.
27. $9 + n = 40$; $n = 31$ It is 31.
28. $75 \div n = 15$; $n = 5$ It is 5.

Challenge

1. B   2. C   3. A
4. E   5. F   6. D

Final Review

1. Girls:boys = 12:15 = 4:5   The ratio was 4:5.
2. Total no. of students : 12 + 15 = 27   Fraction of girls : $\frac{12}{27} = \frac{4}{9}$
   $\frac{4}{9}$ of Miss Gink's students were girls.
3. Total amount : 20.75 × 27 = 560.25
   They would want to raise $560.25.
4. Total amount : 4635 + 6430 = 11065
   Betsy had 11 065 g of raisins.
5. No. of bags : 4635 ÷ 85 = 54...45
   Betsy would need 54 bags. 45 g of golden raisins were left over.
6. No. of bags : 6430 ÷ 75 = 85...55
   Betsy would need 85 bags. 55 g of sultana raisins were left over.
7. Money raised : 0.5 × 35 + 0.65 × 60 = 56.5
   Betsy would raise $56.50.
8. No. of bags : 18 × 6 = 108   Betsy could sell 108 bags in 6 hours.
9. $\frac{4}{5} = \frac{4 \times 20}{5 \times 20} = \frac{80}{100} = 80\%$
   80% of Betsy's raisins had been sold.

10. Money raised : 1.25 × 108 + 1.75 × 88 + 1.45 × 104 = 439.8
    Elaine raised $439.80.
11. Total : 108 + 88 + 104 = 300
    Orange juice:all the juice = 108:300 = 9:25
    The ratio was 9:25.
12. $\frac{108}{300} = \frac{36}{100} = 36\%$ 36% of the juice sold was orange juice.
13. Fraction : $\frac{88}{300} = \frac{22}{75}$ $\frac{22}{75}$ of the juice sold was apple juice.
14. $? - 1.45 \times 7 = 1 + 0.25 \times 3 + 0.1$; $? - 10.15 = 1.85$; $? = 12$
    He gave $12.00 to Elaine.
15. $? - 60 = 255$; $? = 315$ The boys raised $315.00.
16. Total amount raised : 315 + 255 = 570   (570 > 560.25)
    Yes, the students could meet their goal.
17. Time taken : 1200 ÷ 400 = 3   The trip would take 3 hours.
18. Average speed : 48 ÷ (36 ÷ 60) = 80
    The average driving speed was 80 km/h.
19. Cost : 415.37 × (5 − 1) = 1661.48
    The air fare was $1661.48 for the whole family.
20. Cost : 239.45 × 8 = 1915.6
    They spent $1915.60 on accommodation.
21. Cost : 125.75 × 9 = 1131.75   Their food bill was $1131.75.
22. Cost : 1915.6 + 1131.75 = 3047.35
    They spent $3047.35 on food and accommodation.
23. Cost : 625 × 5 = 3125   (3125 > 3047.35)
    No, that would not be a good deal.
24. Factors of 16 : 1, 2, 4, 8, 16   Factors of 24 : 1, 2, 3, 4, 6, 8, 12, 24
    They could put the key-rings in 4 ways.
25. They could put 1, 2, 4 or 8 key-rings in 1 box.
26. Gary's brother is correct because 9 is a multiple of 3.
27. Factors of 24 : 1, 2, 3, 4, 6, 8, 12, 24
    12 is between 11 and 20.   The hat cost $12.00.
28. Multiples of 8 : 8, 16, 24, 32, ...   16 is between 10 and 19.
    Gary's mother bought 16 T-shirts.
29. 17, 33, 65 ; Each number is 1 less than 2 times the previous number.
30. No. of seashells : 2 + 3 + 5 + 9 + 17 + 33 + 65 = 134
    Gary's father would collect 134 seashells.
31. Fraction : $\frac{17}{134}$ $\frac{17}{134}$ of the seashells were picked on the 7th day.
32. C   33. A   34. B   35. D
36. D   37. C   38. B   39. A

Unit 1

1.

m	40	2	4500	800	950	700
cm	4000	200	450 000	80 000	95 000	70 000
km	0.04	0.002	4.5	0.8	0.95	0.7

2.

g	900	8300	50	290	60 000	3440
kg	0.9	8.3	0.05	0.29	60	3.44

3.

mL	2050	450	110	52 000	32 400	9
L	2.05	0.45	0.11	52	32.4	0.009

4. a. 40 cm + 8 dm = 40 cm + 80 cm = 120 cm   False
   b. 500 mm + 6 m = 50 cm + 600 cm = 650 cm   True
   c. 8.2 kg + 200 g = 8200 g + 200 g = 8400 g   True
   d. 0.5 L + 400 mL = 0.5 L + 0.4 L = 0.9 L   False
5. (1.3 kg = 1300 g)   Amount of candies : 1300 + 250 = 1550
   Kelly bought 1550 g of candies in all.
6. (0.75 kg = 750 g)   No. of times : 750 ÷ 100 = 7.5
   Milly would pay 7.5 times the price per 100 g.
7. (14 cm = 0.14 m, 1200 mm = 1.2 m)
   Amount of ribbon bought : 0.14 + 0.8 + 1.2 = 2.14
   They bought 2.14 m of ribbon.
8. 2.14 m = (2.14 x 100) cm = 214 cm   They bought 214 cm of ribbon.
9. (800 g = 0.8 kg) Amount of candies : 1.03 + 0.8 = 1.83
   She bought 1.83 kg of candies.
10. (2.4 kg = 2400 g) No. of bags : 2400 ÷ 600 = 4
    They bought 4 bags in all.
11. (2.25 L = 2250 mL) Amount of juice : 2250 ÷ 5 = 450
    1 container held 450 mL of juice.
12. (450 mL = 0.45 L) Difference : 0.89 – 0.45 = 0.44
    Container A could hold 0.44 L more juice than container B.

Challenge
1. (6.4 m = 6400 mm) No. of tiles : 6400 ÷ 8 = 800
   There were 800 tiles.
2. Weight : 18 x 800 = 14400 (14400 g = 14.4 kg)   It weighed 14.4 kg.

Unit 2

1. Price (store B) : 41.52 – 5.25 = 36.27 (36.27 > 35.98)   A
2. Change : 50 – 35.98 = 14.02   Her change was $14.02.
   She was given 1 $10 bill, 2 twoonies and 2 pennies.
3. (0.7 kg = 700 g) Cost : 1.49 x (700 ÷ 100) = 10.43
   It would cost her $10.43.
4. Change : 12 – 10.43 = 1.57   Her change was $1.57.
   She was given 1 loonie, 2 quarters, 1 nickel and 2 pennies.
5. Cost per gram (store C) : 3.95 ÷ 125 = 0.0316
   Cost per gram (store D) : 2.99 ÷ 100 = 0.0299 (0.0299 < 0.0316)
   Store D's shoe polish was a better buy.
6. No. of quarters : 10 ÷ 0.25 = 40   He would get 40 quarters.
7. Cost : 2.49 x 2 + 1.25 = 6.23
   He would pay 3 twoonies, 2 dimes and 3 pennies.
8. Amount of money : (2.49 + 1.39 + 1.25) x 8 = 41.04
   She had $41.04.
9. Amount of money : (11.16 ÷ 4) x 3 = 8.37   She got back $8.37.
10. Total cost of popcorn and drink : 4.32 x 3 = 12.96
    Total cost of popcorn : 4.59 x 2 = 9.18
    Cost : 12.96 – 9.18 = 3.78   The jumbo soft drink cost $3.78.
11. Money Jeffrey had : 0.25 x 4 + 0.1 x 24 + 0.05 x 16 = 4.2
    (4.2 > 3.78)
    Yes, Jeffrey had enough money to buy a jumbo soft drink.
12. Money earned : 7.05 x 18 = 126.9
    He could earn $126.90 per week.
13. Bus fare per week : 1.85 x 2 x 6 = 22.2
    Money earned : 126.9 – 22.2 = 104.7
    He earned $104.70.
14. Money earned : 104.7 – 25.38 = 79.32
    He earned $79.32.
15. No. of weeks : 600 ÷ 79.32 = 7.56 (2 decimal places)
    He would have to work 8 weeks.
16. Parking fee : 1.75 + 3 x 4 = 13.75   It was $13.75.
17. Parking fee : 1.75 + 3 x 3 = 10.75
    Money Mr Keller gave : 10.75 + 1.25 = 12
    Mr Keller gave $12.00.
18. No. of nickels : 5 ÷ 0.05 = 100   He would get 100 nickels.
19. five thousand nine hundred seventy-five dollars and forty-five cents
20. six thousand ninety-four dollars
21. four thousand two hundred ten dollars and thirty cents
22. three thousand nine hundred eighty-one dollars and ninety-five cents
23. five thousand seven hundred dollars and forty cents
24. nine thousand eight dollars and ten cents

Challenge
25, 5, 10, 5, 5
Amount of money : 2 x 25 + 1 x 5 + 0.25 x 10 + 0.1 x 5 + 0.05 x 5
= 58.25   Gary had $58.25.
He had enough money to trade for a $50 bill.

Unit 3

1. Time taken : (1040 ÷ 1000) ÷ 0.08 = 13   13 min
2. Time taken : 11 h – 10 h 42 min = 18 min   Speed : 2160 ÷ 18 = 120
   He should walk 120 m/min (0.12 km/min).
3. Time taken : (2160 ÷ 1000) ÷ 0.08 = 27
   Time arrived : 10 h 42 min + 27 min = 11 h 9 min
   He would reach Elaine's house at 11:09 a.m.
4. Average speed : 506 ÷ 9.2 = 55   Their average speed was 55 km/h.
5. Time taken : 9.2 – (2 + 45 ÷ 60) – (3 + 30 ÷ 60) = 2.95
   He drove 2.95 hours (2 h 57 min).
6. Distance : 72 x 6 + 50 x (1 + 33 ÷ 60) = 509.5
   They drove 509.5 km.
7. Average speed : 300 ÷ (3 + 12 ÷ 60) = 93.75
   Their average speed was 93.75 km/h.
8. Total time taken : 36 ÷ 60 + 36 ÷ 40 = 1.5 (1 h 30 min)
   Time returned : 12 h 44 min + 1 h 30 min = 14 h 14 min
   She returned at 2:14 p.m.
9. Time : 2 h 45 min + 2 h 18 min = 5 h 3 min
   They reached the museum at 5:03 p.m.
10. Average speed : 138.92 ÷ (2 + 18 ÷ 60) = 60.4
    Their average speed was 60.4 km/h.
11. Time : 5 h 3 min – 16 min = 4 h 47 min   It would be 4:47 p.m.
12. Time taken : 2 h 18 min – 16 min = 2 h 2 min (2.03 h)
    Speed : 138.92 ÷ 2.03 = 68.43
    They would have to drive at 68.43 km/h.

Challenge
Time taken : 6 h 15 min – 2 h 45 min = 3 h 30 min
Distance travelled by car : 80 x (3 + 30 ÷ 60) = 280
Distance travelled by truck : 50 x (3 + 30 ÷ 60) = 175
Distance between the two places : 280 + 175 = 455
The distance between Townville and Littleton was 455 km.

Unit 4

1. Length : 10 x 4 = 40   40 cm
2. Length : (16 + 18) x 2 = 68   The braid border would be 68 cm long.
3. Length : (10 + 12) x 2 = 44   The braid border would be 44 cm long.
4. Length : 17 x 2 + 12 = 46   The braid border would be 46 cm long.
5. Area : 10 x 10 = 100   The area was 100 cm^2.
6. Area : 16 x 18 = 288   The area was 288 cm^2.
7. Area : 12 x 9 = 108   The area was 108 cm^2.
8. Area : 12 x 16 ÷ 2 = 96   The area was 96 cm^2.
9. Area left : 100 – 6 x 6 = 64   There was 64 cm^2 of cardboard left.
10. Area left : 288 – 14 x 12 = 120   There was 120 cm^2 of cardboard left.

11. a. Area left : 108 – 8 x 6 = 60   There was 60 cm² of cardboard left.
    b. Perimeter : (8 + 7) x 2 = 30   The perimeter was 30 cm.
12. Area left : 96 – 10 x 13 ÷ 2 = 31   There was 31 cm² of cardboard left.
13. Width : 180 ÷ 15 = 12   Its width was 12 m.
14. Wallpaper needed : 15 x 3 x 2 + 12 x 3 x 2 = 162
    162 m² of wallpaper would be needed.
15. Area : (15   2) x (12 – 2) – 130
    She would need 130 m² of carpeting.
16. Perimeter : 5 + 12 + 13 = 30   The perimeter was 30 m.
17. Area : 12 x 5 ÷ 2 = 30   She would need 30 m² of tiles.
18. No. of cans : (5 x 3 + 12 x 3 + 13 x 3) ÷ 5 = 18
    She would need 18 cans.
19. Area : 18 x 16 = 288   She would need 288 m² of carpeting.
20.
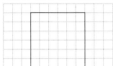
21.
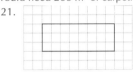
22. Suggested answer:
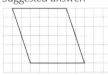

23. Suggested answer:

24. Suggested answer:
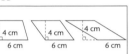

25. Suggested answer:
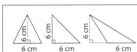

Challenge

1. Perimeter : 10 + 30 + (24 – 8) + (18 – 6) = 68
   The perimeter is 68 cm.
2. Area : 18 x 24 – 24 x 18 ÷ 2 – 8 x 6 ÷ 2 = 192
   The area is 192 cm².

Unit 5

1. 1 mL = 1 cm³   Volume : 500 – 200 = 300   300 cm³
2. Volume : 800 – 200 = 600   The volume is 600 cm³.
3. Volume : 700 – 200 = 500   The volume is 500 cm³.
4. Volume : 900 – 200 = 700   The volume is 700 cm³.
5. D, B, C, A
6. Area : 300 ÷ 5 = 60   The area is 60 cm².
7. Length : 60 ÷ 6 = 10   Its length is 10 cm.
8. Area : 600 ÷ 6 = 100   The area is 100 cm².
9. Width : 100 ÷ 25 = 4   Its width is 4 cm.
10. Height : 700 ÷ 140 = 5   Its height is 5 cm.
11-13 Suggested answers:
11.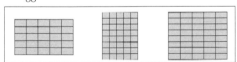

12. No. of layers : 40 ÷ 5 = 8   No. of bricks : (30 ÷ 6) x (50 ÷ 10) = 25
    There are 8 layers of 25 bricks each.
13. No. of bricks : 25 x 8 = 200 ; 200 bricks can be put in the container.
14. Amount of water : (50 x 30 x 40) ÷ 1000 = 60
    It can hold 60 L of water.
15. Width : 120 ÷ 15 = 8   Its width is 8 cm.
16. Height : 1500 ÷ 120 = 12.5   Its height is 12.5 cm.
17. Amount of water : 1500 cm³ = 1500 mL = 1.5 L
    It can hold 1.5 L of water.
18. Volume : 0.5 x 0.45 x 0.2 = 0.045 (0.045 m³ = 45000 cm³)
    The volume is 0.045 m³ (45 000 cm³).

19. No. of pailfuls : 45000 ÷ 1500 = 30   She needs 30 boxes.
20. Volume : 1500 x 40 = 60000   The volume is 60 000 cm³.
21. Area : 60000 ÷ 60 = 1000   Its base area is 1000 cm².
22. Height : 45000 ÷ 1000 = 45   It will be 45 cm high.
23. Volume : 30 x 21 x 1.8 = 1134   Its volume is 1134 m³.
24. Amount of water : 1134 x 1000 = 1134000
    It can hold 1 134 000 L of water.
25. Volume : (30 x 21 x 1.6) x 1000 = 1008000
    There will be 1 008 000 L of water.
26. Amount of water : 30 x 21 x (1.7 – 1.6) x 1000 = 63000
    63 000 L of water should be pumped into the pool.
27. Time needed : 1134000 ÷ 30000 = 37.8   It will take 37.8 hours.
28. Height : (126000 ÷ 1000) ÷ (30 x 21) = 0.2   It will rise 0.2 m.

Challenge

Volume : 4 x 9 x (5 + 4) + 4 x 4 x (16 – 9) = 436
Its volume is 436 cm³.

Unit 6

1. 4 cm, 4 cm, 4 cm; 60°, 60°, 60°
2. 4 cm, 5 cm, 3 cm; 90°, 37°, 53°
3. 4 cm, 4 cm, 4 cm; 60°, 60°, 60°
4. 3 cm, 3.7 cm, 5.5 cm; 40°, 110°, 30°
5. Triangles ABC and GHI are congruent because their corresponding
   sides and angles are equal.
6. Triangles ABC and GHI are acute triangles.
7. Triangle DEF is a right triangle.
8. Triangle JKL is an obtuse triangle.
9. Triangles ABC and GHI are equilateral triangles.
10. Triangles DEF and JKL are scalene triangles.
11. Suggested answer:

12. Triangular prism; 6, 5, 9   13. Rectangular pyramid; 5, 5, 8
14. Hexagonal prism; 12, 8, 18   15. Pentagonal pyramid; 6, 6, 10
16.

17.

18. a.

    b. A square pyramid can be made from this net.
    c. It has 4 triangular faces.
19. a. Suggested answer:

    b. A hexagonal prism can be made from this net.
    c. It has 6 rectangular faces.
20. a.

    b. A pentagonal pyramid can be made from this net.
    c. It has 5 triangular faces.

21. a. Suggested answer:
   b. A rectangular prism can be made from this net.
   c. It has 6 rectangular faces.

22. a. Suggested answer:
   b. A cube can be made from this net.
   c. Suggested answer:

23. A has 2 lines of symmetry. It has rotational symmetry of order 2.
24. B has 4 lines of symmetry. It has rotational symmetry of order 4.
25. C has no line of symmetry. It has rotational symmetry of order 3.
26. D has 1 line of symmetry. It has no rotational symmetry.

Challenge

Midway Review

1. 56.07 km = (56.07 x 1000) m = 56070 m   The distance between the flea market and Kelly's house was 56 070 m.
2. Time : 9 h 47 min + 42 min = 10 h 29 min
   They arrived there at 10:29 a.m.
3. Speed : 56.07 ÷ (42 ÷ 60) = 80.1
   Their average speed was 80.1 km/h.
4. Speed : 56.07 ÷ ((42 − 4) ÷ 60) = 89
   They would have to drive 89 km/h.
5. Length : 48 ÷ 10 = 4.8   Width : 36 ÷ 10 = 3.6   The length and width of her picture were 4.8 dm and 3.6 dm respectively.
6. Area : 48 x 36 = 1728   The area of her picture was 1728 cm^2.
7. Perimeter : (48 + 36) x 2 = 168
   The perimeter of her picture was 168 cm.
8. Length : 48 + 2.5 x 2 = 53   Width : 36 + 2.5 x 2 = 41   The length and width of the frame would be 53 cm and 41 cm respectively.
9. Perimeter : (53 + 41) x 2 = 188
   The outside perimeter of the border would be 188 cm.
10. Yes, it has 4 lines of symmetry.
    It has rotational symmetry of order 4.
11. Change : 50 x 2 − 57.64 = 42.36
    The cashier could give her $42.36 change. There were 2 $20 bills, 1 toonie, 1 quarter, 1 dime and 1 penny.
12.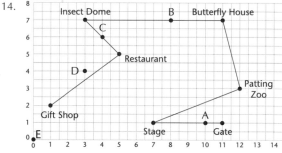
13. Volume : 4 x 4 x 4 = 64   Its volume was 64 cm^3.
14. Change : 20 − (4.79 x 2 + 1.29) = 9.13
    His change was $9.13. There were 1 $5 bill, 2 toonies, 1 dime and 3 pennies.
15. It is a rectangular pyramid.
16. It is a rectangular prism.
17. Area : 4 x 2 + (4 x 3.5 ÷ 2) x 2 + (2 x 3.9 ÷ 2) x 2 = 29.8
    Sally needs 29.8 cm^2 of cardboard.
18. Area : 1 x 3 x 2 + 1 x 7 x 2 + 3 x 7 x 2 = 62
    Sally needs 62 cm^2 of cardboard.
19. Solid A has 8 edges.
20. Perimeter : 4 x 6 + 2 x 2 = 28   The braid will be 28 cm long.
21. Cost : 0.16 x 28 = 4.48   Sally will pay $4.48 for the braid.

22. Volume : 7 x 3 x 1 = 21   The volume is 21 cm^3.
23. Suggested answer:

24. D   25. C   26. B   27. B   28. A
29. C   30. A   31. D   32. D

Unit 7

1.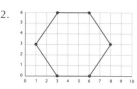
   trapezoid

2.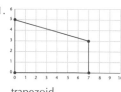
   It is a hexagon.

3.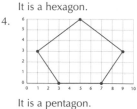
   It is an octagon.

4.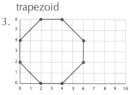
   It is a pentagon.

5. (11, 1)
6. (12, 3)
7. (11, 7)
8. (3, 7)
9. (5, 5)
10. (1, 2)
11. (7, 1)

12-13.
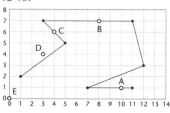

14.

15.

3	Gerry	David		Billy	Emily
2	Raymond	Olive	Louis	George	Ted
1	Elaine	Katherine	Stephanie	Jiffy	
0	Terry	Uma	Rebecca	Vera	
	0	1	2	3	4

16. No, they are too far away from each other.
17. No, they are too close and will talk most of the time.
18. I would assign Billy to (3, 3) because the seat (0, 1) was close to the window.
19. I would assign Rebecca to (2, 0) so that she would be near the teacher.
20. They couldn't sit at (0, 2) or (2, 2).
21. Gerry should sit at (0, 3) and Terry at (0, 0), as Gerry should sit at the back.
22. Raymond should sit at (0, 2) and Louis at (2, 2) so that Raymond could not chat with George.
23. Elaine's seat was at (0, 1) and Stephanie's at (2, 1).
24. Katherine's seat was at (1, 1) and David's at (1, 3).

25. Vera's seat was at (3, 0).
26. There were 3 empty seats. They were at (2, 3), (4, 0) and (4, 1).

Challenge

No, Larry could not easily ski this run.

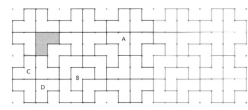

Unit 8

1. 1 and 3
2. 1 and 2 are the rotation images of the shaded figure.
3. 2 and 3 are the reflection images of the shaded figure.
4. (2, 4), (3, 1) and (5, 3)

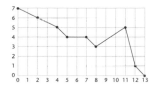

5. The ordered pairs of the vertices are (6, 6), (7, 4), (9, 4) and (10, 6).

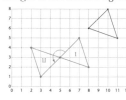

6. The ordered pairs of the vertices are (1, 5), (1, 2) and (4, 2).

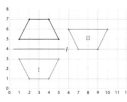

7. The image is congruent with the original figure.
8. a.

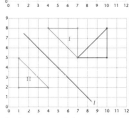

   b. reflection or rotation   c. translation   d. rotation
   e. Suggested answer: I will use 2 rotations to transfer the shaded tile to D. Rotate the shaded tile to get tile C first, and then rotate tile C to get D.

9. a.

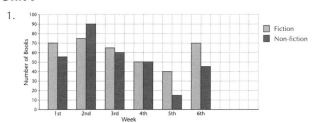

   b. rotation   c. translation   d. reflection
   e. Suggested answer: I will use a reflection and a rotation to transfer the shaded tile to D. Flip the shaded tile to get tile C first, and then rotate tile C to get D.

10.

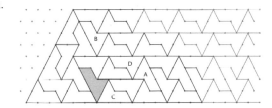

11. The key to open the treasure chest is B.

Challenge

1. Suggested answer:

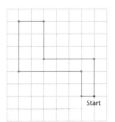 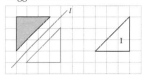 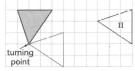

   Use reflection and translation.   Use rotation and translation.
   Flip the shaded figure over the line *l* and translate it 1 unit up and 6 units right.   Rotate $\frac{1}{4}$ turn clockwise about the turning point and translate it 2 units up and 6 units right.

Unit 9

1.

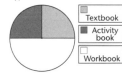

2. Difference : 70 − 55 = 15   15 more fiction books were borrowed.
3. It was the 4th week.
4. It was the 2nd week.
5. Total no. of books : 70 + 75 + 65 + 50 + 40 + 70 = 370
   370 fiction books were borrowed.
6. Total no. of books : 55 + 90 + 60 + 50 + 15 + 45 = 315
   315 non-fiction books were borrowed.
7. It was the 5th week because fewest number of books were borrowed.
8. a.   Types of Math Books

   Textbook
   Activity book
   Workbook

   b. No. of books : 120 ÷ 4 = 30   30 of them were activity books.
   c. No. of books : 120 ÷ 2 = 60   60 of them were workbooks.

9.

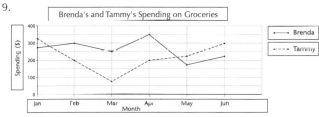

10. Difference : 350 − 200 = 150   Brenda spent $150 more.
11. Difference : 300 − 225 = 75   Tammy spent $75 more.
12. Difference : 350 − 175 = 175   It was April. It was $175 more.
13. Difference : 325 − 75 = 250   It was March. It was $250 less.
14. The greatest difference was in March.
15. Brenda's spending : 275 + 300 + 250 + 350 + 175 + 225 = 1575
    Tammy's spending : 325 + 200 + 75 + 200 + 225 + 300 = 1325
    Difference : 1575 − 1325 = 250
    Brenda spent $250 more than Tammy.

16. Brenda's Spending in February

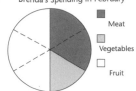

- Meat
- Vegetables
- Fruit

17. Money spent : 300 ÷ 3 = 100
She spent $100 on meat.

18. Money spent : 300 ÷ 2 = 150
She spent $150 on fruit.

19. Tammy's Spending in February

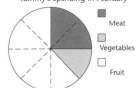

- Meat
- Vegetables
- Fruit

20. Money spent : 200 ÷ 8 x 5 = 125
She spent $125 on fruit.

21. Brenda spent : $150
Tammy spent : $125
($150 > $125) No, she didn't.

Challenge

1. 144˚, 108˚, 72˚, 36˚
2. The size of the angle of red marbles (144˚) is 4 times bigger than that of green marbles (36˚).
No. of green marbles : 120 ÷ 4 = 30   He had 30 green marbles.

Unit 10

1.

	Jan	Feb	Mar	Apr	May	Jun
No. of jellybeans	120	120	120	120	120	120

120 ;   had the same no. of jellybeans

2. Jody would be happiest in April because she got the most red jellybeans.
3. She would be unhappiest in June because she got the least red jellybeans.
4. She got the least yellow jellybeans in April.
5. Difference : 40 – 30 = 10   She got 10 more.
6. They made the discovery in April when the number of red jellybeans started to decrease.
7. It is increasing by 5 every month.
8. No. of yellow jellybeans : 45 + 5 = 50
She would have got 50 yellow jellybeans in July.
9. It is decreasing by 10 every month.
10. No. of red jellybeans : 30 – 10 = 20
She would have got 20 red jellybeans in July.
11. No. of red jellybeans : 30, 35, (40), (40), 45, 50
Median : (40 + 40) ÷ 2 = 40   The median number was 40.

12.

Vehicle	Tally	Frequency
Car	### ### ### ###	20
Van	### ### ### ### ### ###	30
Jeep	//// //// //// //// //// ### ###	35
Truck	### ### ### ### ### ### ### ### ###	45
Bus	###	5

13. He saw 20 cars.
14. Difference : 35 – 30 = 5
He saw 5 more Jeeps.
15. Total of vehicles :
20 + 30 + 35 + 45 + 5 = 135
He saw 135 vehicles in all.
16. Average : 135 ÷ 2 = 67.5
He saw 67.5 vehicles on average.
17. No, he would not have seen as many trucks.
18. Suggested answers:
a. He might have collected his data near a bus terminal.
b. Their graphs have the same title, scale and label.
19. They received junk mail the most.
20. Suggested answer: They might receive some gift subscriptions.
21. It was December.
22. Suggested answer: They got Christmas cards in December.
23. It was December.
24. Suggested answer: They got more flyers for the Christmas season.

Challenge

1.
median (143)
Height : 137, 140, (˙), 144, 151, 165
Peter's height : 143 x 2 – 144 = 142   Peter is 142 cm tall.

2. Mean: (165 + 137 + 140 + 151 + 144 + 142) ÷ 6 = 146.5
The mean height is 146.5 cm.

Unit 11

1. 5 possible outcomes
2. The probability is $\frac{1}{5}$.
3. 4 out of 10 marbles are green or yellow.
P(green or yellow) = $\frac{4}{10}$ = $\frac{2}{5}$ The probability is $\frac{2}{5}$.
4. Yes, since each colour has the same number of marbles.
5. No, the outcomes will not be equally likely because the probability of drawing a green marble is $\frac{1}{9}$, but the probability of drawing a red, blue, yellow or white marble is $\frac{2}{9}$.
6. There are 5 possible outcomes : red, blue, green, yellow or white.
7. No, since there are now more white and yellow marbles.
8. It is most likely a white marble.
9. 2 out of 15 marbles are red. P(red) = $\frac{2}{15}$
The probability is $\frac{2}{15}$.
10. 5 out of 15 marbles are white. P(white) = $\frac{5}{15}$ = $\frac{1}{3}$
The probability is $\frac{1}{3}$.
11. No, the most likely marble should be white.
12. There are 5 white marbles and 4 yellow marbles. To make each outcome equally likely, he needs to put in 10 more : 3 red, 3 blue, 3 green and 1 yellow.

13.

1	H	(1, H)
	T	(1, T)
2	H	(2, H)
	T	(2, T)
3	H	(3, H)
	T	(3, T)
4	H	(4, H)
	T	(4, T)
5	H	(5, H)
	T	(5, T)

14. There are 10 possible outcomes.
15. Yes.
16. 1 out of 10 outcomes is a 1 and a head.
P(1 & H) = $\frac{1}{10}$ The probability is $\frac{1}{10}$.
17. 1 out of 10 outcomes is a 5 and a tail.
P(5 & T) = $\frac{1}{10}$ The probability is $\frac{1}{10}$.
18. 2 out of 10 outcomes are an even number and a head.
P(even no. & head) = $\frac{2}{10}$ = $\frac{1}{5}$ The probability is $\frac{1}{5}$.
19. 3 out of 10 outcomes are an odd number and a tail.
P(odd no. & tail) = $\frac{3}{10}$ The probability is $\frac{3}{10}$.
20. 1 out of 10 outcomes is a 1 and a head.
P(1 & head) = $\frac{1}{10}$ The probability is $\frac{1}{10}$.
21. No, he is wrong. The probability of getting a 1 and a head does not depend on any previous tries. Sally will have the same probability to win as before.